S-DAY

A MEMOIR OF THE INVASION OF ENGLAND

James Stewart Thayer

ST. MARTIN'S PRESS NEW YORK

The locations of many of the military units in the novel are based upon the actual German plan for invading Great Britain during World War II. But the actions of those units, and the placements and activities of other military units, both Allied and German, are inventions of the author.

Library of Congress Cataloging-in-Publication Data

Thayer, James Stewart.
    S-Day : a memoir of the invasion of England.
      p. cm.
    "A Thomas Dunne book."
    ISBN 0-312-04148-9
    1. World War, 1939–1945—Fiction. 2. Great Britain—
    History—Invasions—Fiction.   I. Title.
    PS3570.H347S18   1990   813'.54—dc20   89-77820

First Edition: November 1990
10 9 8 7 6 5 4 3 2 1

To my daughter
Alexandra Amy Thayer

Thanks to
C. James Frush, Peter Lowe, Sally A. Martin, John D. Reagh III, John L. Thayer M.D., Joseph T. Thayer, Amy Wallace, Dexter A. Washburn, Peggy J. Williams, and my wonderful wife, Patricia Wallace Thayer

"We may therefore be sure that there is a plan—perhaps built up over the years—for destroying Great Britain, which after all has the honour to be his main and foremost enemy."

—Winston Churchill

FOREWORD BY
GENERAL SIR ARTHUR STEDMAN

When Colonel Royce asked me to write a foreword for his work on the invasion, I readily agreed. The wounds from those dreadful days may seem too fresh, the fear and shock still too bright in the mind's eye, for careful study. But memory is perishable. The onslaught is best recorded early, just after the clangor has stilled, before time tempers our memories.

This is an account of the most momentous episode in our history since William the Conqueror landed at Pevensey. It is also an intimate portrait of the American general Wilson Clay, whose rank as a combat commander will never be gainsaid, but whose place in the larger history of mankind's journey will remain unsettled for many years.

For those who want to understand those dangerous days, for those who wish to smell the powder of battle and endure the burden of command, I strongly recommend Colonel Royce's narrative.

—Arthur Stedman, GCB, CBE, DSO, MC
Rathwell House
26 May 1948

INTRODUCTION

Germans call the day of launching a military operation *S-Tag*, or S-Day. There was a time when we thought Great Britain would be spared that day.

After the massing of German war materiel on the coasts of occupied France and the Low Countries in 1940, there came a long pause. For most of the next year, Hitler delayed his decision about England and apparently toyed with the idea of marching into Russia. Hope burned throughout England that the German chancellor had forgotten the lessons of Charles XII and Napoleon and that he would exhaust his country's demonic energy on the endless Russian steppes.

That was not to be, of course. Hitler had indeed read his history, perhaps knew Frederick the Great's warning that an attempt to seize Moscow would be "contrary to reason and common sense." By late 1941, it became clear that the Soviet Union was forgotten and that the Germans would attempt what had not been done in almost nine hundred years: to conquer the British Isles against hostile defenders.

American troops began arriving on English soil shortly after Pearl Harbor, and by May 1942 the American Expeditionary Force was in place alongside forces from the United Kingdom and Commonwealth countries. General Wilson Clay was commander of the American army. I was his aide-de-camp.

The term "aide-de-camp" is not often used these days, and certainly was not by the general, who simply called me his aide or his ADC. I was with him almost all his waking moments during that critical time. He ordered that I keep a journal, usually recorded by me late at night and transcribed the next day by a headquarters secretary. From that journal and from operations logs, numerous commanders' war diaries, recently declassified documents, captured enemy records, and over five hundred interviews, I have drawn this account.

"Write a history of a battle?" asked Wellington. "As well write the history of a ball." I have not tried. After-action reports and divisional histories have already been published, and the army's Office of the Chief of Military History will soon release its multivolume study. Many other books on the invasion are sure to follow. I leave the retelling of field-by-field, house-by-house military maneuvers to them.

This is the story of people—servicemen and civilians, Allied and German—swept up in the turmoil of S-Day.

—JACK ROYCE, COLONEL, U.S. ARMY (RET.)
March 23, 1948

PART ONE

War, "the trade of kings."
— DRYDEN

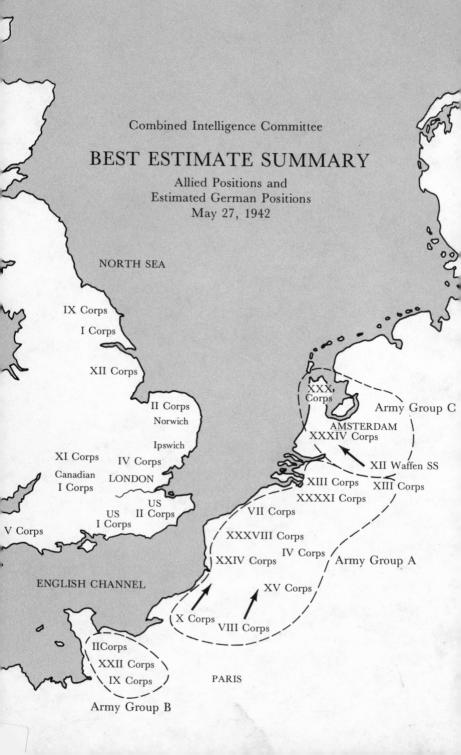

Combined Intelligence Committee

BEST ESTIMATE SUMMARY

Allied Positions and
Estimated German Positions
May 27, 1942

NORTH SEA

IX Corps

I Corps

XII Corps

II Corps
Norwich

Ipswich

XI Corps   IV Corps

Canadian   LONDON
I Corps

US
US   II Corps
I Corps

V Corps

ENGLISH CHANNEL

XXX
Corps

Army Group C

AMSTERDAM
XXXIV Corps

XII Waffen SS

XIII Corps
XIII Corps

XXXXI Corps

VII Corps

XXXVIII Corps

IV Corps

XXIV Corps

Army Group A

XV Corps

X Corps

VIII Corps

IICorps

XXII Corps

IX Corps

PARIS

Army Group B

1

Legends about the great warriors always have a source, often some small event magnified by time and retelling. Down through the centuries has come the tale that Alexander, enraged by his own soldiers' caution, grabbed a siege ladder, set it in place, and was the first to charge over the wall at Multan. Scipio Africanus, the Roman who defeated Hannibal, is said to have shamed his troops into action by charging on horseback alone into a line of Carthaginian cavalry. At Gettysburg, Confederate Brigadier General Lewis Armistead reportedly waved his hat on the point of his sword, rallying his outgunned men to break through Union lines.

I'd often wished I could witness the birth of a legend. General Wilson Clay and a Messerschmitt offered me that chance just before S-Day.

We had landed in the general's Cub several miles from Rye, the ancient town in east Sussex two miles inland from the English Channel. A jeep had been waiting for us, with a British driver, Corporal John Markham of the Royal Sussex Regiment, who had lived in Rye most of his life.

Local drivers met us at all stops because the signposts and milestones, some of them hundreds of years old, had been removed throughout England to confuse invaders. Everything else that identified towns had been painted over or hidden. Churches, building societies, shops, railway stations, all were rendered anonymous. Endless problems resulted. Tank columns turned around on themselves; infantry brigades became lost in marshes; truck convoys wandered miles down wrong roads.

I had slapped the general's four-star magnetized plates on the sides of the jeep, and rifle-carrying bodyguards followed in another jeep. General Clay had just served with George Patton, who always insisted on flags flying from his vehicle, motorcycle escorts, and sirens—a regular parade. He claimed the troops needed to know he was in their area. Clay did not tolerate that pomp, but he made daily tours, no matter how busy he was.

"Look at this." The general pointed at a ridge. "We're skulking under those trees, and the German hasn't even landed yet."

I was sitting behind him in the jeep.

He said, "Not a thing moving, no reinforcing, no build-up. We might as well be in Nebraska."

It should have been a peaceful tableau. A plow sat idly at the edge of a field. When the breeze played with patches of green winter wheat, the stalks briefly took on a silver tinge, reflecting the sun at a new angle. Rock walls rimmed the fields. We passed a stone house and barn that abutted the road, narrowing it. A small black dog emerged from the barn to bark at us.

Closer inspection revealed a land braced for battle. The wheat field was studded with poles, each the girth of a man's leg, a defense against gliders. So many poles dotted the landscape that American soldiers had taken to calling them Clay's spaghetti. We drove under iron bars arching fifteen feet over the road at regular intervals, also to prevent glider landings. Where the field ended at a defile of trees, an antitank ditch had been dug in the road, then covered with wood planks. A local Home Guard contingent had been assigned to remove the planks when enemy armor approached.

Our road wound along a shallow valley, with forested hills rising above the fields on both sides of us. We saw through the trees the indistinct lines of camouflage tarps and nets. Sentries walked the edge of the woods, carefully keeping under the forest shadows.

General Clay twisted in his seat and spoke loudly over the wind blowing around the windshield and the noise of the engine. "We think General Franz Halder told Hitler in 1940 it would take the Luftwaffe just two weeks to destroy the Royal Air Force. Instead, it has taken them two full years." Clay pursed his mouth a moment. "But now the Vickers-Supermarine plant in Southampton is a bombed-out hulk. Same with the Nuffield Spitfire factory. The Rolls Royce engine plant in Derby is in ruins. Most RAF squadrons exist only on paper."

The general once told me that the happiest stint of his career was the four years he taught military history at West Point. Given the slightest opportunity, Clay would still lecture, even if I was his only audience. I always listened attentively; one of the clearer duties of a lieutenant colonel being addressed by a general.

Silent until now, Corporal Markham could not help himself. "I knew we were in trouble when our metal cap badges were replaced with plastic ones a couple months ago. Badges for Spits, they said."

Worn on the front of his cap, the corporal's badge was the distinctive eight-pointed star of the Royal Sussex. Markham was tall enough that he was wedged into the jeep. His right leg was pinned awkwardly between the stick shift and the wheel. He had a rough-hewn face, with a bump on his nose, a knobby chin, and a narrow mouth. His Lee Enfield was tucked under his feet.

"You look good in plastic, Corporal." The general shifted his gaze to the woods on the rise. Several artillery pieces were parked under olive tarps. He scowled and said, "Tell Jones over my signature that his crews are cooking over open fires, and if I can see smoke rising above those trees, so can the goddamn German pilots."

Soldiers should carry rifles. I carried a note pad. I ate with it, slept with it, visited the latrine with it. I penciled a note in it. I also carried a camera on a strap over my shoulder. A 35-

mm Leica, a German product, no less. Major General Burt Jones was commander of the 2nd Infantry.* "Yes, sir."

Clay glanced skyward, narrowing his eyes against the vivid blue. The sun reflected on the four stars sewn near the seam of his cap. He preferred a side cap, which he would fold into a rear pocket when indoors, rather than a brimmed cap. He wore the same clothes every day so his men would recognize him: sharply creased khaki breeches, a tunic, a khaki tie tucked into his shirt below the second button, and a waist-length brown leather coat resembling an aviator's. Except for the stars on his cap, he typically wore no other badges of rank or service and no decorations. He told me it was his soldiers' duty to recognize him even without all the glitter on a uniform.

His hair must have been a rich red in his youth. I heard he was once called Red Clay at the academy. Only once. The story goes that he knocked the offending cadet off his feet, yelling that he was no goddamn Indian chief, and the nickname ended right there. The general's hair was now gray, with touches of auburn, and closely cropped. His grass-green eyes had flecks of brown in them. He had rather pale skin, with a smattering of freckles along his nose and forehead. His grin came easily, as did his laugh. More frequently, when he was lost in thought, his face would have a somber cast, with the infantryman's thousand-yard stare and his mouth turned down.

"The German didn't come two years ago in what he was going to call Sea Lion," Clay added, "because he couldn't gain control of the sky over England. Now that's changed."

I nodded. The general wasn't looking for conversation. The Luftwaffe's dominance of English skies had forced the British and Americans to transport men and machinery only at night. At first light every day, the columns left the roads for the forests to pitch camouflage gear overhead. Tanks, mounted antiaircraft and antitank batteries, self-propelled guns, armored and scout cars, half-tracks and trucks—everything and everyone— remained hidden until dusk. During daylight only essential movement was risked. The general had deemed essential this brief jeep journey from the airfield to the beach near Rye.

*Ranks are given as of S-Day.

6

Clay pulled a sheaf of reports from a folder on his lap. He lifted his reading glasses from his tunic pocket. The wire rim was so flexible he had to wrap the glasses around his face, always left ear to right. I was instantly forgotten. General Clay had a way of making others think they had vanished. I was used to it.

We passed a wood building with white roses climbing a wall trellis. A sign hanging above the door read "Crown and Thorn." On the door was a hand-printed notice with one word, "Sorry." There was precious little beer in England.

The general looked up. "Jack, see to it that Jones also takes the—"

The road abruptly turned on its side. At least, that's how it seemed to me. A wall of dirt and rocks was thrown into the air alongside us, then raced ahead.

"Bloody Christ!" yelled Markham. "We're under fire!"

He braked hard and swerved off the road. I grabbed a tie-down. The fender-well slammed my backside as the jeep lurched into a ditch. I fell to the cargo bed when the jeep careened off the trunk of an oak tree. The general's elbow shattered the windshield. We came to rest between two oaks when Markham's foot slipped off the clutch. The jeep's motor died.

The sound finally reached us, a dull pounding of four MG 17 machine guns mixed with the scream of a Daimler Benz engine. This model Messerschmitt, the 109E, was popularly known as the Emil, and it had destroyed European air forces early in the war. It was no match for a Spitfire, but there were seldom any British fighters around. The shadow of the plane flickered over us, the whine of its engine dropping to a low growl as it sped down the valley.

"You all right, General Clay?" I asked, rising unsteadily to my feet.

Clay held Corporal Markham's chin, turning his face toward him. A red crease crossed Markham's forehead where it had hit the steering wheel. "Report, Corporal."

"John Markham, Corporal. Royal Sussex. I'm fine." His words were rough, and he blinked repeatedly. "Little bump on the head is all."

7

Clay leaped from the jeep. He bit down on his lip, frowning. I followed his gaze. The bodyguards' jeep was turned on its side at the edge of the road forty yards behind us. The bullets had almost cut it in two, and shards of metal protruded at odd angles from the vehicle. Smoke poured from under the hood. The driver was sitting on the road, cupping his chin and rocking back and forth. Splattered with blood, the two bodyguards lay on the dirt, motionless, their M1s near them.

"Here it comes again," Markham said, stamping on the jeep's starter. The starter churned but the engine would not fire. "Christ, I've flooded it." The corporal hurried out of the jeep and fell behind a tree.

The Messerschmitt was banking out of the valley into the morning sun, the black crosses on its wings clearly visible. It skimmed behind the eastern hill, gaining elevation for another strafing run at us.

"Son of a bitch," Clay said under his breath. He leaned over the fender to grab Markham's rifle. He checked the action, stepped from under the tree, then raised the Lee Enfield to his shoulder.

"General, come on," Markham pleaded. "Take cover."

I jumped out of the jeep, prepared to shove Clay to the ground.

The Messerschmitt leveled off, coming at us at an oblique angle to the road. Even though the fighter was backlit by the sun, I could see muzzle flashes from the wings and cowling. The German's aim was low, and clods of dirt burst from the ground a hundred yards in front of us in a wheat field. The eruptions sprinted along the field, closing.

General Clay fired back, repeatedly squeezing the trigger, emptying the ten-round magazine in a few seconds.

The Messerschmitt emitted black smoke, and pieces of the engine blew away, followed by a sheet of the cowling. At the same instant, the rudder tore free. The fighter shuddered, and its port wing suddenly rose, tipping the plane onto its side. The elevators ripped off, and the Messerschmitt flipped onto its back. The hatch popped off, and the pilot's arm emerged as he struggled to climb out. It was too late. The Messerschmitt shot into the ground, parts of it spewing toward us across the field. A cloud of flame instantly engulfed the wreckage.

The general appeared to think nothing of it. He nodded approvingly as a white Ford ambulance emerged from the woods and quickly crossed the field to the overturned jeep. He casually asked Markham, "Can you get her going again?"

The corporal was gaping at the blaze. Dumfounded, he took a moment. "Pardon? The jeep? I think so."

Damage to the vehicle was limited to a sprung hood and a bent push bar. Markham pressed on the starter. After a moment of grinding, the engine rolled over. Clay slammed down the hood, then pushed the rifle back behind Markham's legs and climbed in.

"Don't dally, Corporal. I've got to get down this road."

I returned to my post behind the seats, and Markham backed the jeep onto the road. He shifted into forward, and we began again toward Rye.

Now, this is precisely what I saw, as did perhaps a thousand soldiers of the 2nd Infantry peering down at us from the hills. Of course, no Lee Enfield rifle is going to bring down a Messerschmitt. We learned later that it had been the pilot's hard luck to perform his banking maneuver right above fifteen antiaircraft mobile batteries, quadruple .50-caliber Browning M2 machine guns mounted on wheeled trailers, hidden in the woods on the rise. On the German's second run at us, they all opened up, gleefully firing through branches and leaves, enveloping the Messerschmitt in a web of fire. This was the AA crews' first combat, and they made the most of it, firing eleven thousand rounds between them, we learned later.

General Clay never claimed to have hit the plane and, indeed, was a bit embarrassed by his rash action. Yet, he had fired the Lee Enfield and the plane had come down. Within hours, most Americans in southern England knew their commander had single-handedly downed a Messerschmitt. The legend was born.

We passed to the west of Rye, which was once on the coast, but is now considerably inland due to the shingles and silt that have clogged the bay over the centuries. To reach the town, boats must sail two miles up the Rother on the flood tide, then be prepared to settle into the mud as the tide goes out. The general wanted to inspect the beach again.

We turned off the road and drove onto a low dune near the mouth of the river, the jeep's wheels sinking almost to the hubs as we crossed the sand. We kept well inland of a series of "Danger—Mines" signs. The beach stretched for miles before us, the pale sand contrasting with the radiant blue of the channel and sky.

The beach was littered with twisted metal, cement blocks, wood posts, and wire, reminding me of an abandoned construction site. Flatbed trucks were crossing the beach, carting material and ferrying engineers. Other soldiers were laying wire and filling bags. Fortifications hid thousands of other troops from the Luftwaffe fighters, which might at any moment appear. Each work crew had a spotter, which never lowered his binoculars. Sirens on poles would wail if enemy planes were spotted.

"Jack, take off your coat, will you?" the general said.

"Sir?" I hastily removed my wool overcoat. It was brisk in the back of the open jeep.

"A commander and his staff should never wear warmer clothes than men at the front. Stop at that wire array, Corporal."

We pulled up next to a length of dannert wire, unrolled coils clipped to support posts. Soldiers working with the wire turned to the general as he got out of the jeep. They smiled and wiped their hands on their uniforms.

"Morning, General," several shouted. They stepped eagerly toward the jeep.

"Men, look at yourselves," the general answered with mock anger, pointing at several of them. "You are damn near out of uniform."

The soldiers laughed. Although they wore steel-reinforced gloves, and a few had leather aprons similar to blacksmiths', their shirts and breeches were in tatters, victims of the wire's barbs. Even leather boots were torn, and some were held to-

10

gether by canvas wraps. As always happened, soldiers quickly gathered around General Clay.

"You injured, Private?" Clay nodded toward a soldier, whose blood was dripping along the tongue of one of his boots.

"No, sir." The private looked fourteen years old, with the skin of a peach and wide eyes. "A few scratches."

"That's what you joined the engineers for, right?"

"Yes, sir. For that very reason."

The others joined the general in the laugh. These were the men of the 2nd Engineers Battalion. Many of them had seams of blood along their faces and red blotches on their trousers and pants, the results of wrestling with barbed wire.

"You look after that, Private," the general said loudly, as always with his combat soldiers. "I don't want you working when injured."

"Yes, sir."

A jeep sped toward us along the beach, undoubtedly Major General Burt Jones, commander of the 2nd Infantry Division, whose beach we were on.

The general added, "But I'll be damned if I'll be issuing you a Purple Heart for a few nicks, either."

More laughter, which surged and faded in the channel wind. The jeep rolled up, and Jones jumped to the sand. "Good morning, sir. Nothing like a surprise inspection at 0800."*

Clay and Jones had served in the same unit in the Great War, and this gave Jones license to needle his superior. A crowd was assembling before Clay, who played to it. Again, quite loudly, Clay said, "I heard you were breaking these guys' collective butts, and I've come by to make sure it was the truth."

A round of "It is" and "You heard right" came from the soldiers.

Burt Jones was called Two Inch, but never to his face. It was thought he always wore two-inch platforms in his boots. He was a good five-four or so, alleged platforms included. He claimed he owed his life to his short stature. In the Meuse-

---

*All times will be given in British Double Summer Time. Germany was on German Central Time, one hour later.

Argonne sector in November 1918, mortar fragments had decapitated a taller American soldier running next to him, but had left Jones intact. Nevertheless, Jones walked rigidly, as if he had a poker for a backbone. His features were sized to his stature, with small eyes and a chip of a nose. But he spoke in a rich bass. Without his raising his voice, his orders carried fifty yards.

Jones stepped close, out of earshot of his troops, and said, "The resupply party got here just before dawn. That's their material you see being installed on the beach."

"Is it enough?" Clay asked, undoubtedly knowing the answer.

Jones inhaled loudly. "You know, General, I don't give a damn which day they come. But if I just knew which tide. We're spread too thin."

"Admiral Fairfax believes it'll be low tide." Clay's eyes followed the line of surf. "That'll give them what the admiral calls a dry attack. He argues that in the half-hour between landing and the rise of the tide, our posts and traps can be destroyed by German combat engineers. They'd avoid a high tide, when many of their landing craft would be pinioned and their bellies torn open."

Jones said. "Even so, I think it'll be high tide."

"Same here. A low tide landing means their craft would be grounded as far as four hundred yards offshore. That's a lot of open ground to cover under fire. It'd be like Suvla Bay at Gallipoli, where the 2nd Yeomanry had to cross the dried-up salt lake under a continuous barrage from Turkish batteries. No cover, easy pickings. They were mauled."

"General," interrupted one of the engineers. "We've got a piece of art we think you'll like. You inspired it."

With a glower, Burt Jones turned to the soldier.

Clay said quickly, "Art? Show me."

We walked after the engineer. A clot of troops followed us. I sank in the sand with each step. When we reached a landward rise in the dune, the engineer grandly raised his hand as if introducing an act and said, "Wire sculpture. It even has your name on it."

"Well, I'll be go to hell." Clay grinned widely. "Will you look at that? Pure beauty, Private. Pure goddamn beauty. A high-wire entanglement, a tremendous job."

The sculpture was a criss-crossed barbed wire mesh attached to a maze of wood posts. The entanglement resembled the outlines of a tent city, with stakes and wire guy lines, joined on both ends by dannert wire. It was a city block long and thirty feet deep and appeared impenetrable. We slowly walked along the entanglement. Hanging from wire midway was a hand-painted sign reading "Clay's Dog House."

The general paused in front of the sign. "What's your name, Private?"

"Will Drubowsky, 2nd Engineers Battalion, sir." A wad of tissue was stuck to a cut on the private's lip.

"Private Drubowsky, I'm touched." Clay turned to the crowd and made a production of wiping away a stage tear. "This rates right up there with my wedding day."

Hearty laughs.

"Get a photo of this, Jack."

Clay pulled Drubowsky into position next to him, with the sign visible on their right. The general locked his arm around the private's shoulder. I focused, then pressed the shutter.

Clay raised an imaginary champagne class. "Here's hoping some German bastard tears his *lederhosen* on this fine piece of art."

The soldiers lifted their hands, joining in the toast. They called out, "Here, here," and "Up theirs," and "Here's mud in their eyes."

The general touched his cap to the soldiers, who, to a man, instantly stood taller and snapped a salute. Clay led us back to the jeep. "Burt, I'll see you tonight."

We resumed our places in the jeep. Corporal Markham drove us down a narrow access lane on the beach, well marked with red flags stuck in the sand. To our left, seaward, were the deadly devices we hoped would repel the invasion.

First and foremost were the mines. It takes one ton of mines to cover a hundred yards, and it takes ten man-hours to plant every ton. To be an engineer, then, is to dig holes—hundreds, thousands, of them. The mines were M-7 dual-purpose weapons. Some were bounding mines, which leapt three feet into the air to explode. Others, less sophisticated, simply blew legs off when walked on. More antipersonnel mines sat atop posts, which were planted in long lines, resembling the pylons of rotted piers. These explosives were triggered by wires branching out in many directions from each post. Rows of cylindrical steel antitank mines were buried in the sand, each with five and a half pounds of high explosives.

Cluttering the beach below the mine fields were crude antitank obstacles: triangles of steel, saw-tooth bars resembling gates, cones of cement, even piles of rock—a junkyard of ragged stone and steel. Also embedded in the sand were rows and rows of anti–landing craft stakes, jutting at angles toward the water, resembling phalanxes of fifteenth-century Swiss pikemen, locked together and advancing "at push of pike." Twisted among the stakes were nests of barbed wire. And, above the high-water line, was the general's own invention: posts on which were mounted M1 portable flamethrowers, each with trip wire triggers. "We'll cook their asses," he had said when he showed me the drawing.

To landward of us were the manned obstacles. Piles of burlap sandbags were partly covered with tarpaulins on which were arranged plugs of salt grass. These were camouflaged machine gun nests. As we passed, soldiers set aside their mess tins and stood to wave at the general. He always saluted back. On slopes overlooking the beach were concrete bunkers, their guns pointed not out to sea, but right down the beach. Other guns were hidden in innocent-appearing seaside homes.

Behind the bunkers were batteries of rocket launchers, most commonly M17s, with their boxes of twenty tubes, but also some batteries borrowed from the British. They were mounted on trucks and tanks. Behind all this were the miles of communication trenches and hundreds of hastily poured concrete bunkers, all covered with barbed wire.

If you had asked me then, I'd have said not one living thing could have made it through those defenses. Not a German, not a German shepherd, not a German sand flea, nothing. That's why I was an aide-de-camp. Wilson Clay was the commander of an army, and he knew better.

He turned to me as we sped down the beach. "Jack, you may

be wondering why I took the time back there to admire some barbed wire contraption."

"Of course I know why, General."

"Let me explain, then."

I never knew whether he just didn't hear me or whether he didn't care how I replied.

"Yesterday there were about 150 Luftwaffe sorties over the 2nd Infantry's portion of this beach. Strafing, bombing, dropping leaflets, the works. The 2nd suffered fifty-eight casualties. They've endured this day after day."

I nodded. My teeth chattered against each other. My coat lay on the jeep's bed.

"The same folks who chewed up France and the Low Countries may be sailing to this very spot. Tonight, tomorrow night, next week, soon. My soldiers are fearful, and they have every right to be. So I've got to compensate. I do it by building their morale."

"Should I be taking notes, sir?"

" 'The moral is to the physical as three is to one.' Do you know who said that?"

I thought for a moment. "Babe Ruth."

"For Christ's sake, Jack, the commander of the American Expeditionary Force doesn't go around quoting Babe Ruth. He quotes Napoleon. And Napoleon was dead right."

"Yes, sir."

"A hundred small things assure that my soldiers will follow me and believe in my leadership, such as those snapshots I'm always having you take. They end up in hometown newspapers, soldier arm in arm with his general."

We zigzagged left and right, through a flag-marked mine field. The flags were removed every evening, lest they mark passage for the invaders. More soldiers, hastily continuing preparation of the beach defenses, waved at General Clay. He waved and saluted, again and again, reminding me of a Harvest Queen on her float. The elbow which he had put through the windshield didn't seem to bother him. Markham had folded down the windshield frame.

"What's the most important aspect of morale for troops at the front?" he asked me, mid salute.

15

"Knowing your side has better men and weapons."

"Jack, you're thinking too much. Socks. An army fights on its socks. An officer must make sure his men's socks fit. Loose or tight socks lead to sore feet. And socks must stay dry to keep away trenchfoot. When new socks are issued, morale soars. Don't forget that."

"I won't, sir."

"No army with clean, dry, comfortable socks ever lost a battle, not once in history, as far as I can tell."

"You've spent a lot of time studying socks, sir?"

"You're goddamn right. Corporal, pull up to that fortification."

"Fortification" was a happy euphemism for three reinforced concrete walls with a gun port, something of a pillbox. It was a rough structure with no finishing on the concrete and no floor. Hundreds had been slapped together along General Clay's sector. The barrel of an M1 A1 pack howitzer protruded through the portal.

Several soldiers appeared from behind the bunker when Clay got out of the jeep. They shouted greetings.

"Official inspection tour, men," Clay announced in that patently pompous voice that instantly put the soldiers at ease. He never used that tone with his staff or division commanders.

I followed him across the sand toward the entrenchment. Other soldiers, who had been manning nearby machine gun emplacements, began moving toward us. Several whooped at the honor of the visit. Others climbed out of slit trenches, called out to the general, and broke into trots toward the pillbox.

Clay demanded of the first man who reached him, "Name and unit, soldier."

"Corporal Allen Wilkes, 38th Field Artillery Battalion, 2nd Infantry, sir."

"Show me what you've got," ordered Clay. He followed the gunners into the box. The six-man crew took their positions around the weapon. This was an old howitzer, used for close support, mounted on spoked wheels, firing a fourteen-pound shell to nine thousand yards. The size of the crew was determined not by the number of soldiers it took to fire it, which was only two, but by how many it took to dismantle and cart it.

"What's your load?"

"Steelies, sir." Corporal Wilkes was about twenty years old. He had an open, cheerful face, with canted eyes and large teeth. He looked at odds with his menacing howitzer. His crew surrounded us in the bunker's tight quarters.

"What in hell are steelies?"

"When we played marbles as a kid, that's what we called ball bearings. You'd shoot with them. Most of what's in these shells are damaged ball bearings."

"Grapeshot is what you're telling me."

"Yes, sir."

"So you'll pepper them with steelies? Good for you, Corporal."

Wilkes's eyes followed the barrel out the port. "We will if we can see them, General."

"They'll be sitting ducks, wading in the water, burdened with eighty or a hundred pounds in their packs. Most'll probably drown. But a few might make the beach. You'll see them clear as day down your gunsight."

Wilkes cleared his throat. "General, that's not what I heard. Word has it they've got a fog pill they're all going to swallow on the way over here. Makes them invisible in their own little cloud of fog."

I stared at the gunner and was about to burst out laughing, when General Clay asked in earnest, "Where'd you hear that, Corporal?"

"On the wireless, sir," Wilkes replied sheepishly. His crewmates nodded. They'd heard it, also.

"On NBBS?" The New British Broadcasting Station. "Lord Haw Haw? Is he your source?"

"There's no order against listening to him, sir."

Lord Haw Haw was the sobriquet of William Joyce, an ex-member of the British Union of Fascists who had gone to Germany just before outbreak of the war. With his arrogant, grating voice, he broadcast German propaganda in English from Hamburg.

"And I suppose you believed him about the fog pills and about the electromagnetic ray that can turn cement pillboxes into melting mush?"

"Well, sir . . ." Wilkes stared at his howitzer. I heard the hissing of waves breaking against the shore.

Clay slapped the gunner on the shoulder. "You and I know it's all crapola. And I'll tell you something, Corporal, the Germans think you've got your finger on a button that will spray gasoline two miles out to sea, then set it on fire." Clay laughed, nodding, inviting Corporal Wilkes and the others to join him. "Just think, Corporal. The German thinks we can set the English Channel on fire, huge balls of flame right out of hell, all along the south coast. So he's over there wetting his pants with fear."

Wilkes felt the reprieve of humor. He rocked back with a loud guffaw, and the other soldiers joined him.

"That's not all, Corporal. We've also let the German know in our radio broadcasts that we've planted gravity rods all along the beach, generating huge pulses of extra gravity that'll pull his bullets right into the ground in a limp arc just like piss from a goat as soon as he fires."

"Gravity rods, General?" Wilkes exclaimed. "Those bastards actually believe we've got magic gravity rods?"

I chuckled along.

The general abruptly asked, "Where's your radio, Corporal?"

The young man sobered. "It's with our truck, sir. It's just an old Edison we wired to a White six-by-six."

"Show it to me."

Clay and I followed the corporal out the back of the entrenchment and up the side of a grass-covered hill of sand. Behind it, under a khaki camouflage tent, was the enormous White. The crowd, now no less than a hundred soldiers, walked with us.

Resting on the truck's front winch was the radio, a model made of black Bakelite with imitation ivory knobs. Clay ripped out the power wire, then lifted the radio over his head as if he were a boxer displaying his hard-won championship belt. He marched a few paces away from the truck to plant the radio against a sand berm.

He turned back to his men. "Let me show you what we're going to do Lord Haw Haw after the war." He pointed to several soldiers carrying their M1s. "You four, form a line in front of the radio."

They quickly did so. Their faces reflected their bewilderment.

"Ten hut," barked the general.

The four soldiers came to attention, and they smartly shouldered their rifles as General Clay called out commands. Others stood back.

"Ready." Safeties clicked off. Clay looked right to insure a clear field of fire.

"Aim." He pointed at the radio. "Fire."

The shots crackled. The Bakelite shattered, and tubes and wire blew out the back. The Edison skittered back on the sand. The riflemen lowered their weapons.

"There." He clapped his hands together as if ridding them of chalk. "That's what I think of Lord Haw Haw's bullshit."

The story that appeared on the Associated Press wire and was reprinted in many U.S. newspapers saying the general ordered a soldier to put the radio on his head, like William Tell, to be shot off by the firing squad is apocryphal, probably begun by one of the general's detractors.

The general bade good-bye to the 38th, and we climbed into the jeep, applause following us. We made stops at several other units that morning before we left the beach for Rye.

The town is the loveliest of the Cinque Ports, the confederation dating from the reign of Edward the Confessor, which provided sailors and ships to the crown in return for certain privileges. Rye stands on a promontory, the old cliff line, which before the sixteenth century overlooked the channel.

Below the town now are reclaimed marshes, used for grazing and farming. These marshlands and shingles form a twelve-mile indentation in the coast, from Dungeness to the Fairlight headland. Here England was once protected from sea-borne invaders by cliffs. No longer.

Rye is a town of wood warehouses and maritime inns. It is a seaport, although the sea long ago retreated. The town was fortified against the French in the fourteenth century, and we entered it through the remaining town gate, which lost its drawbridge and portcullis long ago. Burt Jones had provided another trailing jeep, this one with a mounted .30 caliber machine gun. It followed us as we passed storefronts and several pubs.

Few of Rye's citizens remained in town. The area twenty miles inland, from Berwick-upon-Tweed to Plymouth—most of the east and south coasts of England—had been declared a Defense Area. Men and women who were not essential workers and children had been moved inland. No one could visit the coastal area without good reason. The town echoed with their absence. We drove by a poster showing Mr. Squanderbug, drawn over the legend "Wanted for Sabotage." Most windows along the streets had tape or paper over them. On a sturdy stone building was a sign indicating the air warden's post was inside and on a nearby wall was an ad, "Wartime living affects your liver . . . Carter's Little Liver Pills."

A man walked along the narrow sidewalk carrying a basket of haws, red berries that come in May, useful for feeding pigs when there is little else. I saw down a sidestreet the man's penned hogs and several chickens, which throughout Britain had moved into towns for the duration. At another intersection was a news vendor's stand. Earlier in the war vendors scrawled in chalk on homemade placards the plane tallies, "122 for 48," or "45 for 22," as if the war overhead were a cricket match. Of late the scores had been too gloomy, and this vendor's placard was blank.

Corporal Markham drove us around a mound of stones, once a small church. Rubble was everywhere, piles of rock, brick, and charred timber. Buildings had been destroyed at random, giving the town a gap-toothed look. Rye had no particular military significance, but the Luftwaffe was still carrying out Baedeker raids, originally in retribution for the RAF bombings of Rostock and Lübeck, now simply to injure British morale. Bath, Salisbury, Winchester, Canterbury, and many other historic sites had been hit, singled out from the Baedeker guide book. On a water tower was a plane spotter, with his binoculars on a strap around his neck. Spotters were nicknamed Jim Crow.

We turned up a hill toward the Mermaid Inn, which had

hosted smugglers and sailors for hundreds of years, intending to meet the troops of the newly arrived 40th Field Artillery Battalion. Instead, we drove into a nest of activity on the rough stone street. We slowed for the swarm of soldiers. They wore a mix of uniforms, American Army and British Home Guard, and they were agitated.

The crowd parted before our jeep. The shouting gradually died as the soldiers turned and saw stars on the jeep and recognized the general. Standing near the inn's door was a man whose hands were tied behind him. Blood was flowing from his nostrils and from a cut above an eyebrow. He was wearing dark wool pants, a stained leather vest, and a blue shirt, part of which had been ripped away and hung to his knees. He was braced by two military policemen carrying rifles at the ready. The British press called American MPs Clay's Snowballs, because of their white helmets. Next to them was Colonel Ralph Simpson, commander of the 40th. He was reading an army manual with such intensity that he did not look up even as the jeep came within six inches of him.

"Something I can help you with, Ralph?" General Clay asked.

The colonel's head came up. Vast relief crossed his features. He was a rounded man, with a distended belly and an extra chin. Hitler had made mustaches unpopular in the Allied services, but Simpson bucked the trend. His resembled a black bottle brush, which he carefully trimmed so it did not cover his puffy upper lip. "Sir, my prisoner is an Irishman, caught this morning in a flat in Rye with a two-way radio. I'm having a little trouble convincing my men that we should hand him over for interrogation."

Someone behind the jeep shouted, "We'll interrogate the bastard, General. Just give him to us."

A chorus of assent rose from the crowd.

"You've questioned him yourself?" Clay asked.

"He refuses to say a word."

"How'd he get bloodied?"

"My men say he tripped down the stairs as he tried to escape, sir."

"You sure he's Irish?" The general remained seated in the jeep.

"Damn right," one of the Home Guard called out. "Just look at him."

The prisoner was a jut-jawed brunet with a cold gaze. His face was the white of paste, and he had a prominent Adam's apple. I didn't see anything peculiarly Irish about him, but I'm no expert. Despite urgings from the Ministry of Information to "Join the Silent Column," rumors were rife that the Irish had teamed with the Axis en masse, and most were in southern England radioing intelligence reports to their German masters. The notion was preposterous. Then again, this fellow was no rumor.

"The bastards don't know who their friends are," another Guard added. The Guards wore uniforms identical to the British infantry's except for the shoulder flashes. "He's a spy."

The general asked, "What kind of radio?"

"Here's his two-way." A lieutenant from the 2nd Signal Company held up a portable radio and a battery pack, a model the Germans called an *Agentenfunk*.

"How'd you find him?" Clay asked.

"We've got one of the new radio direction finders," the lieutenant answered. He pointed up Mermaid Street to his jeep. Mounted on a roll bar was a circular antenna on a ball joint. "A new Motorola. We've been looking for him for a week. He finally obliged with a lengthy broadcast. The Brits and us broke into his room and found the radio, wired and ready to go, and he was still talking into the microphone."

"Looks pretty suspicious, all right," General Clay concluded dryly. He turned to the soldiers and asked loudly, "What are you men proposing to do?"

"The man is a spy," one shouted. "Working behind our lines, plain and simple."

Another yelled, "We're going to shoot him out of hand."

Several soldiers standing around our jeep nodded vigorously. "Line him up," one called out.

From the rear of the group another shouted, "Let's dish out some of what we've been taking." There was loud consent from many of the soldiers.

Clay motioned them to silence. "Let's think this through,

men. G2 will be mighty upset if they don't get a chance to talk to this guy."

"Look at him." An American sergeant jerked his thumb at the prisoner. "He's going to keep his trap shut right into the grave."

"Let's not be hasty here, Sergeant. There's little difference whether this fellow is shot right now or in a couple of weeks, after Intelligence discovers his story."

"Bullshit, General," a soldier yelled.

"Let us have the son of a bitch," another bellowed.

Clay held up a finger, cutting them off. His words became more abrupt. "I'm not making myself clear, men. This fellow is going to be put behind bars and Colonel Simpson will call G2. Are you following me?"

Borrowing the general's strength, Simpson straightened himself, "Precisely, sir. Thank you." He turned to the guards. "Corporal, you and the private here find where the jail is in this town, lock the Irishman up, and post guards."

The soldiers straightened in unison. One yelled, "Are you shitting us, General?"

Another, with a voice tightened by ferocious anger, "This bastard was working to make sure plenty of us die when his German friends come."

Fists were raised and hammered in the air.

"We can take care of him without help from you, General."

"We heard you were a hard ass, General. But you see an Irish spy close up, and you go soft."

"How many of us will this bastard have helped kill in the next week?"

"Now's our chance."

The soldiers pulsed a step forward.

General Clay suddenly stood in the jeep. He pointed sharply at the gunner in the trailing vehicle, then at the sky.

The burst of .30-caliber shells was loud in the narrow street. Soldiers ducked, some dropped to the cobblestones. Others instinctively looked for a Messerschmitt. The Irishman didn't even wince.

The general pushed out his chest in that unattractive way

often captured on the newsreels. Too much like Mussolini, I told him once. He said in a brittle voice, "You'll learn exactly how goddamn hard I am if this prisoner is harmed. Lock him up." He swept his gaze over the crowd like it was a gun on a swivel. It found the guards. "You heard me. Take him away."

The corporal pushed the Irishman on the shoulder, directing him through the crowd. The other guard followed. The soldiers let them pass.

Clay smiled thinly. "You men save your anger for when the German is armed and coming at you. It'll serve you well then."

"Dismissed," yelled Colonel Simpson.

Chastened, the soldiers seemed only too happy to disperse.

The general lowered himself to the seat and looked over his shoulder at me. "Did you see that goddamn spy laugh when I saved his ass?"

I had.

"I was tempted to change my mind right then, line him up in front of a firing squad like I did to that Edison back on the beach. The goddamn ingrate."

"Not only was he spying on us, he's ungrateful." I shook my head. "Can you imagine?"

"Hardly, no," Markham smiled.

"Just because my aide in the back seat is a wise ass doesn't mean you can be too, Corporal. Let's go."

We backed down Mermaid Street to return to the Cub.

2

Wilson Clay treated the press as if he were an elected official. He granted frequent interviews and told reporters what he could, which was usually little. When he arrived back at his headquarters at Eastwell, Donald McDonald of Reuters and Jerry Ness of United Press were waiting for him at his trailer. He waved them in and said, "Everything is off the record unless I say otherwise."

Both reporters sat in the uncomfortable wood chairs across from the built-in settee. Their reports were censored in any event.

"You two had breakfast?" Clay asked.

"I got an early start, and just had coffee," McDonald replied. The Reuters correspondent was the dean of war reporters, having filed his first stories from Cuba during the Spanish-American War. His hair was yellow-white, the color of an old newspaper. His skin was the same hue, the result of his struggle with malaria, which had almost killed him thirty years before, when he was posted in Panama, and which occasionally recurred. His jaw was unnaturally cut, as if drawn with a T-square. He wore rimless spectacles and this past month had started using a cane. "If you've got breakfast, I'll eat it."

"Same here," Ness said, drawing a pad from his shirt pocket. Ness was a favorite of the GIs because in 1918, during the second Battle of the Marne, he had dropped his paper and pen and crawled out of a trench to drag wounded American soldiers back to safety. Claiming he was a bit deaf, he always kept his left ear cocked toward the person he was interviewing, and he wore a puzzled expression, as if he were not quite hearing the words. He told me once he could hear perfectly well, but people always said more if they thought the reporter wasn't quite getting it all. Ness had a high forehead, emphasized by his dark hair, which he wore slicked back. His eyes, set far back in his face, reflected his intelligence and humor.

"Charley, have the cook set up four breakfasts, will you?"

Corporal Charles Elliot was the general's orderly. He emerged from the trailer's kitchen nook and left for the manor house.

Ness tilted his head at General Clay. "Speculation around the news corps is that they're coming tonight. I don't suppose you have any publishable thoughts on that, do you, General?"

"None."

"Or where they'll come?" McDonald asked. He didn't even have his pen out. He knew the routine.

"No."

"Anything we can send back home?" Ness tried again.

The general's eyebrows narrowed in thought. "If the German attempts an invasion of England, historians will mark it as the beginning of the end of the Third Reich. How's that?"

"A little too quotable, General," Ness said, writing it anyway.

"Put this down, then. The American Expeditionary Force is ready for anything. I have utter confidence in our soldiers."

"We can always count on you for special insights, General Clay," Ness said sardonically.

Clay laughed. He removed one of his shoes and rubbed the ball of a foot. "You wouldn't think someone who sits on his butt all day would get such damn sore feet."

"Can we quote you, General?" McDonald asked.

"No."

"I've got a deadline," Ness pleaded. "I need something."

"Look around my setup here," General Clay suggested. "Tell your readers how I live."

"You must think we write for *Life*," McDonald growled. Nevertheless, he and Ness stood to tour the trailer.

There wasn't a lot of furniture or much of anything else. The trailer had a living room, a galley, and sleeping quarters. It was decorated with framed photographs of his wife Margaret, perhaps a dozen photos, some on the walls, several on his desk. Also on the desk were three phones installed by the Signal Corps. The red phone was a direct link to Washington, the green to the cabinet war rooms in London, and the black to his headquarters in the manor house nearby. Just before the reporters arrived, Corporal Elliot had swept all documents on the desk into a drawer, as he always did.

The general slept on a canvas and wood cot. Detective novels were piled on the lamp table, a fact both reporters noted in their pads. A cardboard trunk containing cold weather uniforms was at the foot of the bed. Another photograph of Margaret stood on a bedside table.

With little to look at, McDonald and Ness moved from the cramped bedroom through the main room, where the general was still rubbing his feet, into the galley. Next to the small sink was a basket of mottled apples, a pile of C-ration tins, and a pitcher of water. Ness poured himself a glass. The shelves were bare.

When they resumed their seats, McDonald commented, "This trailer isn't as swank as I might've expected from a full general."

"I've got all I need," Clay replied in that humble fashion he could generate once in a while.

Charley Elliot returned with breakfast, stacked on trays. He passed them around. The general sat at his desk, and the reporters and I used our knees to balance the trays. Scrambled eggs, ersatz sausage, and a cup of apple juice.

General Clay poked at his eggs, sniffed a forkful of them, then turned to his orderly. "Charley, these look real."

"They are, sir. The old man who owns the place over by the pond brought by a dozen eggs for you this morning." Elliot was a slight man, with curly blond hair and a fidgety manner. His job was to be always at the ready, and he excelled at it.

"You know my rule, Charley," Clay said patiently.

"Yes, sir. You don't eat better than the men in the field. But I thought that since you've got guests this morning, you ought to serve some real eggs."

"Take these away, and bring the powdered ones," The general ordered.

Elliot quickly gathered the trays, almost having to wrestle the plate of fragrant eggs away from McDonald. He pushed the trailer's door open with his foot and sprinted toward the house.

Ness rose from his chair. "I don't see any profit in waiting around for those wretched powdered eggs, General. Thanks for the interview, such as it was."

"Any time." Clay gestured expansively. "Glad to be of help."

As McDonald and Ness filed out of the trailer, the general smiled conspiratorially at me. When the door closed, he asked, "Think they bought it?"

The interview had been a staged production. The detective novels were props. General Clay never read them. His bedtime reading was anything but relaxing. He read Cromwell on the problems of morale and command. He read Frederick's *Instructions for his Generals*, Marshal de Saxe's *Reveries*, and Guibert's *Essay on Tactics*. And he studied whatever he could find written by the enemy: General Eimannsberg's *Der Kampfwagenkrieg* (Tank War), General Guderian's *Achtung Panzer*, even *Tante Friede*, which means Aunt Friede, the German infantry officers' nickname for their manual. General Clay read in German, French, and English, and he never read anything for pleasure.

Corporal Elliot returned, still carrying three of the trays of real scrambled eggs. The general said, "Nice work, Charley."

Elliot placed a tray in front of the general, handed one to me, and kept one for himself. Clay dug into them with his fork. Powdered eggs activated his gag reflex, he told me. He always had a full larder, courtesy of nearby English farmers, who, grateful for his presence, frequently sent dressed out chickens, boxes of fruit, milk, and other farm goods. Once in a while a bottle of Scotch Highland whiskey would arrive at the trailer. Each week he also received in the mail from America dozens of boxes of cookies and candy, canned meat, dried fruit, and the like, always with heartrending notes asking him to take care of the writers' sons. Corporal Elliot had hidden the stockpile of food and whiskey behind the trailer before Ness and McDonald arrived.

His appetite accurately reflected the man. The general enjoyed an iron constitution, despite his Pall Malls and his living on four hours sleep a night. He had only two infirmities. One was a constant ringing in his ears, a symptom of hypertension. Clay claimed he did not have time to take pills, so his doctor was attempting to treat the high blood pressure by having medication surreptitiously added to his food. The other was a stiff and creaking ankle from an old injury.

Perhaps I need to correct an impression here. General Clay was no Gonzalo de Córdoba, the Spanish general who in the late 1400s arrived at a battle elegantly turned out and lavishly provisioned. Clay slept in the spartan trailer, not in the bedroom suite available for him in the manor house. He ate the proffered food not as a display of perquisites, but simply because he could not resist it. Every evening I poured him a whiskey, which he threw back, then another, which he pondered over, sometimes for an hour, and seldom finished. I never saw him drink more than that. The numerous photographs of his wife were certainly not props, but were a genuine expression of his reverence and love for her. At times he would speak to me of Margaret, reminiscing in low, intimate tones, his eyes on one of her photos. I would sit silently, knowing he was talking to her, not me. He had not seen her for more than a year. I write candidly here of his love for her, because in my opinion it vastly overshadowed his relationship with Lady Anne Percival, which I will discuss at some length later.

The show of asceticism so carefully arranged for the Reuters and UP reporters was not a cynical charade. Rather, it was another of the general's attempts to insure his soldiers would trust his leadership. Clay compared the army to a bunch of bananas, some rotten, some green, some yellow. But, he swore, all would follow him when the time came. Civilians at home and soldiers in the theater would read of an earnest man of simple tastes, a father figure, one who shared his soldier's pri-

29

vations, one who read pulp novels and whose shoes were too tight—an endearing portrait.

General Clay gobbled his food. Time spent eating was time lost, he liked to tell me if I lingered to chew. His mouth was still full of eggs when he put down his fork and said, "Let's go."

Headquarters was in Eastwell Manor, just north of Ashford in Kent. The trailer was parked along a brick wall to the west of the house, and we walked through an ornate but untended rose garden toward the building. The manor had over sixty acres of grounds within a three-thousand-acre estate. Queen Victoria and King Edward VII had been regular visitors, and Prince Alfred had lived there. Before the war, the manor had required more than a hundred retainers: gardeners, cooks, maids, stable hands. The building was quite daunting, three stories, with several wings, all made of gray stone. Spires, cupolas, and banks of chimneys topped it. The owner, Lord Ramsey, had ceded the estate to the general for as long as needed, but Clay changed location of his headquarters every four or five days, fearing Luftwaffe raiders. Lord Ramsey had left his hunting hounds, and they were cared for by the headquarters company. From their run fifty yards from the building, they barked and howled endlessly, a grating background to every conversation I had at the manor.

The manor was referred to as AEFHQ, pronounced "Afe-Q," American Expeditionary Force Headquarters. Headquarters was actually in London, and this was the advance command post, but it was still called AEFHQ. Almost five hundred people were assigned to it, including staff members, engineers, signal specialists, military police, and others. Most were billeted in the manor outbuildings and in neighboring homes, some in Ashford. General Clay's close staff assistants lived in the manor house, including his two corps commanders, his chief and assistant chiefs of staff, his G2 and G4, liaison officers, and others. I shared a room on the second floor with Colonel William Strothers, Clay's chief medical officer. From his office in the billiard room, the general guided, dominated, rewarded, and harried his staff.

The billiard room was on the ground floor, facing the north

gardens, which dropped away from the manor house in a gradual slope, with long grass concourses, topiaries, and an empty fountain. The billiard table had been moved against a paneled wall and was used for spreading out maps. Windows had been taped, and blankets dyed black hung around them, to be drawn over the glass at nightfall. The general's desk was flanked by one for his secretary and another for his stenographer. Mine was against an inner wall, near the cue rack, which had a chalk ball attached to it. A fine powder of blue chalk always covered my work.

Clay's G2, Major General David Lorenzo, was sitting in a chair beside the general's desk, waiting. The G2 was forty-five years old, young for the rank. He had a broad nose and dark eyes hidden under vast eyebrows. Lorenzo carried a small notebook he would refer to, but he never offered a written report. Clay required oral briefings so he would not be overwhelmed with the details of written reports. Clay nodded to the G2, but the phone rang before they could begin. He lifted it and listened for a moment. The general believed a commander should answer his own phone during daylight. Not many people telephone a commanding general, except for emergencies, and then callers needed to speak to him at once.

Clay said into the phone, "Fine. Move it up."

He hung up and turned to his stenographer to quickly relay the conversation. The general finally lowered himself into his chair. G2 leaned forward and began speaking about overnight developments and what was known about German air, land, and sea movements. Lorenzo's was an early job. He always met at 4:30 in the morning with his night duty officers. Clay bit crescents into the corners of his mouth as he listened. I was not privy to the conversation. Undoubtedly Lorenzo would do most of the talking and make recommendations. Subordinates who thought their jobs were done when they reported on a problem without also offering a solution did not last long. Lorenzo knew the requirements. He had worked with the general for three years. Clay disliked new faces around him.

There is little romance in leading an army. The general's days at Eastwell or other headquarters locations were usually steady grinds of appointments. But as the invasion inevitably drew near, Clay allowed fewer things to crowd his calendar. "On the day of the battle, I want to do nothing," he had said, believing his observations would be clearer, his judgment more sane, and his reactions to change better. After Lorenzo, Clay was scheduled to meet with Lieutenant General Eugene Girard, commander of II Corps, and others. Then we would be off again in his Cub. Clay told me that twenty years of staff assignments and combat schools had given him calluses on his butt, and he loathed being at his desk.

A week-old copy of the *Detroit Free Press* was in my basket. I glanced at the front page and its war news. There was also a story on General Clay's mother and a photo of her holding up a snapshot of a ten-year-old Wilson Clay. The intense press coverage of Clay had begun two months before, on his promotion and appointment to command the American Expeditionary Force.

Unlike European military officers, most American professional soldiers come from modest origins, and Clay was no exception. The American public found all the elements for a folk hero. Clay was born in 1890 in Davenport, Washington, thirty-five miles west of Spokane, in a three-room clapboard house. Not exactly a log cabin, but close enough for the newspaper photographers who converged on it. The general's father, Tom Clay, who later owned a state bank, was supposed to have killed a man from Sprague, twenty-five miles southeast, in a war over which town would be Lincoln County seat. Davenport won. Wilson Clay never knew whether the story was true and never got up enough courage to ask his father, but citizens of Davenport never tired of speculating about it in front of the son. The general allowed untrue stories about himself to circulate if they were useful. Perhaps he learned that from his father.

Tom Clay abused his son relentlessly. Wilson spent his first sixteen years learning of his inadequacies and being reminded of his failures. He was the object of cruel jokes and public humiliations and the target of countless backhand cuffs. His mother, loving and weak, was powerless to intercede. The general told me once that he wished he could blame his father's mean spirit on alcohol or dementia, but, in fact, he said, "My father simply came into this world packed with bile to his eye-balls." Tom died in the early 1920s. "The bastard choked to death on his own spite." Actually, it was on a piece of ham. General Clay had said he hoped time would diminish the hateful memories of his father. It hadn't yet.

Tom Clay's sourness was the key to his son's success, I believe. The general's dogged ambition to outshine his belittling father drove him throughout his life, even after the old man was gone. Other warriors have suffered cruel fathers. The two greats, Alexander and Frederick, come to mind. Perhaps they too tried to exonerate themselves before their fathers. In any event, you can be sure neither Alexander nor Frederick tolerated amateur psychiatrists as aides, and General Clay certainly did not, so I'll end my speculation.

Tom Clay's persistence in obtaining for his son a West Point appointment was viewed by Wilson as another form of punishment. A military academy had never crossed the boy's mind, the general claimed. Tom failed at first and settled for shipping Wilson to the Virginia Military Institute in Lexington. General Clay said the year at VMI paid a handsome premium, because it allowed him to enter West Point by certificate, without taking the dreaded entrance examination. During that year, Tom called in favors from local businessmen and politicians, asking them to pressure Henry Wade, the United States senator from Spokane, until, finally, Wade appointed Wilson to the academy. My suggestion one evening that his father's obtaining a West Point appointment might have been motivated by something other than the desire to be rid of the boy was dismissed out of hand by the general.

It is well known now that Wilson Clay graduated first in the class of 1915. For the next two years he was an assistant commanding officer at Fort Bragg, North Carolina. He served in artillery in the Great War. "I didn't see the enemy much, but I sent my regards often enough." In 1918, he received the Distinguished Service Cross "basically for not tucking my tail between my legs and running away from my battery one day when I really wanted to."

Clay was discharged as a colonel of the wartime National Army in 1919, reverting to his Regular Army grade of captain.

He was posted to West Point for four years as a lecturer. Then came twelve years of staff assignments and combat schools, during which time he was stuck at the rank of major. In 1933 he was sent to the Philippines for three years, where he made lieutenant colonel.

Clay's meteoric rise began during the 1939 army maneuvers, where his impressive performance earned him an assignment to Washington as deputy, then chief of operations. He visited the White House more often than any soldier except George Marshall, the chief of staff. By December 7, 1941, Clay was wearing two stars.

President Roosevelt wanted to keep Clay in Washington as assistant to Marshall, perhaps eventually to replace Marshall, but Clay desperately wanted a field command. "I came as close to begging as I ever have," he once told me. "It would have been an ugly sight, a major general groveling on his knees."

It is easy, and accurate, to say Wilson Clay thirsted for fame. In his words, "History recalls those in the field. We remember Grant, not Halleck, Lincoln's chief of staff."

His appointment to command the AEF in Great Britain was a surprise, and the press concluded it was due largely to his favor with the president and the chief of staff. Clay brushed aside newspaper terms such as "practiced charm" and "Eleanor's favorite GI."

Credit the president and George Marshall with more than promoting a crony. Washington bristled with desk-bound generals lusting after that command, but the president must have known that competent peacetime military leaders do not always make skilled warriors; they can prepare for war, but they can't practice the real thing. And Roosevelt knew of Clay's talents: Clay understood the qualities and needs of the American soldier, he was skilled at stage management and a genius in administration, and he knew the art of war. The president and the world would soon learn of yet another talent, one the French call *le feu sacré*, the distinctive characteristic of the warrior, an utter determination to conquer or to perish with glory.

The president and George Marshall were looking for the perfect general, one with Charles XII's courage, Eugene's art, Montecuccoli's foresight, and Turenne's ability to seize the critical moment. No such person existed. They settled on Wilson Clay. Some now say this was the gravest mistake of Roosevelt's presidency. Others will always cheer the decision. You will already have guessed that I am a Clay partisan.

He was a lieutenant general all of one month before being promoted again, virtually unprecedented in American military history. The general clearly understood his transition from an obscure staff officer to commander of the American army in Great Britain, from an unknown to a celebrity, and he cherished his new position in the world.

Not that there wasn't a drawback to fame. He railed, but only to me, about the press when they acquired and published personal letters to family and friends. He asked the judge advocate general to prevent their publication and was told there was no legal means to do so. So he began censoring his own letters, depriving them of substance. He called them "dull whitewash."

I looked up from my copy of the *Free Press*. General Clay walked David Lorenzo to the billiard room's door, a hand on his shoulder, talking into his ear and stabbing the air with a finger, gesturing encouragingly. Clay believed it was his duty to be optimistic with his staff commanders. He conveyed his buoyancy and hope at every meeting. His chief of intelligence, Lorenzo, was the most difficult to convince. Clay always underestimated the enemy's strength to junior officers, but it was the G2's job to know better. With a final pat on the back, Clay said goodbye to Lorenzo. He turned back into the room. His face was ashen.

Others were loitering in the reception room, waiting for their turn with the general, but he quickly walked by the billiard table and out the glass door onto the stone veranda behind the manor house. He descended the steps into the garden. I viewed it as my job to follow him.

I found him near a hedge, hidden from the manor house. He was bent over, hands on his knees. He shuddered, but there was nothing left. A pool of vomit was beneath him on the grass. He wiped his mouth with the back of his hand and looked up at me.

"Don't put this in your diary," he ordered.

"No, sir."

"If a quarterback can puke before the big game, why can't I?" He stood and squared his shoulders, then snapped, "Enough fresh air, Colonel."

I walked with him back into the billiard room. This incident in the garden was how I learned that the general was afraid, just like the rest of us.

A short while later we were again squeezed into the Cub, sitting in a pasture used as a runway near the manor house. The pilot talked aloud to himself, doing his preflight check. The take-offs were usually the roughest part of any journey.

General Clay boasted he had stolen the best American pilot in England, Captain Terry Norman. Norman vociferously complained he was wasted ferrying the general around in "this puny nosepicker." He had lost his Mustang in the channel, and there was no replacement. In a fit, he had stenciled "Nose-picker" on the plane. Clay laughed, but ordered the censors not to let the American public learn of it.

Norman lifted a pair of spectacles from his pocket and put them on. I had never seen them before.

"You're wearing glasses?" the general exclaimed. "You're a fighter jock."

"I'm tired of squinting," he said equably. "And now that you've seen me put them on, do you want me to take them off?"

"No," Clay answered hastily. "Not at all."

The engine roared, and the plane began down the runway. I am a large man, and my seat behind the pilot and Clay allowed for little dignity. My knees were almost touching my chin, and my neck was bent over at an uncomfortable angle. Every time the wheels rolled into a rut over a hardened cow pie, the roof banged against my head.

Norman lifted the plane into the air, and the ride at once became smooth. The land fell away from us. We flew over the pond south of the manor, then banked over Westwell. The spires of Ashford were out our port window. Longbeech

Wood was to our right. Below us, sheep speckled their grazing grounds. Fields of grain and hops were cut into the land. Stone walls surrounded orchards. Kent was proudly called the Garden of England. The general gazed intently at the verdant hills and pastures.

After a moment he said, "I've been entrusted with the special stewardship of the land below us, Jack. No matter what is to come, I'm not going to forget that."

Sometimes I thought the general was making a record for posterity, knowing I wrote down his pithier comments. This wasn't one of his better ones, but I noted it anyway.

He turned in his seat and said in a less noble vein, "I had to fight like hell to get it, too. The Brits, full of righteous indignation, wanted to put us Americans on the back burner, set us up in Berkshire and Oxfordshire and some of the other shires, and use us only as reserves. They argued they could defend their own beaches, thank you. They've got five thousand miles of coastline, for Christ's sake. Sometimes I think English optimism is a national danger."

He interrupted himself to address Captain Norman. "This is about the moment in any flight where you lobby me to transfer you back to your unit."

"I've given up on that, sir."

"Saving your breath for swimming, in case you ditch us in the channel? You've got experience at that." The general winked at me. "I heard you had to dogpaddle five miles to shore because nobody would rescue you."

"I like to think they didn't know I was down, sir."

Norman was old for a fighter pilot, and he was the only bald Mustang pilot I saw during the entire war. He said he lost his hair within three months of his twenty-fifth birthday, and his fellow pilots were ceaseless and imaginative inventing nicknames for him. He was from Mobile.

The general returned to his subject. "I asked Roosevelt to insist that as a condition of our participation in this theater American troops would be on the line."

"I'm sure our soldiers are grateful, sir," I said.

"We busted out butts to get here, but we're still being rele-

37

gated to a kiss-your-sister role," he said with distaste. "The British Army is going to see the action while we sit on our thumbs."

"You sure of that?" Norman asked.

"No, but it's AACCS's last, best guess. Only the German knows better, and he's not talking." AACCS was the Anglo-American Combined Chiefs of Staff. Unfortunately, the acronym was pronounced "axis."

Norman pressed his headset against an ear, listening intently, then said, "Folkestone is being shot up, sir. They think it's an E-boat raid. Couple of RN ships are in trouble."

The general said, "Let's take a look."

The pilot grinned and instantly put the Cub on its wing, turning south toward the channel. He was one of those fellows whose entire being atrophied when he wasn't in the middle of the fray.

Clay said, "Captain, this plane isn't going to get there any faster, no matter how hard you rock back and forth."

Norman stilled himself. "Sorry, sir."

Several moments later we flew over the Great Stour River northwest of Ashford. The English call a hill a mountain, a pond a lake, and a creek a river. The Great Stour River is an example. A stone could be thrown over it at most places. To someone from the West Coast of America (I'm from San Diego), England is a miniature. All of Great Britain, including England, Scotland, Wales, and Northern Ireland, is smaller than Oregon, as I once heard Clay petulantly remind Churchill. (The PM replied, "Oregon? That's somewhere near British Columbia, is it not?") It takes a while for an American to adjust to English map scales.

Clay frequently complained to me that the Defense Committee had given him too little of the country to defend. The general's army, the AEF, was comprised of two corps, called, fittingly, I Corps and II Corps. I Corps's sector was roughly from Portsmouth to the River Rother, or about seventy-five air miles along the channel, and extended inland almost to London. II Corps's area was from the Rother east to Foreness Point, about forty-five miles, and included most of Kent, England's southeast county. Thus, the area of Great Britain defended by Americans just before S-Day was the combined size of Delaware and Rhode Island, our two smallest states.

British and Commonwealth soldiers, with a smattering of Free French, Poles, and others, guarded the balance and, by far, the bulk of the island. To the west of the American Expeditionary Force was the British V Corps, spread over Hampshire and Wiltshire and eastern Dorset. Next was the British VIII Corps, responsible for the rest of Dorset and west to Land's End.

On the other side of the Americans were five British corps, ranging from the Thames estuary north to the Scottish border. A Canadian and yet another British corps were in reserve north and east of London.

Something over 85,000 soldiers were in the American sector, all under General Clay. Each American corps was comprised of three divisions and a pool of nondivisional combat units. The divisions each contained between seven and ten thousand soldiers. To get an idea of a division's size, figure that a division on the move may take two hours to pass a given point and stretch for twenty miles.

More Americans were frantically on the way. Almost an entire corps was in transit on the Atlantic on S-Day. Some never arrived, and the rest were too late.

We were five miles north by northwest of Folkestone, over Acrise Place, when Captain Norman spotted the smoke from a fire at the stern of a ship. It was under power, churning eastward away from Folkestone, as if trying to flee the flames on its own aft deck.

After a moment, the general said, "Looks like a Hunt class." It was a British destroyer, an older design, armed with antiaircraft weapons and intended to defend coastal convoys. "The E-boats have done their work. There they go."

Clay pointed at five sets of tell-tale tracks across the water, glittering in the sun, resembling etchings on glass, the E-boats' wakes. Another few seconds passed before we could see the boats themselves, tiny craft from our distant perspective. They were heading back across the channel.

I never met anyone who knew why E-boats were so called by the British and Americans. The Germans called them S-boats, for *Schnellboots*, fast boats. Their principal role was to draw off British naval power, although they could inflict terrible damage when called on to do so. They had sunk the British destroyer *Wakeful* and the French destroyers *Jaguar* and *Sirocco* during the Dunkirk evacuation. With Allied air defense almost nonexistent as S-Day neared, the E-boats had become more aggressive. These five had apparently not even bothered with air cover.

"Why would they leave the British destroyer afloat?" I asked.

"They wouldn't," Clay replied. "They know it's finished."

As if on cue, the destroyer's midships erupted, spewing flame skyward in a roiling ball.

"The fire just reached the magazine," the general said.

Now cut almost in half, the ship began slewing to starboard. We were close enough to see sailors jumping into the channel. Black smoke of the oil-fed blaze trailed away from the craft. An oil slick near the destroyer was also on fire, and spreading quickly. I could see sailors frantically swimming away from flames on the water. A rescue boat, it looked like a tug, was pulling away from the harbor at Folkestone, heading for the gutted ship. I learned later the wounded destroyer was the HMS *Everlast*, which went to the bottom half an hour later. Twenty-two Royal Navy sailors were lost.

Norman banked the Cub at Hougham Court, and we were soon right above the cliffs at the waterline. The plane bobbed up and down in pockets of air. The blue-green French coast was visible across the channel, unknowable in the haze, ominous, full of Germans. We flew over the Warren, just east of Folkestone, where mudstone slides had fallen away from the cliff. The Cub approached the town. Smoke was swirling inland and upward in winding black cones. Several flashes came from the dock area, soundless and insignificant at our distance.

As we drew near, we saw that another boat was ablaze still at its moorings in the harbor. It was a merchant cruiser, and it had a wide hole ripped open at the waterline. It was listing away from the dock, with its gunwales almost to the water. I couldn't see any fire aboard the ship, but smoke was wending out its landward portholes.

Yet another torpedo had rammed a small pier. Much of the

dock had collapsed into the harbor, but a tangle of pylons and planking remained, a perilously balanced knot of wreckage. Soldiers and sailors were running to the scene. A fire truck had just arrived, and I could see the firemen hurriedly unwrapping their hoses.

The general had been uncharacteristically silent for a while. Finally he said, "The Germans are landsmen, Jack. Over the centuries the Spanish, Portuguese, Scandinavians, French, Dutch, and British have competed to dominate the world with their sea power. Not the Germans."

Clay touched the corner of his nose and craned his head to look out the Cub's side windows as the harbor passed under us. He went on: "Hitler has been to sea only once in his entire life, a short trip to Memel on the Baltic, and the son of a bitch got seasick."

The general's voice rose, mixing with the angry buzz of the Cub's engine. "Hitler knows absolutely nothing about the sea or about navies. Nor do his people. G2 told me that a lot of the Kriegsmarine's recruits are so ignorant of the sea that they are astonished to learn the water in the channel rises and falls twice a day, for Christ's sake. Many of their sailors are inducted into their navy only because they indicate a taste for canoeing, or say they visited the beach once or twice in their youths. They simply are not a sea-going people."

Clay sniffed, as if at the unfairness of it. "Yet here they are, poised and ready, undisputed champions of the North Sea and the English Channel, waiting for God only knows what before they set sail, more German assholes than in all of goddamn Pennsylvania."

He turned fully in his seat and glared at me as if I had been arguing. He jabbed a finger right in front of my nose. "If they come anywhere near me, Jack, I'm going to rip them up. All I want is the chance. Just one goddamn chance."

I wanted to protest that it was not up to me to offer him the opportunity, that I had very little say about where the Germans would land. I remained silent.

He turned back to the windscreen. "Head north, Captain. I'm due in London."

Norman maneuvered the plane away from the channel. The

41

back of Clay's neck had turned almost purple. His hands were tightly balled on his lap. He was in a fury—not, I suspect, at the Germans, but at the secondary role he believed he would have in the days ahead. He said nothing more until we were over the East End.

3

"Just before the Germans come, things will start popping," the general had said to me several weeks before.

"Like what?"

"Dozens of piddling, curious events. We'll hear about a few of them right away. Most, we won't. Some'll be very nasty. Many will be designed to lower a fog over the British Isles. A baffling, distracting fog."

General Clay was right, we know now. As he and I flew toward London that morning, the German countdown for S-Day had already begun. It had started the previous night.

I spoke with *Ober-maat* (Chief Petty Officer) Karl Hanneken after the war. At two that morning, he and his three-man team had climbed through the galley hatch of U-513 a moment after the submarine surfaced in the choppy waters of Pentland Firth. He was wearing a cumbersome dry suit, and climbing was difficult. On the conning tower above him were the *Kapitänleutnant*, the first officer, and two spotters. The commander leaned over the wind deflector, a steel lip surrounding the conning tower. The spotters carried binoculars, useless on a black night.

The *Kapitänleutnant*, wearing the white peaked cap of a U-boat commander, whirled his hand, indicating to hurry. Hanneken could just barely see the radio aerial, foghorn mount, and bedstead radar above the spotters. The sub was running on its batteries, and the only sound was of the water lapping at the hull.

The sub was abreast of Hearston Head, on the eastern coast of South Ronaldsay Island in the Orkneys. I've never been to those islands, and Hanneken knew them only by maps and photographs he had studied. His memory of the Orkneys that night was of freezing water and darkness. Farmers, shepherds, and dairymen live at this northern tip of Scotland, but most British sailors who served in the Orkneys remember the island as windswept and barren.

Scapa Flow is a sea basin fifteen miles long and eight miles wide, surrounded by the Orkney Islands. It was the chief Royal Navy base in the Great War, and it was there that on June 21, 1919, the Germans scuttled their own surrendered fleet. In the Second World War, Scapa Flow was the Home Fleet's base. Because of its distance from Luftwaffe and *Kriegsmarine* bases, Scapa Flow was the Germans' most difficult target of the war.

That morning it was Karl Hanneken's target. He lifted an inflatable boat and an air hose through the hatch. His team quickly unrolled the boat and attached the nozzle. The boat filled rapidly with air. Two crewmen joined them on deck and were handed air tanks, regulators, and fins from below. Because the team members would not have fit through the hatch wearing their equipment, they had frequently rehearsed suiting up on a pitching submarine deck. The crewmen helped the team into their equipment, then helped strap Schmeisser submachine guns wrapped in oil cloth to the midriff belts of two members of the team.

Within moments, Hanneken and his men were ready. The boat was lowered down the hull on lines, and the team followed it down the side of the sub. Hanneken slipped on the steel, and his face slapped against the hull. He could not see the blood and did not realize for hours that he had broken his nose. Equipment boxes were lowered to them. The team cast off and began paddling north.

Hanneken told me how clumsy he had felt, encased in the dry suit, crowded into the inflatable boat, an awkward craft that seemed to fight them. Every few seconds a wave would crest the low-riding boat, drenching the team. One crewman did nothing but bail. There were no visible landmarks. Lights on the island were blacked out. Every so often Hanneken would cup a hand around the waterproof flashlight and illuminate the compass attached to the boat. They paddled for an hour toward the Sound of Hoxa, the mile-and-a-half-wide passage between South Ronaldsay and Flotta islands that led into Scapa Flow.

Hanneken was a member of the *Aufklärungsstreikräfte*, the Reconnaissance Forces. The Germans had no equivalent of the American Rangers or the British Special Service Brigade. With the exception of the paratroopers, German special forces were created ad hoc, as need demanded. The Navy Reconnaissance Force, under *Vizeadmiral* Hermann Densch, was largely for intelligence gathering, but hidden in the organizational chart was 10th *Marineabteilung*, the obscurely named 10th Naval Detachment, in which, after vigorous examinations, Hanneken had found himself. Hanneken had joined the navy to escape the army and the Waffen SS. "I thought boats would be easier. I misjudged that, I suppose. At the 10th, all I did was train for twelve months."

All his training was for this journey, paddling in a rubber raft between two Scottish islands. He might have seen Stranger Head and Hoxa Head to his left and right, smudges on the horizon, black on black, just before the team came to the buoys. It was too dark to be sure. A submarine net was strung across the sound, hung from a line of black buoys. Hanneken tied the boat to a buoy, scraping his hand on barnacles. His team members unfastened their submachine guns and lowered them to the boat's deck. The equipment box was secured to a strap that ran along the side of the boat. They wiped spit on the glass on their masks, fitted the masks over their faces, inserted mouthpieces, and slid into the water.

For half an hour, the sailors attached explosive charges to the net, along the buoy line and under the floats. The waves were high enough to break over their heads. The charges were modified *s-minen-42*s in glass cases. Hanneken retrieved from the boat a battery pack and timer enclosed in waterproof cloth. He secured the mechanism under a buoy.

Another half hour was spent connecting the charges to the battery. Finally, Hanneken tied to buoys on each side of the charges small red and green navigation lights, ingenious spring-loaded pop-up devices manufactured by a toy company in Munich, which would not be noticed by early morning Royal Navy patrols. Each light was on a timer. The team climbed back into the raft and grabbed the paddles.

Hanneken was exhausted and numb to his soul, but he and the others paddled mightily. In one hour, the U-boat would resurface for only ten minutes. If the sailors of the 10th Marine Detachment were late or lost, they were on their own.

U-513 was not the only German submarine working the waters near Scapa Flow that early morning. There was at least one other net-mining operation, launched from U-478, and there was the commando raid on Wideford Hill on Pomona (Mainland) Island. These raiders, also of the 10th *Marine-abteilung*, concealed their boat in the rocks at Quanter Ness, then climbed in the darkness uphill past Chambered Cairn.

Near the outer barbed wire defenses, the five raiders dug shallow trenches and lay down to wait, covering themselves with camouflaged tarps. Not one of these commandos survived the day.

William Dawes was a locomotive engineer whom I spoke with while interviewing his son, Lawrence, after the war. Lawrence had been a Hurricane pilot with the 96th Squadron at Cranage. Lawrence invited his father along with us to a pub in Durham, where he proposed I conduct the interview.

I had my first glass of porter that day, which alone would have made our talk memorable. Research for this work required me to sample most of England's beers and ales. After a pint with an American, an Englishman begins to remember our common heritage and becomes more voluble and takes on the tone of one addressing a younger brother.

Lawrence commented that many RAF pilots hid injuries so they could continue flying. One day his crew was mounting a refurbished 20mm cannon in his Hurricane, and the cannon was dropped on his foot. He flew with a fractured instep for the rest of the war. He added, "But I was scarcely injured as badly as my father here."

The senior Dawes flicked his fingers in a deprecating manner. He had used a crutch on the way to the pub.

"He lost his leg," Lawrence said, slashing with his hand, indicating the abruptness with which the leg had gone. The son had leaf-green eyes and a narrow nose with a small bulb at the tip. "Just before the Germans came, in one of their last rail-yard raids, it was. He wears a wood peg now."

"Your locomotive was hit?" I asked.

William Dawes gently shook his head. He was sixty-eight and had a mesh of lines around his mouth and patchy gray hair. We expect everything on older people to wrinkle and fade. But the color of the eyes always remains true to youth. William's eyes were still the same sparkling green of his son's. "It was four in the morning. By that point in the war, most rail stock was moved only at night, to be sure. My engine, an American Southern on Lend Lease, was out of service for a while because the coal tender was being loaded. I was in the barn, in the switchroom." He sipped his ale. "Of a sudden the walls blew inward. I wish there were more to tell."

"There certainly is more, Father," Lawrence said, probably not for the first time.

William stared at his porter. "They believe it was a five-hundred-pound bomb, and it landed about a hundred feet away."

Lawrence annotated, "The Germans were using what they called *Knickebein*, which means something like dog-leg, a system of directional radio beams, transmitted from German stations which intersected over the bombers' target. Accurate at night."

"Accurate enough to find me, anyway." William waved away further technical explanations. "The sirens had just gone off, but they were late. I wanted to roll my engine into a cement roundhouse to protect it. I just got to the door when the bomb hit. For a split second, I thought I'd been lifted off my feet and pitched against the wall. What actually happened was that the wall was thrown at me, and everything on it. The calendar, a framed photograph of an old steam engine, a clock—all right at me. Half the building hit me. Then, as soon as you could say knife, the rafter came down, crushing my left leg. How the timber got only one leg, the doctors never guessed. And only then came the sounds of the explosion, like thunder in my ear."

He pulled at his ale, then asked, "Do you think the Germans had delayed-sound bombs, Lawrence?"

"Not then, anyway," the son smiled.

"I spent four months in hospital. But my rail yard was maimed worse than I was. An antiaircraft regiment from the Staffordshire Infantry was assigned to the yard, with a number of the big sixty-inch searchlights."

"They can spot a plane at three and a half miles," Lawrence said.

"And the AA crew hit two of the bombers. But the Germans were determined this time. They wanted my yard. We'd been bombed on five prior occasions, damaged quite badly. We always had it back in operation within days. After that morning, though, there wasn't much left of the yard but twisted steel and parts of locomotives and boxcars scattered around the craters."

We spent another hour in the pub, learning primarily about William Dawes' three operations, "the scalpels running seconds ahead of the gangrene, like a ghastly foot race toward my crotch."

Dawes' switchyard near Sheffield was not the only rail installation destroyed by the Luftwaffe during the same hours Karl Hanneken was mining the sub nets. From London north to Middlesbrough, inland from the North Sea, switchyards, railroad bridges, important crossings, and long lengths of mainline track were destroyed by Heinkels and Junkers. It was night, and "Not even the dog-leg could be bang on," as Lawrence said, so the Luftwaffe made up for their lack of pinpoint accuracy by using over three hundred planes, the Observer Corps later estimated.

In counterinvasion studies done before S-Day, AACCS had correctly anticipated the Luftwaffe would undertake a massive air strike at rail installations immediately preceding the inva-

48

sion. The Combined Chiefs believed the bombing's purpose would be to impede the British in rushing reserves to the invasion front. The Heinkel and Junkers railway raids that night were further proof that the Germans would soon be at hand.

I have read Clara Gaudet's letter to her daughter Anna, written just before Clara's execution. Anna showed me the letter, handling it carefully, as if the words might spill off the page. Because my French is halting, she helped me through it.

Written on onionskin and wrinkled badly, as if tamped into a boot or a hat at some point in its journey, the letter was a painful, defiant missive describing the elder Gaudet's life as a member of the French Resistance in Normandy, and of her proudest moment of the entire war, her radio broadcast from Le Havre, which had been received and decoded at Bletchley just before S-Day.

Mme. Gaudet was a physician, educated at the Sorbonne. When the Germans occupied France, she continued making rounds to her patients' homes throughout Le Havre, using a bicycle after the Wehrmacht pressed her Renault into service. She had documents allowing almost unrestricted travel in the city, and she always had ready explanations if she was stopped late at night.

Le Havre is a major port and was a center of Wehrmacht and Kriegsmarine activity. The city is due south across the channel from Brighton. An invasion on the southern English coast would be launched from Le Havre and other Norman ports. Clara Gaudet reported weekly on German troop movements in and around the city.

Her radio had once been a pack wireless set used by a German infantry squad for unit signals. A more powerful transmission amplifier and a frequency multiplier had been installed by a resistance man who had not introduced himself. The radio was hidden in the loft of a barn near Montivilliers, a short bicycle ride inland from Le Havre. The antenna was concealed in a wind vane on the barn's roof. Her broadcasts were at night, when her signals carried farthest. She kept them short because she had been told the Le Havre Gestapo was using a new radio direction finder, with its circular antenna mounted on the cab of an Opel Blitz truck.

She kept her coding pad in the false bottom of a milk can. The pad was a thick block of sheets of alternating green and black paper, green for enciphering and black for deciphering. The paper was made of cellulose nitrate, once used for film in the movie industry. She kept a vial of potassium permanganate with the pad, which, when thrown on the paper, would cause an explosion, consuming the pad without leaving a latent image.

That early morning Clara Gaudet had encoded her message by candlelight in the loft. Then she dug the radio pack from under the hay and opened it like a standing suitcase. The batteries were on the left and the dials and knobs on the right. She pulled the Morse key and the earphones from the compartment below the volume control. The first few times she had used the key her hand had been shaking so violently she kept getting the repeat signal from England. She was steady that morning.

Mme. Gaudet first sent a series of Vs, paused, and immediately heard the return Vs in her headset. Bletchley had her. She pressed the key rapidly in a series of dits and dahs for no more than sixty seconds, knowing well the importance of her message. Three nights before this signal, she clicked, the Wehrmacht's 8th and 28th divisions, which made up VIII Corps, had abandoned their encampments along the Seine between Le Havre and Rouen. They had moved at night, their armor, trucks, field cars, soldiers, everything. She had heard they headed northeast toward Brussels, but could not be certain.

I've seen a copy of her deciphered message, and it was considerably less wordy than my retelling. With RDF equipment on the prowl, Bletchley rarely risked a request for a confirm. This time they did. She repeated the message, then signed off with another series of Vs.

The letter to her daughter closed with heart-breaking vows of love, made even more so because Mme. Gaudet, sitting in her tiny cell, knew her fate. Anna, who was twenty years old when I talked with her, told me of her pride in her mother's accomplishment that night. The war would have taken a different course had it not been for her mother, she said. No one would argue that.

the house

Ava Singleton's cottage at the Goldings, just south of St. Leonard's Forest, midway between London and the channel, was set squarely in a half-acre of vegetable garden. Before the war, grass had grown in front of the cottage, and roses had been wrapped up and over an iron bar at the front gate. But vegetables had replaced the grass and the iron had been given to the Ministry of Works' salvage drive. She told me she had also wanted to donate the garish cement birdbath at the side of her home, which her long-dead husband had made from a mold, but the ministry would not take it. Her cottage had three rooms and was heated by a log fire in the sitting room. Her bedroom, little bigger than a closet, was off the kitchen.

At about the same moment Bletchley was receiving Gaudet's signal, Ava Singleton was awakened by the rattle of nearby gunfire. It seemed to be coming from behind her shed, where she kept her wheelbarrow and rakes. And then from somewhere near the Bedfords' home down the road. She was familiar with the sound of shotguns. Her husband had been a bird hunter, and she occasionally went with him into the field. But this was entirely different—many shots, right after each other, the crackling sound rolling together with urgency. Many weapons, she thought.

Last night she had heard on the BBC that the War Ministry had issued an Invasion Alert No. 2, meaning an invasion was probably to occur within two days. It was their fifth alert in the past month, but she was taking all of them seriously.

And now the Germans were here. She threw back her blankets and lowered her feet to the floor, pushing them into her slippers. She lifted her robe off the hook on the back of the door. She was curiously calm.

Mrs. Singleton had lived all her life within five miles of the Goldings and had made few trips elsewhere. She took for granted that German spies and parachutists and tanks would come to the Goldings once the invasion was under way. She did not know enough about the rest of England to imagine them going anywhere else. She wondered what Germans looked like.

She trundled into the kitchen and pushed aside the blackout curtain. She could hear planes overhead, as was usual during recent nights. More shots were coming from behind her shed, louder. She could see the shed in the dim light, with its door open so the dog could come and go. Nothing new to be seen.

She walked through the sitting room to the front door and opened it without hesitating. She stepped out onto her narrow stone walkway between the rows of beans and tomatoes. Still nothing to be seen, and now the firing behind the shed had quieted. But the Bedfords still had their hands full. The noise was like the machine guns she had heard on BBC recordings of the fighting in Africa.

She admitted to me that she jumped when the branches started rustling in her apple tree near the birdbath. Most of the tree was hidden by the corner of the cottage, but she could see a few branches shake. Then the tree was still. She padded along a bean row toward it.

I asked her how she remained so steady during all this. She replied, "I was an old woman during the First War, and I was even older during the Second. Nothing excites me."

Apparently not, because when she turned the corner of her home and found a German paratrooper dangling from her apple tree, still swaying, his parachute stuck in the higher branches, all she did was stare up at him.

She said, "My first thought was that they grew them small in the Reich. This fellow was a midget."

Then she felt a fine disappointment when she realized that her paratrooper was made of hay stuffed into a small uniform, with a cloth doll's head, and arms sewn up to the parachute lines. Not even the coal-scuttle helmet, the very symbol of Nazi terror, was real, but was painted on the head. She reached up to feel his cloth boots. They were heavy. Probably rocks for weight, she thought. She was put out that if the Germans were going to drop dolls, they wouldn't even bother to make them life-sized.

Mrs. Singleton was wondering how she would ever climb into the tree to cut the doll down when the first tank came roaring down the road. It had a white star on it, the emblem of all Allied forces. Probably those knotty Americans, she thought. Her village was full of them. Every time one of their tanks came by, it left a sheen of dust over her vegetables. She squinted in anticipation of the cloud. The Bedfords had a telephone and must have called. Another tank rolled by, then another vehicle, which Mr. Bedford later told her was an armored personnel carrier.

She walked toward the shed and called for her dog, a golden retriever named Jedediah. He emerged slowly, and when she patted him, she could feel he was shaking. The dog followed her around the tool shed toward the grove of pear trees. Jedediah was not born to be a hero, and he walked alongside her, pressed into her leg almost hard enough to topple her. She had walked this path a thousand times, knew it so well she was not even aware it was night.

She found the noise-maker lying on the ground between two pear trees. It was attached to a small parachute, and was nothing more than a string of firecrackers with a pressure-activated detonator. All that was left of the firecrackers was a tumble of paper. Her small orchard still smelled of gunpowder.

"Well, posh," she said, and began back to her cottage. "You come and sleep inside with me the rest of the night, Jedediah. You look like you need a good watchperson."

Mrs. Singleton told me she found reason that night to be glad she had no telephone. Down the road, when Mr. Bedford was visited by firecrackers and two dummy paratroopers, he made a frantic call to the local Home Guard regiment, who passed it along to the Americans. Moments later, their tanks ground through his garden over apple trees, snapping them off at the ground. "And completely, I say, completely, tearing out my raspberries," he told her later. His small greenhouse was crushed underneath the treads, not one pane surviving. One tank fired into his barn, which was razed. "I have my suspicions, Mrs. Singleton, that the Americans had already seen the dummies and were just getting in a practice round."

Mrs. Singleton returned to bed, Jedediah in tow. Later that

morning the radio would report that paratrooper dummies had landed in dozens of places along the south and east coasts, even some as far north as Edinburgh. She had utterly no idea what to make of it. Neither did AACCS.

The British Foreign Office's Department of Communications was at Bletchley Park, in the town of Bletchley, about fifty miles northwest of London. The first mansion was built on the estate in the 1870s, and expanded many times through the years. Even so, the department added numerous other buildings to house the seven thousand people who worked there during the war. Bletchley was the heart of the British radio interception and code-breaking efforts.

On watch in the Netherlands and Baltic Intercept Section that morning was Commander Joseph Morehouse, a Royal Navy officer serving with the Foreign Office. Morehouse came by his position honestly, as his uncle was Nigel de Grey, who in 1917 had solved the Zimmermann telegram, in which Germany promised to return Texas, New Mexico, and Arizona to Mexico if Mexico would declare war on the United States. President Wilson released the intercepted and decoded telegram to the press, and it helped turn American public opinion against Germany. Morehouse's duty was to gather on tape as many radio signals from Holland and the Baltic as possible. "I was in intercept," he told me, "rather than in code-breaking because, shall we say, I simply didn't have my uncle's knack."

Morehouse's section was in one of the new buildings at Bletchley. On the roof were numerous antennas: rotary beams, a trap, several quads, a long-wire directive array, and others. Despite the impressive number of antennas at Bletchley, most of his signals were picked up at intercept stations on the east coast and relayed over telephone wires.

Morehouse's desk was at the head of an aisle of radio operators. They sat six to a side, with banks of electronics in front of them: crystal converters, VHF receivers, 110-MC amplifiers, grid-dip meters, signal generators, oscillators, and Edison and Motorola recorders. The array seemed strapped against the walls by a mesh of wires. Light was low, and the men's faces

54

were washed in the green and amber of the dial lights. The room was filled with amplified Morse and scratchy snippets of German conversation. Morehouse spoke German and read Morse, but what he heard, as always, was in code.

At precisely six that morning, Commander Morehouse's head jerked up from a transcript he was reading. Something indefinable was occurring. A part of the room suddenly seemed to be missing.

"Sir," one of his operators said, "I've lost all signals."

"Me, too, sir." The second operator turned a dial. "I'm scanning and not getting anything."

Except for the low static of empty radio bands, the room was eerily silent. In the six months he had been posted to this room, Morehouse had witnessed this only once before, a month ago. Radio silence often precedes a military operation, but the abruptly empty airwaves last month had been a Wehrmacht feint. He walked down the aisle, bending over one radioman after another, glancing at their dials. Finally, he asked, "What is happening, Barnett?"

Barnett threw two switches and slowly rolled another knob. "I don't know yet, sir. Perhaps the same as in April. Give me a moment."

Morehouse's section was monitoring the Wehrmacht's Army Group C, which in the previous week had moved into Amsterdam, Rotterdam, and the smaller ports at Ijmuiden, Wijk Aan Zee, Den Helder, and the West Frisian Islands along the Netherlands' north coast. Army Group C was commanded by Erwin Rommel, proven in Africa. AACCS believed Rommel had been given authority to strip from other Wehrmacht and Waffen SS corps any divisions he desired for the invasion. Bletchley's latest estimated order of battle for Rommel's Group C included the new XXX Corps, made up of the 7th and 15th panzer divisions and the 15th Light Division, veteran units to be feared. Also in the Army Group C was the XXXIV Corps. Rommel's troops were crammed into the Dutch ports, waiting for their signal.

"I can't get even one reading, sir," Barnett said. "There's nothing to hear."

For weeks Army Group C had filled Commander Morehouse's recorders, day after day and night after night, a relentless onslaught over the airwaves. Now, suddenly, utterly nothing. The Army Group had suddenly covered itself with a blanket of radio silence. Morehouse sprinted to his desk and lifted a telephone. "Get me Admiral Reynolds immediately. Yes, I know what time it is. Do as I tell you, and quickly."

George Stephens was a dairyman in Lincolnshire, a few miles south of where the Humber empties into the North Sea. Stephens was a veteran of the Somme. "Trenchfoot, trenchmouth, ringworm, scabies, dysentery, prickly heat, and that's my entire war record."

That early morning he woke to his dogs' barking. They were border collies, three of them, reliable and earnest, not often causing a commotion. Like everyone else in England, Stephens was aware of Invasion Alert No. 2, and he had just heard planes overhead. He climbed out of bed, stepped into his pants, and reached for his shotgun, which he brought into the bedroom whenever there was an alert. The gun was an over-under, and so well handled over the years that the maker's mark had almost vanished.

Without opening her eyes, his wife Carlene said, "It's just the bombers, George. Like always."

"I heard something else," he answered. "So did the dogs."

He stepped out of his house toward the barn. The collies were confined to a run next to a milking shed, and they were still yelping when he got there.

He held a finger to his lips. "Hush, you."

The dogs paid him no heed. Crouched like an infantryman, Stephens rounded the barn. Just to the west was a low-rising hill, too stony even for grazing. There, caught in a passing glimpse of moonlight, was a man in a parachute harness.

This was not a doll. The fellow was gathering up his parachute, rolling it under his arms. Strapped to the parachutist's stomach was a large pack.

"I've thought back over the next fifteen seconds so many times, it seems like an hour in my memory now," Stephens recalled. "I walked closer to him, praying he wouldn't turn to see me. I know my bare feet were making sounds on the rocks, but he didn't hear me because my dogs were still yowling."

"It was dark," Stephens continued. "In my mind I saw a German army uniform and was quite struck later to see his farmer's clothes, pants just like mine, and a blue shirt."

Stephens was forty feet away when the parachutist heard him. The man turned slightly and at the same time drew a Luger from a holster strapped to his leg.

"I was going to say something like, 'Friend or foe?' but he didn't give me time, you see."

"What did you do?" I asked.

Stephens looked at me as if I'd gone daft. "Why, I shot him, of course."

The burst of birdshot hit the German squarely in his stomach pack. It jolted him, and he staggered back a step, dropping the chute.

"But I don't think it hurt him—just destroyed his fancy radio. It got a bit dicey then."

"How so?" I ventured again.

"I glimpsed his pistol, coming up toward me once more, but I raised the shotgun a fraction and pulled the other trigger." Stephens added with mischief, "He lost his head over that one."

So he did. George Stephens gloried in the showdown. The German war machine had personally tested him, and he had triumphed. If only his country would do as well.

Gunboats, motor torpedo boats, minelayers, antisubmarine trawlers, sloops, and drifters patrolled the perimeter of Britain. In 1940, the Royal Navy had two to three hundred of these craft at sea at any given time, predominately on the most threatened eastern and southeastern seaboards. By May 1942, however, the Luftwaffe and Kriegsmarine had exacted their heavy toll, and the Navy was hard-pressed to have fifty ships on patrol.

Lieutenant Richard Keyes was the mine engineer aboard the minelayer HMS *Pettibone*, which that morning was four miles off Benacre Broad, on the Suffolk coast, northeast of London. At 5:30 that morning, Keyes was overseeing the repair of a launcher on the aft deck—a tedious, cold duty. He could not have known he was three minutes from earning the Distinguished Service Cross, the first of the invasion.

Keyes was on one knee, a pair of pliers in his hand, when the battle stations klaxon rang and the *Pettibone* veered hard to starboard. He dropped the pliers and ran forward, catching up to an AA gunner sprinting to his weapon.

"What is it?" Keyes yelled over the alarm.

"U-boat off the starboard bow, sir. On the surface."

The gunner swung the barrels of his dual Polsten 20-mm guns to starboard. Keyes steadied himself against the rail and peered into the night.

"That's when I stopped thinking, I believe," he told me after the war. "Our searchlight flicked on and caught the submarine spot on its beam. The sub was dead ahead. It was a tiny thing, really, looking for all the world quite harmless."

The submarine was one of the Kriegsmarine's *Kleine Kampfmittel* (small battle units), a V80 midget, seventy-two feet long with a six-foot beam and a crew of four.

"Three German submariners were on deck, trying to keep their balance as the sub rolled in the sea. The midget was sinking. The bow was in the air, and the Germans were inching higher and higher along the deck to keep above water, all the while trying to keep their hands in the air, surrendering—small wonder with our AA gun aimed at them."

Just as the British armed forces are penurious in granting bravery decorations, the recipients of those awards are usually hesitant in describing their heroics. I prompted him: "What spurred you to dive overboard?"

"My captain stepped out of the bridge and yelled down, 'They're scuttling their sub. Stop them.'"

"So you jumped into the sea?"

Keyes had a broad forehead and heavily lidded eyes. He paused before every sentence. "Colonel, in the Royal Navy your superior tells you what to do, not how to do it. I had just been given an order to prevent the submarine from sinking."

His expression was purposely deadpan, so I adopted his tone and asked fatuously, "So tell me, was the North Sea cold?"

He smiled. "I thought I was living my last moments, it was

so cold. And it was enough of a swim, perhaps forty yards, for my stupidity to chill me further." He ran a hand through his hair. "I had no idea what had brought the sub to the surface disabled, or why it was now sinking."

Lieutenant Keyes grabbed the sub's metal deck grating, now at a considerable cant, and pulled his feet under him. One of the Germans stood between him and the small conning tower. The others were forward, standing on the nose. All still had their hands above their heads. Keyes moved on all fours toward the tower, the water following him as the sub continued to slide under the water.

The sub's aft hatch was secure. He crawled higher. The German said something, indecipherable to Keyes, and positioned himself between the lieutenant and the tower.

"Get out of my way," Keyes ordered as he approached. The lieutenant was backlit by the searchlight. The sub had a two-dimensional quality, like a photograph, all in shades of gray and black, as had the crewmen, wearing shining wet suits and appearing otherwordly.

The German blocked him and said something more. He sounded calm and reasonable. Keyes pushed him off the deck into the water and clambered for the tower.

"I knew nothing about submarines," he remembered. "I didn't have a clue what I was doing."

When he reached the short conning tower, Keyes gripped the periscope and levered himself over the tower rail. Just as he dropped onto the conning deck, the fourth crewman's head emerged through the hatch. When Keyes kicked him in the face, the submariner slipped back into the craft. The lieutenant heard waves splash against the conning tower. Another minute, and the sub would slip below the surface.

"Lights were still on in the control room below. I gripped the hatch ring and lowered myself as far as my arms allowed. My feet didn't find anything, so I let go, and landed on the German crewman. I don't know whether I'd kicked him into unconsciousness or whether landing on him did it, but he was out by the time I gathered my feet under me."

The lieutenant found himself in the only crew space on the midget submarine, the control room. "It was filled with wheel controls, cables, tubes, compasses, fuse boxes, gauges, and all the plumbing. The room was so narrow I couldn't extend my arms in any direction. I have no idea how four men fit in there."

The sea was gushing up into the room from the grate over the control room deck, swirling and bubbling around Keyes' knees. The lights flickered. The German sputtered. Keyes looked quickly about him. The submariner's head hung limply.

I asked, "How'd you shut off the water?"

Another modest grin. "I started turning every wheel in the place. No small task, mind, there must have been a dozen of them. The deck was by then at a considerable angle, and I kept slipping, sometimes to my knees. All the while, the water rose. Drowning, that's the real drawback of joining the Royal Navy. And that's all I was thinking about. Jesus, I didn't want to drown. I turned those wheels in a panic."

"But you finally found the right one."

"Something lost is always found in the last place you look. That's how it must be with submarine controls. Yes, I found the shut-off valve, and I swear it was the last one in the room."

By then the water was to Lieutenant Keyes' chest. The light sputtered out and plunged the chamber into darkness as black as the sea bottom. The submarine groaned and hissed. Water splashed into Keyes' mouth, and he gagged and spit. He reached for pipes to support him as he waded toward the hatch. He was startled when the unconscious floating German bumped him. The lieutenant found the rungs and climbed toward the night air.

Only the rim of the conning tower and the bow were still above water, but the sub had stopped sinking. Two of the topside Germans were in the water, both clinging to life rings which had been thrown from the trawler. The third submariner was still on the bow, his gaze shifting uncertainly between the British ship and Keyes.

"Come here," the lieutenant yelled as his head crested the conning tower's rail. He signaled the German with an arm, then pointed down the hatch.

"I give that fellow credit. I didn't have to tell him again. He slid down the deck toward the tower. I lowered myself back into the control room to water level, now about three feet below the hatch. I reached around underwater until I found that fourth German, not knowing if he was alive. I dragged him up as far as I could, and the topside German pulled him up the rest of the way. I hurried out of there. Carrying the German, we jumped into the water."

Keyes and the German submariners were hauled to the trawler's deck. The fourth German was quickly resuscitated. The Kriegsmarine sailors were locked in a storeroom and armed guards were posted outside the hatch. After a line was rigged to the submarine, the control room was emptied of water with the *Pettibone*'s portable pump. The sub was still low in the water, but stable. The trawler made slowly to port, its prize in tow.

In the British fashion, the *Pettibone*'s captain said nothing to Lieutenant Keyes. Not until the DSC was announced did Keyes learn what his captain, who made the recommendation, had thought of his little swim.

I have chosen these incidents virtually at random. There were many others that morning. Little incursions by the Germans, deceptions picayune and otherwise, touches of violence. As General Clay had warned, the Germans were parrying and feinting with Allied intelligence, and a shroud of confusion was descending on Great Britain.

Several days earlier the general had exclaimed, "I don't want to go down in history as America's great blind commander, another Custer, who was told by scouts that there were more Sioux and Cheyenne over the next hill than the 7th Cavalry had cartridges. If I could just have a glimpse over the next hill."

Well, he couldn't, at least not an accurate glimpse. The Germans were making sure of that.

4

German planes had not settled for destroying the landscape. They also devastated the language. A full moon, once a lovers' moon, had become a bombers' moon. A cloudless night was termed a smoking night, due to the smoke screens from oil-burning canisters, the most bothersome of all bomber defenses. Londoners had begun calling the River Thames Bombers' Lane, because Luftwaffe planes flew to the city along the estuary.

We were flying along Bombers' Lane toward London. To our right were the ruins of the oil tanker farms at Thameshaven. The fires there had been burning for months. The joke was that the Luftwaffe used the smoke column as a navigation aid, and the Heinkels returned to the tanks at once whenever the smoke threatened to die down.

The general and I came to London almost daily for meetings, and there was usually some new smudge on the horizon, some neighborhood which had ceased to exist the night before, some factory destroyed, some new outrage to peer at as we flew overhead. The Germans had begun their all-out bomber attack on August 13, 1940, which they called *Adlertag*, or Eagle Day. They had been coming back since, each bomber escorted by two fighters, which often flew fifteen thousand feet above their wards, ready to pounce on anything that dared interfere. As the months passed and the ranks of RAF interceptors had dwindled, many Luftwaffe bombing runs were made at only four thousand feet. A plane hardly needed a bombsight at that height.

The East End and the docklands had suffered most. Bethnal Green, Stepney, Hackney, Brick Lane, Bow, and East and West Ham were gone. There were only crater-pocked, wreckage-strewn, ash-covered expanses, which from the air appeared as one imagines the moon might. Industrial areas to the west of the city had also been gutted. Brentford, Hounslow, many more.

"Will you look at that, Jack?" the general said from the co-pilot's seat. "I'd heard it'd been hit yesterday, scarcely believed it. But there's the proof."

Coming into view under the Cub's fuselage was the Tower of London. I could see its dry moat, double castellated walls, and the four towers of the White Tower. From our angle, it should have been framed by the Tower Bridge, to my eye the loveliest structure in the city. Built in 1894, with Gothic towers over two hundred feet high, it was the last bridge over the Thames before the river flows into the sea, the pride of the river.

The bridge was not there. Instead, only the two foundation piers remained, topped by mounds of rubble. The bascules had fallen into the water, as had the decks to the north and south of the foundations. Steel suspension spans lay over the rubble, twisted together like snakes basking on rocks in the sun. The neighborhood south of the bridge was still on fire. Spots of flame were visible through the smoke. Bricks and stone and shattered glass covered Tower Bridge Road. Glittering in the sun, the glass made the road appear like a river, as if bright light was reflecting off waves.

Just north of the bridge site, the warehouses of St. Katherine's Dock had also been heavily damaged, not for the first time in the war. Ivory House's roof and clock tower had collapsed. Fire was still curling through the building's windows.

"A bridge is a tough target," Captain Norman said. "Dive bombers, probably. Brave pilots, what with all the balloons around."

The balloons over the city resembled a cloud layer. They belonged to the 30th Balloon Barrage Group, under Group Captain J. W. Smithers. A Ministry of Information propaganda film, *The Lion Has Wings*, showed a preposterous sequence in which Luftwaffe pilots recoiled in horror at the sight of the balloons. Londoners scoffed at the film and at the balloons. We learned after the war that the film was not too far off the mark. The silver behemoths frightened German pilots. In fact, a Junkers attacking the Tower Bridge had plummeted into the Thames when its wing was sheared off by a tethering cable.

Norman tipped up the Cub's port wing, and we veered north a few degrees over the city. Many Londoners believed the Germans were making it a point of honor to destroy St. Paul's Cathedral. Unbelievably, they had not succeeded, although the entire neighborhood, blocks around, had been flattened. Volunteers slept in the cathedral every night, putting out fires blown their way from near misses.

Looking down on St. Paul's, General Clay said, "The Brits are an adaptable bunch, I'll give them that. For a while they claimed that as long as Big Ben stood, there'd always be an England. Then when it fell, it was Buckingham Palace. As long as there was a Buckingham Palace, there'd always be an England. Now it's St. Paul's." He shook his head. "I wonder what they'll pick next. As long as there's a Dr. Johnson's house, there'll always be an England. Doesn't quite have the same ring to it."

He laughed without mirth, then drew on his Pall Mall. He turned to me. "You know why Winnie thinks the Germans are destroying the landmarks, don't you?"

I shook my head. Winnie. Even to my tin American ear, the nickname was brazen effrontery. The Cub lurched in an air pocket, and I grabbed the edge of my seat.

"Hitler is obsessed with a bloodless victory."

"It's hardly been bloodless," I said.

"Goddamn it, Jack, don't chip away at my stories. Relatively bloodless, then. Hitler thinks he understands the British, since

64

they are Anglo-Saxons like the Germans. His comments about the English have a proprietary quality. From the very first, Hitler was amazed Great Britain entered the war. And once Britain declared war, he was puzzled by its adamant refusal to make peace."

The general held his cigarette between thumb and forefinger over his palm, like a forester. "Hitler has never stopped dreaming of British panic, revolution, and surrender. He doesn't understand that the British are incapable of thinking of capitulation. It's a foreign concept to them, something French, from Paris, like lingerie."

"And that's the reason for the terror bombings," I concluded.

Clay frowned at my stealing his punchline. "You'd think Hitler would have learned that civilian bombings don't always bring results. Madrid was bombed for twenty-eight months, and there never was wholesale panic. Because Hitler thought the British government would collapse, he never planned on really coming. Now, with the British as stiff-necked as ever, he's got to."

I said, "What you mean, then, is that the imminent invasion isn't really the führer's fault."

The general turned to our pilot. "I asked for an aide-de-camp, and I got an asshole-de-camp. Isn't that the military for you?"

We flew over Lincoln's Inn Fields, then banked southwest over Shaftesbury, then Piccadilly. Below, London's main avenues were dappled with ruins. Sticks of high explosive bombs had torn long streaks of destruction across the neighborhoods. The bombs chose their targets with no more logic than a tornado in the American South, touching down here and there in a willy-nilly way, devastating several buildings in a row, then mockingly sparing several, then touching down again. The Luftwaffe was running out of targets, yet they still came to London almost nightly. There seemed to be a weary petulance to the German bombing.

We began descending to the airstrip south of the lake called the Serpentine in Hyde Park. When the general liked a subject, he was a bulldog with a bone. He started again, "Von der Goltz wrote at the end of the last century that it is no longer possible to frighten an enemy into submission. Hitler should have read him. Twenty thousand whirling dervishes howling their battle cries didn't break the British square at Omdurman in North Africa in 1898. The Highlanders' terrifying war cries at Culloden Moor in 1746 didn't drive the British from the field."

Terry Norman said, "Nothing'll make an enemy turn tail like a rebel yell, General. You ever heard one?"

"Captain, I'm trying to make a point here."

"A rebel yell will make your skin crawl. Listen to this."

The general held up a hand, too late. Our pilot filled his lungs and loosed a screech that rattled everything in the Cub's tiny cabin and made the hairs on the back of my neck stand. I swear it registered on some of the plane's instruments.

Norman ended it with a smile. "If the dervishes had had the rebel yell, Britain would have lost Africa. No question about that."

General Clay turned forward in his seat. He put a finger in his ear and rubbed it around. The rebel yell's effect on ears already ringing from hypertension could only be imagined. He said under his breath, "Christ, we might lose this war yet."

The plane soared over Hyde Park Corner and settled into its approach paralleling the Carriage Road. The lake and trees seemed to rise up to us. At one end of the park were three-story mountains of rubble, growing daily, resembling the mysterious, prehistoric barrows that mark the English countryside. Hyde Park's grass was strangely silver, and when the wheels met the grass, a gray plume rose behind us, swirling away in the prop wash. We bounced along, raising clouds of this gray dust as we taxied toward a waiting car.

Norman switched off the engine as soon as we drew alongside the automobile. He said, "I don't want to get any of that crap in my cylinders, whatever it is."

I followed the general out the hatch. When my foot landed on the ground, a puff of powder squirted from under my shoes.

We left Norman at the plane. Our driver was one of Churchill's orderlies, a Scot named Bruce McWhorter who always drove for us in the city. He held the Bentley's door open and explained, "Bombs hit the coal dump at the west end of the park last night. Coal dust everywhere now, all over the park. Could hardly breathe last night around here. I was wearing a scarf over my nose and mouth."

We entered the rear doors of the car. The general began reviewing documents from a folder he had brought along. I sank back into the Bentley's seat. We rolled onto Kensington Road toward Knightsbridge. Not even the opulent scent of the Bentley's leather could mask the smell of the bombed city, the unforgettable blitz odor: a mix of domestic gas, charred timber, broken sewer lines, water-doused fires, and a hint of high explosives.

We rounded Hyde Park Corner, passed the Wellington Arch, and drove along Constitution Hill. Because it was through Green Park, the avenue was one of the few in London that did not have hills of brick and stone lining it. Other than canvas-topped Humber Snipes, three-ton Austins, and other military trucks, few vehicles shared the road with us.

General Clay looked up from his paperwork and stared out the window for a moment. "Did you ever visit London before the war, Jack?"

"No, sir. First time was when I came with you."

"It's unrecognizable now, and I don't mean just the wrecked buildings and the craters and rubble everywhere and the pall of smoke that's always overhead. The bombers are abrading the soul of the city, and it may never recover. Everyone here has lost family members and friends, but there's more to it than that. People here drew strength from the immutability of their city and their lives. Nothing ever changed. Now everything is different."

He glanced at his wristwatch. "The children have been taken to the country. There are block-long lines for food and virtually everything else. Two years ago, most Londoners wouldn't have anything to do with the black market. Now it's a second economy, and folks here are wondering at their inability to do the patriotic thing and avoid the black markets."

The general returned the wave of a pedestrian who had recognized him. "And the smaller things. Having to feed potatoes to their dogs. The banning of the ringing of church bells except to announce the invasion. The warning sirens and the

67

all-clears night after night, sometimes as many as ten times a night. These and hundreds of other nuisances are grinding away at them, making them less British, less resolute and enduring."

He paused a moment, then added, "And now this. Jesus, this is going to be tough for the Brits to take."

We had reached the Queen Victoria Memorial opposite Buckingham Palace, rather, what remained of the palace, which was very little. A night bombing three days before had torn apart the structure. The edifice had been reduced to hillocks of Portland stone and bricks. Those parts of the palace familiar to the public, the Ball Room and the Bow Room, had vanished, though ragged portions of the gold-capitaled pilasters and the corbeled doorways could be seen protruding from the stone piles. An enormous crystal candelabra had been dug from the ruins, and lay in an inglorious, fractured heap behind the iron fence.

Flying the royal standard over the palace when the monarch was in residence had been discontinued early in the war. During the bombing, the king had been in Leeds reviewing soldiers of the British I Corps and the royal family had been at Balmoral. Even so, fifteen members of the household staff had perished in the blasts and ensuing fire.

All that remained upright of Buckingham Palace were a few jagged brick spires, charred black and tottering so precariously it was judged wise to topple them. Perhaps a thousand people had gathered near the gates to watch a wrecking ball swing from a crane in the forecourt. The ball hit a segment of wall, and bricks and mortar fell to the ground, sending up a roll of dust.

As we slowed for the crowd, the general said, "This'll be hugely demoralizing."

I understood him to mean the bombing of the palace, until he said a moment later, "To finish the job for the Luftwaffe by bringing down the last of the walls with a wrecking ball is a terrible decision. The ruins should sit there for Londoners to gaze on every time they pass by."

He fished a cigarette from his tunic pocket and said, "After all the pounding these people have taken, they need an Alamo.

This should have been it. I'd say so to Winnie and Montgomery, that SOB, but it's too late."

I hasten to mention that General Clay had enormous respect for Bernard Montgomery, particularly for his genius at managing the set battle, but the British general "affects me like a cold sore," Clay often said. I almost never heard Clay mention Montgomery without adding "that SOB," much like the letters following the names of British valor award winners, such as VC for Victoria Cross.

"Honk the horn, Sergeant," Clay ordered. The crowd was blocking the Bentley's progress. "We're late. I received a telex from Roosevelt yesterday asking me to be more prompt for the meetings with Churchill, if you can imagine. Winnie must have complained to the president. Christ, many is the morning I've waited two hours for the PM to get out of bed."

McWhorter tapped the horn, and we waded through the bystanders. Several times the general returned greetings with waves. When we resumed speed, he said again, "An Alamo. That's what is needed."

I wanted to say that the British already had enough Alamos, that the entire country would soon be an Alamo, but I remained silent.

General Clay began one of his trademark orations, this one about promptness in the military, which lasted all the way to the War Rooms, and which will be happily omitted here. Instead, I'll introduce myself.

The British call an aide-de-camp a dog's body, someone always under foot and easy to kick. That's all I knew about military aides when I was first assigned to General Clay. He never did outline my duties, and, with the exception of the diary he directed I keep, I invented my own tasks. My job evolved, and by S-Day I was acting as a staff troubleshooter, handling relations with the press, scheduling the general's appointments, and channeling his orders.

To my regret, not once did any newspaper or radio ever suggest that I was a power behind the throne, a Richelieu or a Rasputin. I suppose my dispensable nature was too apparent.

In fact, in many command and staff photos that appeared in stateside newspapers during the war, I was the only person not named. The caption under the famous *Life* photograph taken by Margaret Bourke-White reads, "With the weight of the free world on their shoulders, Prime Minister Churchill and General Clay spread a map on a tree stump at the Prime Minister's retreat at Chequers. Also present is an unidentified aide." My wife's next letter to me began, "My dear Unidentified."

I have three degrees from the University of California at Los Angeles. My Ph.D. thesis is entitled "Lieutenant General John Burgoyne's Strategy to Restore King George III's Rule in His Rebellious American Colonies; Defects in the Design." Quite a read, I might add, if you are interested in that sort of thing. I was hired by the War Department as a lecturer in military history and strategy soon after leaving the university, and I taught as a civilian at West Point and at combat schools around the country for a number of years. For a while, Major Wilson Clay was a fellow staff member at the artillery officer's school in Washington.

My knowledge of military history was the nexus of my relationship with General Clay, I believe. The anecdotes of war that he would extract from his remarkable memory and parade before me—at times it seemed he was flogging me with them—acted as a religion for him, offering him guidance and support. Perhaps he viewed me as a disciple.

To say we were friends during those days would be an exaggeration. Our wives became quite close, though. Clay was the hardest worker I ever met. He thought nothing of his seventy-hour work week. He spent the little time he allowed himself for socializing with staff-level officers and congressmen or administration officials. Among Wilson Clay's many gifts was the ability to make friends with influential people. I am a student of command and of Clay, but I don't pretend to understand this talent.

By 1939 one didn't need a doctorate to see the war coming, so I joined the army, tired by then of teaching, thinking that I'd prefer to fight than teach fighting. The army promptly sent me back to West Point, this time in uniform. I made repeated requests for transfers to line duty, all of which were denied. Finally, when I heard Wilson Clay was being sent to Europe as a divisional commander, I wrote him asking for work. I tried to avoid pleading in my letter, but failed, so much did I want to be in the war. I also shamelessly asked my wife, Barbara, to ask Clay's wife for help. This and, as the general delighted in pointing out, only this succeeded.

A few more personal notes. I was thirty-five years old at the time of S-Day. Barbara and I have one child, a boy, born since the war ended, who is now two years old and who appears on his way to becoming a gifted surgeon. I have three bald brothers, but I boast every hair I ever had, and it is seal brown. I wouldn't call myself handsome (and if I won't, no one else will), but my features are presentable. My nose is a bit too wide, and I can't quite hide my Adam's apple. My eyes are blue or green, depending on the light, and my wife loves them. I have a strong laugh and what I think is an attentive manner. People like being around me.

I cannot truthfully expand my role as General Clay's aide. I was one of those people you see walking the heavyweight champ from his dressing room to the ring. Much of the time my presence meant only that General Clay didn't have to talk to himself. Other times I could be handy. On my uniform was the badge of a general's aide, an eagle clutching a shield decorated with stars and stripes in colored enamels. On the shield were four stars, corresponding to Clay's rank. After the war I returned to UCLA as a professor of history. I now keep the badge in a drawer of my desk there, and I lift it out and ponder over it and recall those days more often than I'd care to admit.

The general was not one for compliments, but he inadvertently paid me one once, and modesty won't prevent me from passing it along here. Our wives back in Washington were lamenting our absences over wine one evening. The next day Margaret Clay wrote her husband asking if he would arrange a leave so I could return to the States and my wife for a few days. His reply, according to Margaret, was that I would be missed more at AEFHQ than I was being missed in Washington. I swelled with that one.

71

*   *   *

We arrived at Great George Street at 1:15 that afternoon. The government offices are between Whitehall and St. James Park. To the south was the half-ruin of Westminster Abbey. The Gothic Nave, built in the sixteenth century and once the tallest in Britain, had been destroyed by Luftwaffe bombs. Its soaring vaults had collapsed onto the monuments in the nave's aisles and transepts, all of which were now piles of rock and dust. The rest of the structure, including the two western towers, the Chapter House, Cloisters, Sanctuary, and the chapels, remained undamaged, and services were still being conducted daily.

The cabinet war rooms had been built in the basement of the Great George Street offices because of the building's proximity to Whitehall and because of its steel-framed structure. The basement complex had been reinforced with tons of concrete and steel I-beams. Engineers promised that even a direct hit on the building above would only flicker the lights and loosen dust in the subterranean rooms. Most who worked there called it "the hole in the ground."

General Clay nodded at the guards, and I followed him down the stairs. We were joined at the bottom of the steps by Lieutenant Ed Paley, Clay's London headquarters secretary. "Sir, Senator Longley is here to see you. Insists on it, in fact."

Clay glared at the lieutenant. "What is he doing in London, for Christ's sake?"

"Fact-finding tour, he claims, sir. He said he could not alert you to his arrival for security reasons. The president issued him a BIGOT, and he's been waving it around down here."

The BIGOT security card was the most secure in the ETO, and allowed its holder to know all details of the invasion defense.

"Lest you hadn't already concluded this, Lieutenant, Senator Longley is the north end of a horse walking south." Clay removed his cap and pushed it into his pants pocket. "I've got too goddamn many things to do to meet with a politician. Is the prime minister here yet?"

"He's been delayed a few moments, sir."

72

"Show the senator into my office."

The general and I walked along the main corridor. It was Clay's nature to both say he had no time and then to make time for Senator Lawton Longley, the Democrat from Louisiana, chairman of the Senate Foreign Affairs Committee and a long-time supporter of President Roosevelt. The general was not about to have the powerful senator return to Washington to whisper negative things about the AEF commander into Roosevelt's ear. Longley was known to imagine slights and nurse grudges. He was not anyone to toy with.

As he walked, Clay said over his shoulder at me, "Don't stand between Longley and a mirror, Jack. It'd be too dangerous. He loves mirrors like most men love women."

The war rooms were a series of small cubicles, most not much larger than the desks inside. They included a radio room, the shorthand-typist station, a map room, the mess, a transatlantic telephone room, a number of offices and quarters for high-ranking war personnel, the cabinet room, and the prime minister's quarters. The long corridor was filled with soldiers and sailors, all moving briskly.

We entered General Clay's office. He made do with an oak desk and chair, a filing cabinet, and a cot, which was placed against the wall under a clock. A light in milk glass hung from the ceiling. Also overhead was an air duct, painted tan, with adjustable nozzles. A banker's lamp with a green glass shade was on the desk. On one wall was a curtain hiding a map. Under the cot was a bedpan. Because there was no plumbing in the war rooms, Clay loathed staying the night there and always attempted to return to his advance command post or his rooms at Grosvenor Square.

Clay had just lowered himself into the chair when Paley ushered Senator Longley into the rooms, then retreated. You'd have thought it was Margaret Clay rather than the senator. The general leaped up, a broad grin suddenly on his face. He held out both hands and charged around the desk to greet the senator.

"Lawton, if you'd have told me you were coming I would have prepared a reception, a little drum and bugle in your honor."

The senator beamed and pumped Clay's hand. I'd seen photographs and newsreels of the senator working his home state. He invariably wore a white suit, black suspenders, spats, and sometimes even a boater. Outside Louisiana, he dressed like a Wall Street banker. For his meeting with the general, he had chosen to wear a paratrooper's camouflage jacket and pants. I thought I could hear Clay's teeth grinding behind the grin.

"The president sent me over to gather information and report back, Wilson."

Which General Clay knew meant that FDR sent him over to get him out of FDR's hair.

"And I'm glad he did, Lawton. Those twice daily briefings the president receives from my office can't completely keep him informed, I know. Hell, they're only fifteen to twenty pages apiece."

Longley helped himself to the general's chair. Clay locked his hands behind his back and rocked on his toes, the smile frozen on his face. He introduced me. I was worth only a dip of the senator's chin.

"Well, tell me what you need to know, Lawton," the general said.

The senator's black hair was two-tone, white near his ears, while the remainder was black. "A skunk's coloring," General Clay told me later. Longley had teeth as white and as perfectly spaced as piano keys. His eyes had friendly lines around them, giving him an avuncular appearance. He was as tall as I am, but had broader shoulders. He had played football at LSU. Eighteen of those ballplayers were appointed to federal government jobs within days of his first senate election victory, along with twelve of his immediate family and countless friends. "Sucking on the government tit, the lot of them," Clay had said.

"Tell me, Wilson," the senator asked, "are you positive the Germans are going to invade?"

The question was so brainless, indicative of such a vast expanse of unknowing, that General Clay's mouth actually dropped. He recovered quickly. "Let me show you how we know, Lawton."

He crossed quickly to his files and pulled out several folders.

He leafed through them a moment, then lowered a few to the desk. He stood over Longley's shoulder.

"These photos were taken by recon planes, usually De Haviland Mosquitoes. They've been analyzed by the Photographic Interpretation Unit at Wembley." The general slid the top photo under the senator's nose. "This was taken over a harbor near Amsterdam. What looks like a herringbone pattern are two long docks with barges tied to each side of both docks. There are over two hundred craft in this one photo."

General Clay pushed the top photo aside, revealing another. "These show a number of inlets in Zeeland, in southern Holland. You see more of the same barges." He brought up another photograph. The image was partly obscured by clouds. "We believe this photo shows the German navy's new *Marinefährprähme*, a special landing craft they have been mass producing for half a year."

"You mentioned barges. You mean the type that ply the European canals?"

"The same. The Kriegsmarine has requisitioned tugs, motor vessels, trawlers, lighters, and launches from throughout Europe. At least five thousand vessels. It has virtually paralyzed canal, coastal, and fishing traffic, seriously reducing trade with the Baltic and shipment of supplies to Norway. The withdrawal of merchant ships, especially coal and iron ships, has impaired ore imports from Sweden. We believe that collecting and adapting invasion vessels has put such a severe strain on the Germans' limited shipyard facilities that almost all other naval construction has come to a standstill."

"I worked on barges on the Mississippi as a lad, Wilson. They wouldn't seem to be the ideal landing craft."

"The Germans are modifying them." He returned briefly to the file cabinet, then placed a six-by-eight photo in front of the senator. "The bow of the barge you see here has been replaced with a collapsible ramp, which will act as both a sallyport and a gangway for men and vehicles. Some have been given a concrete deck for carrying tanks. These barges have a loading capacity of five to eight hundred tons and a draught of six feet. Most of them are not self-propelled, but will rely on tugs."

"This is a remarkable photo. Good clear shot, like someone just held up a Brownie and snapped it. Who took it and how did it get back to England?" The senator had left most of his Southern accent in the States.

"I wasn't told," Clay smiled briefly. Longley undoubtedly wanted a few war stories to take back home. During the Great War he had served as a typist at a Navy Reserve base in New Orleans.

"All these barges and ships are in Holland?" he asked.

"Not at all." The general pulled the curtain cord to display a map. He drew an arc from the North Sea to the English Channel. "Kriegsmarine HQ Coblenz and HQ Rotterdam have clogged these estuaries in north Germany, the Elbe, Weser, and Ems, and the bays and river outlets in Holland and Belgium. Antwerp, Rotterdam, along here to the Seine. We estimate that the Kriegsmarine has a million and a quarter seagoing tons ready for the crossing."

"What's this one show?" Senator Longley asked.

"An assembly area near Amsterdam, an enormous staging area."

The general bent lower over the desk. "We think those are Krauss-Maffei half-tracks, which carry troops and can haul AA guns. This line of vehicles here at the south end of the area are *Panzerjäger*, which are self-propelled guns, tank hunters."

The senator flipped through photograph after photograph, each showing a concentration of war materiel. Tanks, armored cars, artillery tractors, trucks, scout cars. Howitzers, antiaircraft guns, prefabricated huts, bulldozers, and excavators. Enormous stockpiles of food, clothing, and medical supplies. Horses and bicycles.

General Clay said, "Those little things that look like bumps are tents for Wehrmacht and Waffen SS troops."

Other photos showed row after row of tents, perfectly aligned grids. Churchill estimated there were half a million men waiting to cross. The impression from the photos was of the enormity of the German invasion effort, and of its perfect, methodical order. Men and materiel cluttered the coasts of Germany, Belgium, Holland, and France. The photos bristled with the imminent danger. The coastland seemed about to sink under the weight of it all.

The general lifted another photograph. "And here we see a large encampment under construction, this one in Zeeland. Here's a photo of another, near Bruges in Belgium. The square within a square in each of the shots is a fence within a fence. Note the small buildings at the corners. The bastard German is building POW camps for British and American soldiers. He plans on his ships and barges being full of men both ways."

Senator Longley stared at the photos without comment. His face had lost its practiced composure. Finally he gathered up the photos and handed them to the general. "Quite an eye-opener, those photos."

"Not eye-opening enough, I'm afraid. Most of these are dated. The Luftwaffe is heavily patrolling the coast, looking for our recon planes. This past week we lost three high-altitude recon De Havilands out of four attempts. Our ability to obtain air reconnaissance has been almost eliminated."

Clay returned the folders to the cabinet. When he turned again to Senator Longley he said, "We know they are coming, Lawton, simply because it is impossible to hide an operation of this size. The Germans know it, and so do we. The surprise will be when and where they come."

"What's your best guess when?"

"I thought they'd try it thirty days ago and was proven wrong." The general remained standing. "The tides weren't perfect, but the Allies were much less prepared than now. I thought the Germans would accept that trade-off."

"What's your next guess?"

"The enemy will make the crossing at night so darkness will conceal the strength and direction of their attacks. The German will want about an hour of daylight prior to the amphibious assault to complete air and naval bombardments. He wants a moon for airborne assaults. Whether he'll come at high or low tide is a matter of heated controversy here, but I think it'll be high tide. So we believe the enemy must land at or just after dawn and at or about high tide. These conditions exist for only a week in any given lunar month. We're in this month's critical period now."

The general returned to his map. "Tides for landing in Norfolk, which is the county here above London on the east coast, become suitable five days later than they are for landing in Sussex, here on the south coast. Three days ago Sussex was ripe. Now it's the east coast's turn to be nervous."

Lieutenant Paley pushed open the door. "The prime minister has just arrived, General. He's in his quarters and will be in the cabinet room in a few moments."

Clay glanced at Paley. "He can wait a moment until my briefing of Senator Longley is complete."

I swear the senator flushed with pleasure. Longley had met his political match in the general.

"Finally, Lawton, there's another reason we know they are invading. Hitler has insolently announced it to the public. Three months ago, at the tenth Winter Relief campaign at the *Sportspalast*, Hitler, with great zest and confidence, yelled over the public address system, '*Wir fahren gegen England.*' His audience, mostly nurses and social workers, applauded hysterically."

Senator Longley rose and patted the general on the back, one campaigner bucking up another for the task ahead. "I won't have you keeping Churchill long. I'll relay to the president and my committee members all you've said, Wilson." He stepped to the door. "Remember, I'm behind you."

The general took the proffered hand in both his. "I know you are, Lawton. Winston and I are counting on your support."

Another gratified grin from the senator, then Lieutenant Paley escorted him down the hall.

General Clay looked at me. " 'Winston and I are counting on you.' Christ on a crutch, you'd think the senior senator from Louisiana would know bullshit when he's standing in a bucket of it." He squared his black tie. "Let's go hear more bad news."

5

When disaster looms, the British look for a leader rather than a scapegoat. Winston Churchill entered the cabinet room, and we rose like a jury. He walked briskly around the table to his post nearest the world map and nodded once before lowering himself into the chair. He was wearing a black, rumpled pin-stripe suit, a burgundy tie, and the knowing smile and sparkling eyes of one who has already won the battle. Lately, Churchill's public face had not been lasting through these sessions.

We settled into our seats. Pipes and tobacco were produced. Churchill chewed on a cigar. He seldom lit them, by the way, just gnawed them down to empty rags. Water was poured into glasses from several pitchers, and folders were opened. This was a meeting of the Defense Committee, comprised of portions of the War Ministry and the Anglo-American Joint Chiefs of Staff. Sitting near Churchill were the only other men not in uniform, Deputy Prime Minister Clement Attlee and Minister for Coordination of Defense Lord Lindley.

The table, covered with green cloth, was a rectangle with a gap in the center. Overhead were massive steel beams, double riveted and painted red. Several fans and a clock were on the wall. Arranged round the room were portable blackboards and map boards. The room was ten feet underground.

General Clay sat opposite the prime minister, quite a distance from him, since the table was twelve or so feet across. On Clay's left was Lieutenant General Henry Bisset, commander of the Canadian I Corps. The Americans, four of us, were grouped together. Admiral Walter Stanton, commander, U.S. Atlantic Fleet East, was to Clay's right. Stanton's aid, a lieutenant commander from Chicago, was near me. We aides, about fifteen of us, called ourselves the Flying Buttresses. At each meeting we leaned in our chairs against the walls as if holding them up.

"Shall we begin?" the prime minister asked as he pulled another cigar from his breast pocket. He stared at it a moment, turning it in his hand. From his expression, it was impossible to tell if he was pondering the fate of the free world or an imperfection in a tobacco leaf. He cleared his throat grandly, a British art. "Let's start where we ended yesterday. Bring in the meteorologist."

A nagging dread was that the weather would blind us to the attack. German air, land, and sea operations required a minimum level of weather conditions. Whenever the North Sea and English Channel were tossed by storms, committee members shared a palpable sense of relief. We prayed for white horses, as the British called white caps. The Meteorology Committee, a subgroup of the Defense Committee, met twice daily, at five in the morning and ten at night.

One of the few advantages we enjoyed over the enemy was more accurate weather reporting. The Germans were forced to predict the predominately western weather patterns based on data from Ireland and Norway and periodic weather patrols in the east Atlantic by four-engined Fw200s stationed at Lorient. In contrast, the Allies gleaned information from stations in Northern Ireland, Iceland, Greenland, the Faero Islands, Labrador, Gibraltar, and the eastern United States. Weather in the North Sea could be reliably predicted twenty-four hours in advance. In the channel, forty-eight hours.

Group Captain Dr. Richard Swarthmore was shown into the room, looking uncomfortable in his RAF uniform, which hung limply on him. Swarthmore was a civilian meteorologist on loan to the Royal Air Force. He led a team of experts collected from the Admiralty and from the Air Ministry at Dunstable. He stepped quickly to a map displaying eastern and southern England.

"Good afternoon, Dr. Swarthmore," Churchill said, his wonderful voice filling the room to its corners. Despite frightening intelligence reports from all fronts, I was convinced that with that voice, we could not lose the war. "I want you to tell me your children have been playing with your barometer."

Swarthmore was accustomed to the prime minister's perplexing openings. Churchill liked holding forth a moment before each session. "My children, Prime Minister?"

"You remember, I am sure, that the night before the devastating storm of 27 November 1703, Daniel Defoe in London glanced at his barometer to find that the bottom had quite fallen out of it. He accused his children of playing with the instrument. Defoe did not know that the gale of the century was hours away. I want you to tell me, Doctor, that your barometer has fallen to unprecedented lows, and that our seas will shortly become impassable."

"I am afraid I cannot, Prime Minister." Swarthmore pushed a lock of his hair to one side. His face was the pasty color of one who never saw the sun. He had dark patches resembling oysters under his eyes. Swarthmore's job allowed little sleep. "A high-pressure ridge, reaching from Iceland east to the Outer Hebrides, continues to force depressions southward. Yesterday I said that depressions may be forming between Newfoundland and Ireland, which will make the weather eastward deteriorate. These are developing, but we remain under the calming influence of the broad high-pressure zone. Those depressions are moving our way, but too slowly to interfere dramatically with channel weather in the next three days."

"*Hitlerwetter*, is it then, Doctor?" Churchill asked. Hitlerweather, or perfect sailing, as German radio was openly calling it.

"For the next twenty-four hours there will be a patchy two-thousand-foot ceiling over the North Sea from Edinburgh south. A touch lower further north. Seas will be level two to three. The channel will be clear, with the possible appearance of spotty clouds at three or four thousand feet and with a slightly freshening wind. Fair weather, Prime Minister."

81

"Do all the members of your team agree?" Admiral Peter Fairfax challenged. He was commander of the Royal Navy Home Fleet. He and his superior, Admiral Parker Gilford, commander in chief, Allied Naval Forces, were on the hallway side of the room. The other Royal Navy representative in the room was Lord Erskine, admiral of the fleet and first sea lord, sitting next to Attlee.

"Admiral, there is little to disagree with in our report," Swarthmore replied. "This is a predictable front, with little movement and few surprises. Yes, the team agrees."

"There is a saying that in war weather is neutral," the prime minister said. "A regrettable fiction in our case. Doctor, on your way out will you ask General Cadogan to join us?"

General Roger Cadogan was head of the Combined Intelligence Committee, which drew members from all British and American forces. Cadogan reported to the Defense Committee daily and sent reports three times each day. He marched into the room.

I'm always surprised to see an overweight Englishman. Cadogan carried a substantial bulk that pushed out his uniform and robbed his face of angles. Rumor had it that he shaved several times a day to avoid a five o'clock shadow.

"Prime Minister, there have been developments since we spoke last." Cadogan began his briefing this way each day, much like a radio announcer's distinctive sign on. Nobody questioned his right to do so, because he was always true to his word, bringing some new, startling glimpse of what was to come.

He said, "We have analyzed the submarine caught by the *Pettibone* this morning in the North Sea near Benacre Broad. It is a V80 midget which carried no weapons other than one pistol. The sub was fitted with a Netz radio designed to send continuous signals once the sub has surfaced. It also had an Asdic-type apparatus, called a Nadel BE, made by the Kroner Radio Works in Hamburg, which broadcasts sound waves through the water to be picked up by underwater listening devices on German ships."

"It's a pathfinder, then, is it?" asked General Sir Allen Barclay. Other than the first sea lord, Barclay was the ranking military officer in the room. He was chairman of AACCS and chief of the Imperial General Staff. The British are careful with precedent. Barclay sat next to Lord Lindley, who was to Churchill's immediate left at the head of the table.

"Yes, sir. The submarine's equipment is designed to guide other ships to it."

"That submarine is a plant," General Arthur Stedman exclaimed. He was commander in chief, Home Forces. With several others in the room, Stedman was convinced the increasing evidence pointing to an invasion on the east coast was part of an intricate deception. "There have been no satisfactory explanations why it foundered. The Kriegsmarine let us find it."

"Arthur," Churchill said mildly, "let's hear what else General Cadogan has to say, shall we?"

Cadogan said, "There is certainly a chance it is a deception, General. We are considering that possibility. However, other evidence is mounting."

He lifted a blank piece of paper from a display stand, revealing an enlarged photograph. He reached for a pointer. "As you know, we have recently had very few successful reconnaissance flights. But one made it through yesterday. Here is a photograph taken by a Mosquito flying from our Photographic Reconnaissance Unit base at St. Eval in Cornwall. It shows a pasture on the French coast near Dieppe. The field is apparently a staging area for tanks. Our analysts say that these twelve structures you see here," he tapped the photo, "are supposed to be medium tanks, which the Germans call the PzKpfw III, short for *Panzerkampfwagen*. They are the Wehrmacht's standard battle tank."

"Supposed to be?" the prime minister asked.

"Sir, if you will look closely at this photograph you will see that the Wehrmacht was careful, but not quite careful enough. A tank cannot cross a field of any sort without leaving track prints. This is what these double lines are crossing the pasture." Cadogan drew patterns with the stick. "But this one tank has left no track marks, either in front or in back of it. It has apparently sprung from nowhere onto this field."

"What you are saying, General, is that those tanks are not tanks at all, but mock-ups?" The question came from General

Alfred Alexander, commander in chief, Joint Army Operations. Alexander, an Old Harrovian and a graduate of Sandhurst, as were many in the room, including the PM, spoke with a pointed public school accent, also called a plumstone accent, meaning he spoke as if his mouth were full of plum pits.

"We are quite certain that this tank—and probably the others in this field—is in fact made of canvas and wood. These tank tracks have been cut into the ground with some sort of implement, perhaps a lawn roller. They forgot to roll on the tracks behind this one tank."

"That doesn't sound very German, forgetting like that, Roger," Wilson Clay commented.

After all these British speakers, General Clay's words sounded broad and flat, a hillbilly's language. Several of the British officers smiled, as always at Clay's first words at a meeting. They weren't being unkind. People grin when someone belches in church, and I think that's what the British heard when an American spoke.

"Granted, it does not." He hesitated, then lowered his pointer. "But despite evidence to the contrary, the Germans are human. Here they have made a human mistake by forgetting to put tracks behind a decoy tank."

Fairfax asked, "Then did the Luftwaffe deliberately let our reconnaissance plane through?"

"Evidence points that way," General Crawford Douglas replied. He was commander in chief, Allied Air Forces, the only RAF officer at the meeting. "Our pilot reported only dispirited antiaircraft fire, and no chase from the Messerschmitts. No other recon flight has had such a jolly time of it lately."

Churchill said, "So by installing the decoys, the Germans want us to believe there are more tank columns in northern France than there actually are. Or, by deliberately omitting a tank track and knowing we'd discover it, the Germans want us to believe their forces in northern France are largely phantoms. Which is it, General?"

"I cannot tell you, Prime Minister." Cadogan's voice was strained, as if Churchill's question were an indictment.

Churchill summarized the endless arguments of these meetings when he added, "Do they think we think they think we think they think?" He threw up a hand as if casting away all further speculation and chuckled unconvincingly.

The prime minister always tried to allay the tension during these councils with an offhand remark. Fewer and fewer were joining him in a laugh. These men knew they were making the onerous decisions that would echo down through the generations. The British had a studied nonchalance during moments of great emotion and decision. They resumed their positions around the table each day, placid on the surface, portraits of British stoicism. But of late their facades of calm and reserve were being stripped away by the daily grind of command and their trepidation.

"Look at a man's hands—they're a telltale," General Clay once told me. Around the table, fists were knotted so tightly that hands were white. Several men drummed tattoos on the table. Admiral Fairfax repeatedly pulled at his fingers, as if setting disjointed knuckles. Lord Erskine constantly rubbed his upper lip with two fingers, as if trying to wipe away a clinging bit of lunch. General Douglas endlessly rotated an ashtray.

Tension was worse during the part of the month when the tides were right, and worse again when the weather was fair. The meeting the day before had disintegrated into a shouting match, such an uncharacteristic event that it startled even those who had done the shouting.

Churchill drew his palm along the table, smoothing the cloth. "What else do you have for us, General?"

"We have heard from a reliable resistance source in Normandy that two Wehrmacht divisions, the 8th and 28th, which had been encamped in the valley of the Seine, have suddenly left the area and may be marching toward Amsterdam. And a few moments ago we received another radio report, this one from Merksem, near Antwerp, that the Wehrmacht 30th Division may be passing through to the north."

"You say reliable," General Barclay said. His face was so narrow and his nose so thin that his eyes almost touched. "How reliable?"

"These two contacts have sent information before that we have been able to confirm, but there is always the possibility they have been compromised, as you know."

"And the rest of it, General Cadogan?" Churchill prompted.

"You have read my midday reports, so you know that this morning at 0600 hours Wehrmacht units from northern Germany through the Netherlands to Belgium began a complete radio silence. Their unit orders, which constitute the bulk of their coded transmissions, are now presumably being delivered over telephone lines or by messengers. And just an hour ago, German forces along the French coast also went off the air. As you know, German units underwent radio silence like this in April for several days."

"Last month the silence turned out to be either a rehearsal or a feint," General Douglas said. "What about this month?"

"The Germans do not trust their own radio codes. On occasion we break one, and we gain information until the code changes. Radio silence lets them rest more comfortably. Last minute orders will remain their secret. This month? Another simulation, a bluff, or the actual launch? We can only speculate, General Douglas."

Douglas pounded his fist onto the table. "What I'm asking, General Cadogan, is if the bloody Germans are coming tonight? And where? Those two things are all I want to know. Why won't you tell us where and when?"

Cadogan stiffened. "I am a reporter. I will inform you of all I know, and the committee's task is to draw the conclusions."

Tension shimmered in the room. Finally the Allied Air Forces commander inhaled deeply and dipped his chin at Cadogan, an apology. The room was quiet for a moment. One by one, the committee members turned to the prime minister. Defense decisions were ultimately his. Churchill never formally polled the committee, but he always tried to gain consensus advice. He knew he could be crashingly wrong, witness Gallipoli.

I should briefly describe the chain of command. Doggedly following Wilson Clay around as I did, I could easily exaggerate his pre-invasion role. I don't wish to do so here. Despite more

American troops and equipment arriving daily, the defense of England remained primarily a British undertaking.

The War Ministry was charged with governing Great Britain and directing the war effort, with Churchill as its principal. Reporting to the ministry were the Imperial General Staff and the Anglo-American Joint Chiefs of Staff, which met together as the Defense Committee. Reporting in turn to the Joint Chiefs were the commanders of the Allied Naval Forces (Gilford), Joint Army Operations (Alexander), and Allied Air Forces (Douglas), all British officers.

Then, on yet a lower rung, were the battle chiefs. The American Expeditionary Force commander (Clay) and the Home Forces commander (Stedman) reported to Alexander. Commanders of the U.S. Atlantic Fleet East (Stanton), the Royal Navy Home Fleet (Fairfax), and the Eastern and Southern Approaches (Admiral Sir Hugh Pembroke) reported to Admiral Gilford. Finally, all air operations were under General Douglas, including the American Army Air Force East and the RAF Fighter Command and Bomber Command.

"General Cadogan, is there more?" the prime minister asked glumly.

"Yes, sir. You have read my report on the German paratrooper killed by a farmer just south of the Humber early this morning. The commando's wireless was the same equipment that was being used by the Irish spy your troops captured near Rye this morning, General Clay."

"A German radioman on the east coast, another on the south," Alexander said. He had a high forehead and eyebrows that could climb most of it. "We know the German's aren't targeting both our east and south coasts. It would be a logistical impossibility. So one of the radiomen was a decoy, and the other was going to guide the invasion. Which was which?"

"We have examined their equipment and interrogated the Irishman at length. We received no clue either way."

General Barclay said, "The Germans would not have told the decoy he was a decoy."

"There is more," Cadogan said.

Mouths turned down around the room.

"General Laidlaw of the 2nd Infantry was thorough. He had troops from his reconnaissance regiment search the area. They found a second parachute which had been buried a quarter mile away from where the first German was killed. They also found footprints heading west toward the Lincolnshire Wolds, but have been unable to find him."

The inevitable question was asked by Arthur Stedman, "Were we supposed to find that parachute?"

The chief of the Intelligence merely shook his head.

"Will you summarize for us, General Cadogan?" Churchill asked. His hands were folded in front of him as if he were in prayer.

"We have new evidence—if that evidence is taken at face value—that our North Sea coast may be the target of the invasion. The pathfinder submarine, the increasing radio activity before the blackout this morning, and, of course, the intensified bombing of rail installations along the east coast last night, on which you've seen preliminary reports from the Observer Corps and Coastal Command, all point that way."

Cadogan walked to the best estimate map on the wall to the prime minister's left. He brought up his pointer. "As you know, we are faced with three German Army groups, A, C, and B, arranged from the Netherlands south and east along the coast to the Cherbourg Peninsula. Rommel's Army Group C is in Dutch ports, here and here."

He moved the pointer. "Army Group A, under Von Rundstedt, which remains near Antwerp and south roughly to here." He struck the board at Ostend, on the Belgium coast near the French border. "Von Rundstedt's army also includes the divisions we think are marching north. CIC believes that between 45,000 and 50,000 Wehrmacht soldiers have left Normandy between Le Havre and Dieppe, and are heading northeast."

Cadogan stepped along the map. "Finally, Army Group B, with just three corps, remains here in Normandy, largely from Caen east. We know of nothing new here. There are other German divisions inland on the continent, of course, but these are troops of occupation."

"Thank you, General," the prime minister said, dismissing him. When the door closed behind Cadogan, Churchill went on, "I have always thought the Germans would choose our east coast."

. "So you have said on numerous occasions," Clement Attlee remarked. The leader of the Labour Party was dry, unemotional, and self-effacing, Churchill's polar opposite. But he and the prime minister worked together with surprisingly little disharmony.

"I'll say it again, Clement. The Wehrmacht movements described by General Cadogan reinforce my argument. Our east coast has open, gently shelving beaches, a requirement for an amphibious assault. Many of the beaches on the south coast are flanked or dominated by cliffs, or are overlooked by escarpments of downland, much more difficult for landing craft."

"And the East Anglian plain offers better opportunities for blitz warfare than does the quilted, intricate terrain of Kent and Sussex," General Alexander added. "The German's first goal will be to isolate London, which will be easier from the east."

Admiral Gilford disagreed. "The Germans would have three or four times the sea distance coming to our east coast than to our south coast."

Lord Erskine spoke his first words of the meeting. "They will be able to land eight or ten divisions anywhere they choose before we can counter them. If the invasion armada crosses the North Sea to our east coast, the Royal Navy will have an improved chance to cut off the German's second wave and their efforts at resupplying the first wave. The Kriegsmarine surely knows this. So they will choose the shortest sea route possible, to our south coasts. Kent, Sussex, Hampshire, from France."

"Eight or ten divisions anywhere they choose?" Alexander was sputtering. "Do you think, Lord Erskine, that the British Army has been spending all this time laying out welcoming mats?"

The first sea lord had a scimitar nose and veiled eyes. His features gave away nothing. His voice was a rich baritone, and he used it with effect. "I have long maintained the Germans will gain tactical surprise, despite your gallant efforts, General."

"Poppycock," Arthur Stedman injected. "Sheer and utter poppycock."

"I agree with Lord Erskine," Admiral Gilford joined in. "Eight or ten divisions, tactical surprise."

The first sea lord asked, "Have you ever been to sea, General Alexander?"

"Not often," Alexander admitted icily. "Every time I do, I have an uncontrollable urge to urinate."

Lord Erskine inhaled sharply, gathering himself for an outburst, but Churchill held up his cigar, cutting off the squabbling. "Let us not have history record we were discussing bodily functions at the critical hour."

We had heard this argument countless times. Early on, the location of the invasion was utter guesswork, and even Scotland, the Shetlands, Ireland, and Iceland were mentioned. Then the committee became divided along service lines, with the army believing the German target would be the east coast and the navy arguing the south coast. As evidence mounted over recent weeks that Rommel had formed a third army, Army Group C, in the Dutch ports, and with Cadogan's new intelligence that certain German units were moving north, the view favoring the east coast was prevailing. RAF General Douglas had before this meeting supported the navy position, but as he told General Clay later, the heavy bombing of the railways along the east coast the night before had convinced him otherwise. The first sea lord and Admiral Gilford tenaciously clung to their cross-channel argument.

The prime minister said, "Even though our best information is that the east coast, somewhere along the coasts of Essex, Suffolk, Norfolk, or Lincolnshire, will be the location of the invasion, I counsel caution. These late developments should not prompt us into hasty redeployment."

"Prime Minister," General Alexander asked, "is that precisely what Hitler hopes we are doing in this meeting today, absolutely nothing? We have kept XI Corps and the Canadians in reserve, and I believe we must now release them to reinforce the eastern counties."

"Lord Lindley?" Churchill asked his minister for coordination of defense.

"I quite agree with you, Prime Minister." Lord Lindley sat forward in his chair, peering left and right. There was a delicacy to him, with his peaked lips, moist eyes, and milky skin. Strangers might have taken him for a weak man, a mistake. "At this point, panicked redeployment can only be what the German High Command wants from us."

"Then it is decided," Churchill said. "We have very few reserves and will keep our XI and the Canadians back and commit them only when needed. What is next today?"

General Clay caught himself raising his hand like a schoolboy. "I want to propose realignment of some of my units from a two-one to a one-two defense."

"We have been down this long road before, have we not, General Clay?" Alexander asked. He pushed his chair away from the table in a resigned manner.

"Yes, and I'll try it again. I wish to pull back certain battalions of the 4th Motorized from the Hastings-Eastbourne area, the 35th Infantry from Folkestone, and the 1st Armored behind Worthing."

"A little early to call a retreat, is it not?" Alexander asked bitingly.

Clay rudely sucked on a tooth before he said, "One of the most endearing of British traits is your indifference to outside suggestions or criticisms. But let me impose on you anyway. The strength of our defense can be measured not by the number of troops on the shoreline, but by the number of hours in which a strong counterattack can be delivered."

"Once invading vessels have landed, they will never leave," Alexander said. "Nelson wrote that in 1801, and it is still true today. We must destroy them on the beach. The Germans must not get as far as the saltgrass at the top of our dunes."

Clay said with some heat, "I can prove mathematically that the brunt of their amphibious attack cannot be stopped on the beach."

"Spare us your multiplication tables this afternoon," Alexander said wearily.

Clay pointed at Alexander and said, "Your Lord D'Arbernon said, 'An Englishman's mind works best when it is almost too late.' But he was giving you the goddamn benefit of a doubt."

Furious, Alexander rose from his chair. "You—"

Churchill stabbed them to silence with his cigar. Alexander stiffly resumed his seat.

Alan Barclay toyed with a folder as he said, "In any event, it is simply too late to transfer those divisions."

"It is never too late if the battle hangs in the balance," Clay countered.

This was another argument that had racked the Defense Committee. Stedman and Clay regarded the North Sea–English Channel wall of fixed defenses as an ephemeral hindrance, another Maginot Line. Keeping the Germans out of the country, irrespective of where they landed, would be difficult, perhaps impossible because the Allied navies had not nearly enough remaining destroyers or patrol vessels to cover the entire coast from Dorset to Edinburgh. And the fixed defenses were still weak. Instead, the battle commanders favored massed counterattacks against German penetrations. A static defense repels by fire, and the Allies had insufficient fire. Counterattack defeats by movement, and even undermanned and underequipped units could move. "Counterattack is the soul of defense," Clay had said before.

But the weight of British chiefs had fervently pushed for an intractable defense on the shore line. They believed that the ordered movement of large land formations, necessary for counterattack, would be almost impossible under constant air attack, which, with recent Luftwaffe air superiority, was guaranteed. And, more simply, deliberately leaving a porous sea wall defense, of virtually admitting the Germans into the country and hoping for the best, was a particularly noxious notion.

Barclay and Clay argued back and forth for several minutes. There have been few amphibious landings in the modern era, and much of what the generals said was speculation. When they began pointing fingers at each other, Churchill ended the argument by saying, "General Clay, I must side with my chiefs. Should the enemy not come during this vulnerable time, we'll take up the issue again. What is next?"

The meeting lasted another thirty minutes, largely regarding issues of supply. When Churchill said, "We will meet here again tomorrow, if the Germans allow it," members of the

Defense Committee broke off into smaller groups to continue discussions.

The prime minister pushed himself slowly from his seat. He waved Clay around to him, then said, "I've got ten minutes until the War Ministry meets, so I'll be having a drop of tea in my quarters. Will you join me?"

"Of course, sir."

"You too, Colonel Royce."

I was always astonished when the prime minister remembered my name. Had I tail feathers, I would have flared them. He and Clay had met socially at Chequers and 10 Downing Street and other residences. They enjoyed each other's company. Perhaps it was the game they played. It was the prime minister's turn to serve, to choose the topic. Churchill and Clay leaned toward each other as they walked, deeply into their talk before they reached the hallway. I trailed after them.

Before I tell of their contest, let me mention a few incidents from Wilson Clay's early life that may shed some light on him. I've collected them like others collect stamps or autographs. People always wanted to talk about him. When they learned I was his aide, they cornered me and exhausted their memories of him, perhaps thinking they were adding to some official history and setting the record straight.

By far the most frequent anecdote I heard involved the Plebe Production, the spring show first-year students put on for the faculty and other cadets at West Point. For an entire academy class, Clay's skit remains the most vivid moment of their first year. Although only one of several plebes in the piece, Clay received all the blame and all the demerits because he delivered the punchline.

Major General Clinton Robinson was superintendent of the academy at that time. He was known as a stickler on everything from precision drill to participation in athletics, but his overwhelming passion was hygiene. From his office poured forth orders regarding sanitation. Nothing was too clean or crisp. One week before the skit, he instructed all cadets to wash their hands a minimum of 120 seconds before each meal. "Robinson was asking for it," one of Clay's classmates told me, recalling the skit with glee.

During the Plebe Production, five cadets stood on the stage at rigid attention, while another cadet, dressed as Robinson, reviewed them. The cadet perfectly exaggerated Robinson's pompous lift to his chin and the way he tapped his swagger stick on his thigh. He stepped along the line. "Straight tie, chin up. Excellent."

He stopped at the fourth cadet to stare at his uniform. "I've just noticed, Cadet, that each of you has a fork in your uniform pocket. Tell me why."

"Sir, we use them to lift bread slices from the platter, so we won't touch the other slices with our hands."

"Excellent," the cadet-general boomed. "That's the spirit."

There was hearty laughter from the audience.

The mock general next paused in front of Wilson Clay, who also had a fork in his pocket. The general then asked, "Cadet Clay, I've also noticed that each of you has a string hanging from your fly. Tell me why."

"Sir, we use them to pull our things out in the latrine, so we won't touch ourselves with our hands."

Gasps from the audience.

"Excellent," barked the mock general. "There's initiative for you." He thought for a moment, then asked, "But tell me, Cadet Clay, how do you get your thing back in?"

Clay answered, "I don't know about the others, sir, but I use my fork."

Pandemonium swept the hall. Some cadets laughed so hard they fell off their chairs. General Robinson—the real one—indignantly marched out of the room. Clay was in his doghouse for the remainder of his stint at the academy.

Another story was told to me by Lieutenant General Alex Hargrave, commander of AEF's I Corps. Clay had been a sickly youth who missed a year of high school because of persistent pneumonia. His father blamed the boy for the disease. When Wilson recovered, he vowed to build himself up, and did so with an unremitting dedication to exercise and physical challenge. He layered muscle on himself by lifting barbells and tossing a medicine bag. He went out for football his junior year at Davenport High and was cut straight away. But in his senior year he made the team as a running back. Then he made the academy team.

Clay set no records, but in an era before platooning he played every minute of every game for three years. In his last game, he broke his wrist in the third quarter, but played until the contest ended. Hargrave recalled Clay's obsessive drive during the games and his pushing his teammates. He also remembers Clay telling him once that he hated football.

"To tell you the truth," Hargrave said, "football wasn't much fun for us other players because Wilson was in the game."

Clay used the same techniques courting Margaret. "He lay siege on me like I was a medieval fort," she laughingly told my wife. "I agreed to his marriage proposal as an act of surrender."

Margaret Banning may have been the first woman Clay ever showed an interest in. She claims it was because they were negative images of each other. While Wilson at nineteen was blustery, abrupt, opinionated, and a bit stumbling, Margaret was poised, subtle, and charming. They did have one thing in common, willfulness. Wilson wore his on his collar, but Margaret hid hers under layers of social skills.

She was the daughter of a wealthy founder of the St. Paul and Spokane Railway Company, which was later bought out by the Great Northern. She and Clay met at a social held at the Spokane River Club when the cadet was home on Christmas leave in 1911. His was the third name on her dance card, and after their dance, he refused to release her hand, telling others on her card that their turns had been canceled. "He was the only fellow in the dance hall in uniform," Margaret said, "so the other boys thought he could order them away."

On the following day, Wilson arrived at the Banning home in a horse-drawn buggy, unannounced and uninvited. When the butler inquired of his mission, Clay replied he was taking Margaret on a picnic. Six inches of snow covered the ground. Perplexed, then amused, Margaret let herself be shown into the buggy, where she found a pile of blankets and a wicker basket of food. They drove down the hill to sit on the river bank, wrapped in blankets "to eat the coldest meal of my life."

Clay left the next day for West Point, but barraged Margaret with letters, which became increasingly presumptuous. She happily returned them. "He seemed so dashing, and I didn't mind a little harmless flirtation in our letters. What could he do? He was three thousand miles away."

She underestimated him. By the time he returned to Spokane that summer, it was understood he would ask her to marry him the first moment they were alone. "I became engaged to a man I had never kissed," Margaret told my wife.

Apparently Margaret Clay made the descent from an heiress to the wife of a junior army officer without difficulty. But all her life, wherever they were posted, from Fort Bragg to Washington, D.C., she returned alone to Spokane for six weeks every summer, once again to indulge herself in the family's fortune.

To my knowledge, he never dallied with other women, at least until he met Lady Anne Percival, and I'll relay my spotty knowledge of that relationship shortly. The acid test probably came during the Great War, and I've heard the story from several of his friends from those days, including General Jones. During R&R in Paris, fellow officers of the 4th Artillery chipped in a total of three dollars to hire a prostitute to make a surprise visit to Clay's hotel room. Clay apparently paid her another three dollars to sit chastely in a chair for thirty minutes, then tell his friends he was the best ever.

The artillery officers learned the truth when they offered the hooker yet another three dollars to provide details. I asked General Clay about the story. He shook his head, but volunteered pleasantly, "The palm of my right hand still shines from those days."

I'll share a few more glimpses of General Clay. Nothing endears soldiers to their commander more than stories about how the officer will take care of them, come hell or high water. A favorite among AEF troops was how during the bitterly cold January of 1918 Clay raided the priceless, antiquarian library of a French chateau. He ordered pages torn from thousands of books so the paper could pad the lining of his men's uniform coats.

On another occasion, after a miserably cold day of dragging howitzers across the French countryside, his troops faced a long night bivouacked in a freezing pasture. Against orders not to disrupt the civilian population when at all possible, Clay led his men into the cozy confines of a nunnery near Soissons, herding the startled sisters of the Holy Trinity into the kitchen while his exhausted men sacked out in their cells.

But best remembered stories involve Wilson Clay's restless drive and his ferocity as a commander. Hargrave laughingly told me how Clay stared at his watch during a one-hour truce called to remove the wounded from no-man's land at Château-Thierry. Clay mouthed the passing seconds, then ordered a salvo launched the instant the hour was over.

Another time, German infantrymen breached the American line and began swarming toward Clay's battery. Clay either did not receive or ignored the order to abandon his guns and retreat. Rather, he ordered the muzzles lowered to fire grape-shot pointblank into the advancing German lines, round after round, until the barrels were glowing. This next can't be verified, and may have been embellished over the years, but I heard that during the heaviest incoming, with the Kaiser's infantry visible through the smoke, one of Clay's gun bunnies threatened to bolt. Clay held a .45 to the soldier's temple and asked how far he'd like to go. The soldier hastily picked up the tongue of the shell sled and went back to work. Moments later the German drive stalled.

These snippets of General Clay's life were traded back and forth among his soldiers. They were rolled over and savored, discounted and expanded. American soldiers might catch only a glimpse of their commander as he sped by in his jeep, might not ever hear his voice. But these yarns completed their sketch of him and made him larger than life.

Now, about Lady Anne Percival. I am loathe to bring her up, but some commentators have seized on her relationship with General Clay, suggesting she drastically impeded his judgment during the battle, that she became a "field wife" to the general, to use the Red Army term. I need to tread lightly here, because appearances were less than reality. At least, I think so. Let me lay out some of the evidence.

Lady Anne was the widow of Sir Roderick Percival, who was

97

killed during a test flight of a Hurricane in 1939, and the daughter of Earl Selden, the world's leading armor theoretician. There is some question whether the earl had ever been inside a tank, but his 1934 work *Armored Warfare* was a seminal study on its use. Generals Guderian, Rommel, and Brauchitsch admitted reading it, and it is still a standard work at the United States Army's Command and General Staff School at Fort Leavenworth.

The earl was in his seventies in 1942 and may have supposed his life's work was behind him. Then the American general came calling. Clay's first meeting with Earl Selden began simply enough. In a significant breech of decorum, Clay and I appeared without warning at his country home, Haldon House, in Surrey, southwest of London. After we were shown into his study and announced by his butler, Clay said only, "Earl Selden, I am an artilleryman. I need your help."

The earl had a reputation for being curt and ill-natured. Yet he rose like a young man, beckoning us in. He remains the only man I've ever met who did not look ridiculous in an ascot and a smoking jacket. He had a raft of white hair, parted in the middle, and an ivory mustache sculpted with wax, the tips sharp enough to chip ice.

The room looked as if it had not changed since the age of Queen Victoria. Ponderous red swags hung on the windows. Much of the furniture was covered in tufted silk damask. A Bosendorfer piano, the dimensions of an automobile, was in a corner. Dried flowers were in an arrangement on the mantle, as if they had been there all that time. A dozen family photographs in silver frames sat atop the piano. The earl was a noted collector of Wellington and Peninsular War memorabilia, and three mahogany display cases were near a wall.

The session lasted three hours, with Clay and the earl hovering over a contour map I had brought along, using pins and tags. I had never before seen the general take instruction so passively. He had finally met someone who knew more about fighting a war than he did.

At eleven o'clock that evening a woman entered the study. It seemed that a stage light picked her up, illuminating her arresting features and creating an aureola around her hair and shoulders. Music might have swelled and applause rolled down from the seats. I have no other way of describing her entrance. She was followed by a small dog, a white and tan pekinese with a pug nose and bushy tail that swished side to side.

The general and I stood quickly. The woman's hair was raven black, and she wore it bobbed and tucked in at her neck. Her skin was the color of frost. Her lips were burgundy and full, with a upward lilt, as if she found us Americans amusing. She was wearing an iridescent silk blouse that cast off numberless hues, making her seem illusive and transient. Her eyes shone with knowledge and wit as she drifted across the carpet to the earl.

She bussed her father's cheek and bid him good night. Her voice was both mature and breathless, a mix of challenge and invitation. Yet all she was doing was saying good night to her father. The earl did not introduce her. Maybe he knew better. Even he could not take his eyes off her. The old man glowed with pride and, it seemed, wonderment. She began toward the door.

General Clay abruptly asked, "Earl Selden, may I borrow some brandy?"

"Why, of course. Rude of me not to have offered."

Clay turned to her. "Will you have a refreshment with me, ma'am? Some brandy, perhaps?"

The earl almost coughed out his bridgework.

She replied, "I would enjoy that, Major."

"It's general, ma'am. General Clay."

"Yes, undoubtedly." She smiled. Her teeth must have had some sort of electrical work that made them glow from within. "Have Smalley call me when you and father have finished for the evening."

"I wouldn't want to tire your father," Clay said quickly. "We're done."

The earl glowered at Clay in such a manner that I feared for the alliance. He harumphed in the proper British manner, then levered himself out of his chair.

As he passed us, he said, "Good luck, General." There was

a curious tone to his voice. Looking back, I think he was about to add, "You'll need it," but declined, perhaps thinking the general deserved whatever came his way.

Anne Percival was born in the home in which we sat, but had spent most of her youth in the East Africa Protectorate, later called the Kenya Colony. Earl Selden owned a cotton and coffee plantation christened New Surrey, so named because it was about the size of the English county. Lady Anne's upbringing was supervised by her mother and two nannies, one a Welsh woman and the other a Kikuyu. The earl visited infrequently, preferring the study of armor to farming.

A number of young women from Africa entered Wycombe Abbey, the girls' school, in 1915, most of them tomboys, admired and snubbed for their worldliness, their equestrian ability, and their smattering of native phrases. But Anne Percival also brought a sparkling intellect and relentless spirit and soon developed a scarcely concealed sensuality and provocative candor. A few of the teachers at the school still roll their eyes at her name. She was a confidante to many, a ringleader for all, a girl who broke up cliques and reformed them at will, and a prankster who laughed longest if the joke was on her. She organized a strike against the school's kitchen over the porridge, and it is believed she organized the throng of girls who tied their Latin teacher to a chair and left her in a room all of one night, to be found by a janitor the next morning. The school sighed with relief when she left, but she was widely and fondly remembered by her classmates.

Lady Anne was married four times. General Stedman once said she "used up her husbands and tossed them aside." Her first was Edwin Wooleridge, son of the Fleet Street press magnate, whom she left after three years, "having taught him everything and learned nothing," as she put it, according to Stedman. Her second husband was Baron Fairchild, who thought life on his estate in the Cotswolds might domesticate his new bride. Instead, she wore him down to nothing over the next several years, then returned to the family apartment in London, some say in triumph. Next she married into the Grimaldi family, to a nobleman who had more money than stamina. She lived in Monaco for six years, but left him a juiceless husk. I remember reading about the controversy over the unprecedented annulment in *Newsweek*.

Her self-prescribed station in life was at the elevated center of everything, whether it was a small conversation, a dinner party, or a gala ball. She demanded, and received as her due, the attention of anyone near her. One might think ill of anyone else for such a requirement, but she wore this mantle with grace and amusement. She had a way with the self-deprecating comment, disarming and endearing.

I have heard that Lady Anne's father was in a way relieved that she had been widowed, rather than divorced of her last husband, because the usual storm of controversy that followed her would not whip up this time. I don't know how she took the death of Sir Roderick, but it did not long slow her travels or deter her from her social rounds.

It is popularly believed that Lady Anne devoted most of her time to sexual intrigue, stealing in and out of the bedrooms of the powerful and wealthy throughout England and the Continent. I have it on good authority that this was untrue, mostly. But she did nothing to quell these whispers. She enjoyed the notoriety, and everywhere she went she caused an uproar, much as the oars of a skiff leave expanding rings in the water as the boat moves along.

In all the time I served General Clay, I committed only one act that was disloyal to him, other than recording some of his gamier comments in my journal. After it became clear that he and Lady Anne intended to see more of each other, I discreetly asked a friend of mine, a subordinate of General Lorenzo who must remain nameless, to investigate the lady. His report was fascinating, but not alarming, at least in terms of a possible security leak.

A so-called journalist recently suggested that Anne Percival displaced the general's aide, me, as his late-night confidant, as the person with whom he could relax. This was flatly untrue, and an affront to my war contribution, however meager. But she did fill a barren space in the general's life at that time, one that neither I nor his wife in the States could do.

Yes, her beauty was such that it befuddled men who gazed on her. And, yes, she nourished her titillating reputation. But in General Clay she found someone she could not at once charm and vanquish, who would not join the parade of the dazed behind her. For both of them, the attraction was the sheer intellectual challenge that this refusal presented.

They began that night. After the earl had shuffled off, she poured the brandy, two snifters, not three. She gave him a glass, trying to pin him against the back of his chair with her eyes. I had apparently leached into the wallpaper, vanished without leaving a trace. It was not necessary to clear my throat politely, reminding them I was in the room. I was already gone.

She had opened the joust, calling him a major, but he had done his homework. "Anne Percival," he rolled her name around in his mouth. "You go by Percival these days? One could lose track."

She tilted her head and laughed, sounding like a carillon. "I thought I would wait until Roderick's body cools before I take another name."

She lifted the snifter to her lips, watching him over it. I had a vision of her as a bidder at a thoroughbred auction, calmly assessing musculature and lineage. The pekinese was at her feet, panting happily.

She said, "I'm having a gathering next Sunday here to celebrate a friend's birthday. Sixty or seventy guests. Tell me, will the Germans get this far by then, or should I postpone it?"

I had never heard anyone speak lightly of the impending invasion. The British had laws against it, I thought.

She went on, "I would invite you, General, but you would be distracted and wouldn't be fun at all."

"I've heard the Wehrmacht called many things," Clay replied, "and distracting is the kindest."

They talked for another hour. General Clay brought to the conversation the same intensity he used in command. It was a scintillating tour de force. They worked Oscar Wilde, tsetse flies, Abraham Lincoln, and Idaho potatoes into their talk, and it all made marvelous sense. I laughed aloud several times, but they weren't playing to me.

At midnight, she shook his proffered hand, and they said good-bye. I followed General Clay to the jeep. As we walked

102

along the hedge toward the vehicle, he seemed surprised to see me. He said, "I thought you were waiting in the jeep."

After the war, a few reporters suggested we left the earl's home the following morning instead of at midnight. This is untrue. I have been asked many times the nature of General Clay and Lady Anne Percival's relationship. I have faithfully set forth their first encounter. I will just as candidly describe their later meetings. You, and history, must judge their relationship.

The prime minister's quarters underground were spartan by any standard. A cot covered with an olive wool blanket was against a wall. Every room in the complex seemed to have a wall map behind a curtain, and Churchill's was no exception. On a desk were several telephones and a set of pens. A glass-fronted bookcase was near the desk, and I imagine the floor between them was well trod. Churchill led Clay to a card table, on which was another phone. He lifted it to call for refreshments. I remained by the door, the loyal retainer, until the prime minister frowned for effect and motioned me to join them. I fairly sprinted.

"You were a military history instructor at West Point for a time, I know, Wilson."

"I was, Prime Minister."

"Then you, better than perhaps anyone but me, understand the effects of weather on a military operation."

"I do," Clay replied. "And perhaps even better."

Both men sat back in their chairs while an orderly entered to place tea on the table. General Clay tapped a foot against the table leg, his warm-up. The flashing silver service was jarringly out of place in the room.

The prime minister blew over his tea before taking a sip. "After winds destroyed the Spanish Armada, England took for its motto, 'He blew and they were scattered,' and the channel winds became known as the Protestant Winds."

A hard opening serve. Fifteen-love.

General Clay nodded sagely. "The English debt to the weather is certainly great. At Blenheim in 1704, a thick mist hid the Allied approach, and the French and Bavarians suspected nothing."

Fifteen-all.

"Not as great as you suspect, Wilson. A hard rain before Agincourt saved Henry V, because the French cavalry charge became mired in mud." Churchill lifted his tea cup again. His eyes were alight.

Thirty-fifteen. My silent count always seemed to work.

"At least as great as I suspect, Prime Minister. Napoleon told Admiral Trevill, 'Let us be masters of the channel for six hours, and we are masters of the world.' But channel gales arose, and helped defeat Napoleon's proposed invasion of England. The weather forbade him those six hours."

Thirty-all.

"Weather has not always been our ally, Wilson. The heat during the Third Crusade prior to the Battle of Arsuf debilitated Richard I's troops."

Forty-thirty.

"Are you suggesting Richard lost that battle?" Clay asked.

Nice backhand. Deuce.

"I would not lead you astray. But you of course know that contrary channel winds kept William the Conqueror in port for six weeks."

Advantage Churchill.

Clay used his cup as a prop. He never drank tea. A few seconds passed.

"You were about to say something?" Churchill goaded.

"This jabbering has parched my throat," the general answered lamely. He raised his cup.

The prime minister's serve was vicious. "During the Seven Years War, British troops were surrounded by forces of the Nabob of Bengal at Plassey. They were severely outnumbered, but were saved when rain ruined the enemy's powder. The British had thought to cover their own powder with tarpaulins."

Game, set, match, Churchill.

After a long pause, Clay admitted defeat, but not gracefully. "I have too much on my mind to fill it with minutiae, Prime Minister. Others might, but not me."

Churchill grinned at me. "Aides usually keep diaries. Do you, Colonel?"

"Yes, sir."

"Be sure to include this exchange, then. I don't want history to miss this one."

"It would be an incalculable loss, sir."

Clay asked me accusingly, "Siding with the people who hung Nathan Hale, Jack?"

Churchill helped himself to more tea. "I don't always play games with the past, Wilson. I use it to understand our plight." He brought out another cigar. "What do you suppose is the most-invaded island in the world?"

Clay thought for a moment. "Ceylon."

The prime minister nodded approvingly. "Yes, Ceylon. Great Britain is no Ceylon. A century and a quarter have elapsed since a foreign country seriously threatened England on her own soil. And 1797 was the last time the British infantry in England went into action."

"That would be the small French invasion at Fishguard."

Churchill waved his cigar with approval. "We have had our share of invasions, as you know. Forty-nine to 1798. But fewer than most islands. Our isolation has been our security. Water-borne invasions shatter the calm and complacency produced by long periods of unchallenged national existence. The Incas in the sixteenth century. China and Japan in the nineteenth."

Churchill rolled the cigar in his mouth. "The threat of an invasion has faded from our national consciousness. And so you see us awkwardly struggling with it in the war cabinet room. And you see my countrymen coping with it daily."

When he pushed his cup away, we knew our visit was over. Clay and I stood quickly.

After hearing Churchill time and again on the BBC, I thought his voice foreign in the depth of its sadness. "War is a tragedy anywhere and anytime. But for an Englishman, war on the home soil is more than tragedy. It is an alien conceit. The image will not form in the mind. How does one prepare for the unthinkable?"

General Clay had no answer. The prime minister walked us to the door, the gravity of his words seeming to slow him. He lifted his chin. "But we shall see. They haven't hurt us yet, not much."

For once, the great man was wrong. At that moment, the disasters that became known as the Three Blows were underway, and they would bruise Britain and America to the bone.

6

Troops called the ship the Gray Ghost because its Cunard colors had been painted over with camouflage gray. The RMS *Queen Mary* was the queen of the express liners. The liner and her sister ship, the *Queen Elizabeth*, were Great Britain's most prestigious and visible symbols of maritime might. Before the war it won the fabled Blue Ribband for the record Atlantic crossing, just under four days.

Since 1940 it had been a troop transport, shuttling Australians, Canadians, Britons, and Americans around the world. On this voyage it sailed east from New York carrying 10,554 United States soldiers and a crew of 910 officers and men, the first time in history more than ten thousand persons had voyaged on one ship. The weight of *Queen Mary*'s passengers was such that the troops were ordered to remain perfectly still as they sailed over the Holland Tunnel, to prevent the GIs from gathering on one side to bid farewell to New York City. A list of even five degrees would have caused the ship to scrape the top of the tunnel.

The captain had not known the Cunarder's precise course until it passed the Ambrose Lightship, when he opened sealed orders given him at the shipping office. Gourock, on the Firth of Clyde, near Glasgow.

I spoke with Private Dennis Rawley four months after the war ended. He had boarded the ship in New York carrying the same equipment as everyone else: a helmet, a canteen, a full field pack, cartridge belts, two barracks bags containing summer and winter uniforms and a few personal belongings, and his M1 rifle. He was handed a blue button and told to attach it to his uniform blouse. The ship was divided into three self-contained, vertically separated areas, red, white, and blue, and the soldiers were restricted to their portion of the ship. Blue was the stern.

Private Rawley was frightened at the beginning of the trip. Rumor had it that Hitler had offered the equivalent of a quarter million dollars and an iron cross with oak leaves to the U-boat captain who sank the *Queen Mary*. But Rawley had been told that twenty-four oil-fired watertube boilers pushed the ship through the water at almost thirty knots, faster than anything the Germans had afloat. For most of the journey, the *Queen Mary* would not bother with convoys. It would simply outrun the Kriegsmarine. Nevertheless, his fear returned when 150 miles out of New York the four destroyer escorts signaled "Good Luck" and fell away.

Cunard billed the *Queen Mary* as the "Stateliest Ship Afloat," and Rawley had expected his trip to be in the lap of luxury. By the time he found his standee bunk, jammed with a hundred others in the dry swimming pool, the private was sorely disappointed. Miles of plush Wilton carpeting, all the fragile fittings, over two hundred cases of crystal, china, and silverware, the better furniture, and 2,100 stateroom doors were in storage in warehouses along the Hudson. Thousands of canvas bunks, stacked six high and separated by only eighteen inches, had been installed on the promenade deck, the ladies' drawing room, the squash court, and every other conceivable place above and below decks. The *Queen Mary*'s two thousand portholes and windows had been blacked out. Austin Reed's famous tailor shop in the Main Hall had been made into a stockade. Other shops had been converted to military offices. The cocktail bars had been transformed into dispensaries and the main ballroom into a hospital. Steel blast shutters were installed above the bridge windows. Hundreds of sandbags protected vital areas of the superstructure. Little luxury to any of this, he thought.

Topside, among the louvers and exhaust ventilators, were a six-inch gun, five three-inch high-low angle guns, thirty-four 40mm and 20mm cannons, four Browning heavy machine guns, and four antiaircraft rocket launchers. Daily drills made for quite a show, and large crowds gathered, especially for the rockets.

A degaussing girdle which neutralized magnetic mines had been installed on the ship, along with an Asdic underwater noise-detection system. A mine-sweeping paravane system, consisting of two torpedo-shaped devices secured by cables to a winch on the bow, were designed to cut the mooring cables of submerged mines.

On the third day out, at the same time General Clay and I were having tea with the prime minister, Private Rawley was sitting on a bench in the prewar first class dining room, which served as the enlisted personnel mess. The mess seemed to be in chaos. Meals were served continually from 6:30 in the morning to 7:30 at night, two meals a day in six staggered sittings. While one group ate, another waited in line near the first group's shoulders. The mess was a din of clanging kits and silverware and shouted conversation that rose to storm level. A choking haze of cigarette smoke filled the room.

During that meal the private sat next to a left-hander, who kept bumping Rawley's elbow, spilling his peas back to his tin. Before he could swallow his last bite, a line of new arrivals walked up behind them and demanded their turn at the tables. Rawley shoved an entire biscuit into his mouth and rose from the table.

He returned to the crap game on B deck. The rule against gambling was universally ignored. Rawley estimated that at any given time there were four hundred crap and poker games on board. Christ, it was fun, meeting those fellows, rolling the dice, telling filthy jokes, and chewing each other up. The gamblers hadn't cared if Rawley didn't know anything about craps. He settled down among six others of C Battery, 49th Field Artillery, laying a dollar on the line. The shooter, from the Bronx, knew all the lingo and kept up a mesmerizing patter as he tumbled the dice in his hand, then rolled them out. He was on a streak, with a pile of bills in front of him big enough to use as a pillow. Another seven, a natural, just like before the meal. The shooter swept up Rawley's dollar. The private put down his last dollar against the shooter. Learning had been expensive. The dice rolled. A four. C Battery cheered. Four was a tough point.

"Little Joe, coming out," the shooter urged, rattling the dice and tossing them. Sure enough, each die showed two spots. The men groaned. The shooter jubilantly pulled the bills to him.

"Busting out saved my life," Rawley told me. "I didn't have one thin dime in my pockets, so I left the game and went up number four companionway to A deck, then aft toward the three-inch gun mounted on the former Veranda Grill. The ship's emergency steering gear was under the gun. I had no reason to go there, other than I didn't have anything else to do."

Rawley walked toward a lifeboat, one of twenty-four aboard the *Queen Mary*, each with a capacity of 145 people. It didn't take a slide rule to figure out that, if worst came to worst, seven thousand soldiers would go into the drink. Twice daily abandon-ship drills were held only to give the troops something to do, Rawley believed. The lifeboats were elevated on davits and hung over the side of the *Queen Mary*. He leaned over the deck's starboard rail and ran a hand along one's keel.

The private had an open, guileless face, with broad cheekbones and a mouth that tended to drop open. Wind ruffled his sandy hair. He stared at the horizon. Before this journey, Rawley had never before seen an ocean. There was a lot of it, he concluded. All of it scary.

He didn't like to dwell on disaster. Thinking about it only invited it to happen. He grinned at himself and pushed crazy ideas out of his head. He leaned over the rail, glancing forward. The ship's curved hull hid the bow and formed its own vertical horizon, a pleasing sweep of steel.

That horizon suddenly buckled, as if it had been shaken out like a blanket. Rawley gripped the rail. "I saw the hull quiver, and for a second I thought it might have been the return of

110

seasickness I suffered the first day. Or maybe the ship's hull was somehow reflecting the Atlantic's waves. I just kept staring at the ship's side. A guy behind me was playing a ukulele. He didn't miss a note. Funny, the things you remember. And then the second torpedo hit."

Ambush is the preferred technique of all navies. There was speculation later than the U-boat knew of the *Queen Mary*'s route, that New York's resident community of Axis spies had determined the ship's course and the sub was lying in wait. But less than a dozen people knew the precise zigzag course the *Queen Mary* would take, and none of them was even remotely a suspect. In fact, the *Queen Mary* had sailed entirely by coincidence into U-414's periscope crosshairs.

The submarine had been the northerly boat of a *rüdeltaktik*, or wolf pack, a tactic introduced in 1941, when the Kriegsmarine began losing many of its seasoned U-boat commanders. The wolf pack demanded fewer skills of its skippers. When a convoy was spotted, the sub tailed it and alerted shore-based HQ, which guided the pack to a convoy. Not until the pack had gathered were the torpedoes launched.

U-414's commander would have identified *Queen Mary* on sight. So fast was the liner that he may have had just enough time to square away his sub and flood the tubes. He launched, in sequence, four torpedoes before the first struck the ship.

Private Rawley felt the second impact. The ship rose and fell, not enough to topple anyone, but the crowd was abruptly silent. The ukulele stopped. Troops ran to the rail to peer at the ship's hull.

"I still couldn't see anything wrong," Rawley recalled. "But the ship began to slow. The soldiers around me started to yell and crowd me at the rail."

Although the crews remained British and were paid by Cunard, after Pearl Harbor the *Queen Mary* had come under direct operational command of the United States in a reverse lend-lease arrangement. Consequently, a U.S. Navy board of inquiry conducted the first investigation. A principal focus was the reason the ship had sunk so quickly. The board concluded that due to unparalleled aiming or luck, the second torpedo coursed into the first torpedo's blast hole, ripping through the additional steel plating that had been placed around the engine room. The *Queen Mary* was wounded to its core.

Water poured into the engine room and E deck and the ship began listing to starboard. "What did I do?" Rawley asked me. "Hell, I climbed up the rail and stepped into a lifeboat. Training or no training, I wasn't about to be left behind. It took about sixty seconds for that boat to fill, and another two torpedoes hit the *Queen Mary* during that time."

U-414 was a Type VIIC submarine with four tubes, carrying fourteen torpedoes. The *Kapitänleutnant* must have known this was his prize of the war. After the first round of four torpedoes, the U-boat turned several degrees starboard and launched four more. At 1,019 feet, the *Queen Mary* was one of the largest targets afloat. Six of the first eight found the ship.

With water roaring into it at midships, the Cunarder slowed quickly. By the time U-414 had loaded the third round of four torpedoes, the *Queen Mary* had slowed to five knots and was listing twenty degrees. The *Kapitänleutnant* could take his time closing in on the ship. Three torpedoes of the third launch tore into the open wound midships. The fourth hit but did not detonate. It didn't matter.

"A hundred and forty-five capacity," Rawley snorted. "What a laugh. Must have been two hundred on that lifeboat when they began lowering it. Frantic troops still on board the ship were beaten away from the packed lifeboat. And was I ever in for a rude surprise."

I admit I was startled when Rawley held up his left hand. He laughed when my eyes widened. His fingers were only an inch long. They had been severed at the second knuckles. He said, "I was holding onto the goddamn cable when the lifeboat started down. It ran my hand right into the pulley, pinching the fingers all off. Still have my thumb, though." He waved it. "At least I can still hitchhike."

Rawley said he yowled and shook his hand as if it were on fire, splattering the nearby soldiers with blood. One fellow near the lifeboat's bow calmly collected the private's fingers in his cap and passed them to Rawley. He tossed them away in horror and supposed they became fish food. The private was in such

112

pain he had no recollection of the boat reaching the water or the scramble to break out the oars. Beginning a slow roll, the *Queen Mary* loomed over Rawley's boat, filling the sky. He remembers the massive hull coming for him, ready to crush him.

A soldier lost his grip on the liner's rail and plummeted some hundred feet into Rawley's boat, killing himself and another he landed on. Other lifeboats dangled from their cables, descending slowly to sea level. The cable on the end of one boat spun off its winch, dropping the boat's bow and pitching soldiers into the water. Rawley's boat made haphazard progress away from the liner as the oarsmen struggled with their strokes.

"Christ almighty, my hand hurt, but even so I remember the shouting from those above me, trapped on board. They were being pushed against the rail as a mob ran up from the lower decks. The railing broke in a couple places, and men were pushed off the deck, a stream of them, falling into the water. And I heard what sounded like a long scream, almost a siren, spooky as hell. I learned later it was air being forced up the *Queen Mary*'s ventilators as water flooded the lower decks."

Rawley and the others on his lifeboat watched as the *Queen Mary*'s topdeck and stacks tilted toward them. Thousands of troops ran madly about, searching for an escape. As the angle of the deck increased, they began sliding toward the starboard rail, then tumbling into the air and cartwheeling into the Atlantic. Smoke still poured from the three stacks.

The *Queen Mary* settled onto its side, troops cascading off all the while. The sea foamed with soldiers. Because of the ship's sudden list, lifeboats on the port side could not be lowered. Only ten boats made it away from the doomed liner. Rawley's boat had less than half a foot of freeboard, and waves were already cresting into the craft, so there was no turning back to rescue anyone. The lifeboat pulled away from the *Queen Mary*. A corpsman gave Rawley a shot of morphine.

The liner quickly settled into the sea. Rawley's memory faded as the drug took effect, but he recalled thinking the *Queen Mary* looked like a setting sun lowering itself into the water. Dennis Rawley told me his lifeboat was found by a U.S. Navy destroyer at dusk that day.

The soldiers and crewmen rescued by Allied navy craft, primarily from lifeboats, numbered 1,922. A few others survived by clinging to flotsam. Most never made it topside. Over 9,500 troops and crewmen went down with the Cunarder, four times the number lost at Pearl Harbor a few months before. Every city, every town, every country crossroad across the United States seemed to have lost sons. The *Queen Mary* entered the American consciousness. And the sinking was a glimpse of the fury to come.

The Battle of Scapa Flow began with a brilliant feint. At the same moment the U-414 launched its first torpedo at the *Queen Mary*, RAF sentry Perry Orvin felt his right leg collapse under him. He bounced on the ground and lay there a moment before feeling any pain. Only then did he look at his calf. A bullet had passed through it. He had not heard the shot. With the first tentacles of shock reaching for him, he remembered his duties and reached for his Lee Enfield.

"I swear I had looked down the hill the moment before I fell," he told me after the war. "I didn't spot a thing. Nothing to see, actually."

The commandos of the 10th *Marineabteilung* had been concealed below Orvin's duty station all morning, their brown and white tarpaulins camouflaging them. At precisely one o'clock, they left their hiding places and began running uphill toward the Chain Home Low (CHL) radar station on Wideford Hill on Mainland Island. Their first shot brought Orvin down. The commandos must have thought they had killed the sentry, because they moved quickly over the rocks and sparse grass toward the installation's barbed wire perimeter. Orvin heard the tinny rattle of a Schmeisser submachine gun. Fighting back the cloud of shock, he swung his rifle toward them and quickly emptied the clip. Three of the commandos fell.

Orvin told me that the remaining Germans must have been exceptionally well trained, because only three of them returned fire, while another five remained at the fence, hurriedly cutting through it with wire cutters.

Dust kicked up around the RAF sentry. A bullet bit into his shoulder, breaking his collar bone. Another plowed along the length of his back, leaving a shallow trench that would require 120 stitches. Orvin reached for another clip, blinking repeatedly against the encroaching darkness. He snapped the clip into place, but faded into unconsciousness before he could fire again.

Orvin's sergeant, Claude MacArthur, a Scot from Dundee, was passing the time of day with two radar technicians, leaning against a warning sign on the west side of the site, his rifle slung over his back, when he heard the shot that felled Orvin. He threw down his cigarette and grabbed the rifle off his shoulder, with no idea what was happening. A burst from a Schmeisser blew down the technicians and ripped into MacArthur's shoulder, spinning him to the ground.

Lying there, his neck at a sharp angle, blood pouring from his wound, he watched the commandos race across the field between the fence and the CHL hut. As they neared the wood door, another technician stepped out and was cut in half from blasts from several submachine guns. The first commando to reach the door threw in a stick grenade, then dropped to the ground. The shack's door and windows erupted.

OKM (*Oberkommando der Marine*) ordered the commando raid presumably because radar stations were extremely difficult to destroy from the air. The 350-foot-high lattice masts were porous, and Luftwaffe bombs would have sailed through them. A blast nearby would have done little damage to the mast. The height of the tower inhibited dive-bombers. The control rooms and electronic gear were underground. Even direct hits would have had little effect.

Leaving one raider at the door, the commandos charged into the hut. MacArthur heard submachine gun fire from the cement stairway inside, then, fainter, from the control room. MacArthur tried his left arm. Pain flared from his shoulder to his waist. The commando on watch saw the movement and loosed a half-second burst at MacArthur. The technicians' bodies caught most of it, but one bullet punched through MacArthur's left boot.

Seconds later the Germans emerged from the hut and separated into teams, running to the mast's stanchions. One commando unrolled wire from a spool. They wore wet suits, backpacks, and ammunition belts resembling Sam Brownes. Strapping explosives to the antenna's posts took only a moment. All the while, MacArthur's hand crept to his rifle. One of the Germans shouted an order, and they retreated to the breach in the barbed wire. MacArthur lined his rifle at their backs.

"I pulled the trigger," he told me in his thick Scot's brogue. "The rifle butt bounced against my shoulder, and I yelped with pain. Madder and madder, I jerked the trigger again and again. And, so help me, I did not hit a one of them. They disappeared down the hill. I wanted to weep."

The charges were attached with electrical cord to a timer. Three explosives packages detonated at the same instant. With the caterwaul of wrenching metal, the mast sank in on itself, its guys at first preventing it from toppling to one side. Cross pieces twisted and buckled as the tower shrank like an accordion. With new slack in the guys, the mast began to totter.

"The worst of it, to tell you the truth, was watching that tower make up its mind where it wanted to fall, then choosing me."

It landed less than an arm's length from Sergeant MacArthur. "The bullets couldn't kill me, but fright nearly did."

He was found moments later by other sentries who had run up Wideford Hill from the direction of Kirkwall. One had a walkie-talkie and alerted headquarters. The commandos were three hundred yards offshore in their raft when a Spitfire made its first strafing run. The pilot made two more for good measure. The commandos' bodies washed up on Mainland's shore, but none of them was whole.

In the two months before S-Day, radar stations on England's east and south coasts continually saw signs of substantial enemy muster. The Luftwaffe kept planes aloft to confuse the defenders about possible aircraft concentrations, and this was also true over the German-held airports in Scandinavia, the nearest to Scapa Flow. However, the Home Fleet's base had been chosen with the possibility of enemy air strikes well in mind. Luftwaffe bases at Sola, Bergen, Herdla, and Vaernes, all in occupied Norway, were three hundred miles from the flow, six hundred round trip.

116

The fleet at Scapa Flow had been relatively safe because the Junkers Ju 87B, the dive-bomber that was the edge of the German sword during the invasion of France, had a range of only 620 miles with added external fuel tanks. In other words, the Junkers, nicknamed the Stuka after the abbreviation of its role name (*Sturzkampfflugzeug*, or, roughly, dive-bomber) could make it to the flow, but had no time to engage if the pilot wanted to return to base. With its pinpoint dive-bombing, the Stuka was the most deadly aircraft against Royal Navy ships, but the vast distances of the North Sea protected the Home Fleet.

Similarly, although the Luftwaffe's high-altitude bombers possessed the range, their required escort fighters did not. A Messerschmitt, for example, could fly only eighty minutes before its tanks went dry. Even when crossing the far narrower English Channel, a Messerschmitt was left with only twenty minutes over English soil.

Within ten minutes of the destruction of the CHL station, both RAF squadrons from Wick airfield assigned to protect the Home Fleet were circling the flow, searching the horizon. At full complement, the squadrons would have had twenty fighters on the line plus two in reserve. Because of losses, each Wick squadron had only nine serviceable craft. After forty minutes without enemy contact, the Spitfires and Hurricanes began returning in rotation to Wick for refueling.

The feint was the delay that forced the RAF fighter to return to the airdrome, twenty-five miles south of the flow on the Scottish mainland. When half the fighters were refueling, the Luftwaffe struck the Home Fleet.

The sky above the flow suddenly filled with enemy dive-bombers. Even as the planes began their runs, sailors aboard the Royal Navy ships doubted their eyes. The massive cranked wings and spatted undercarriages meant these were Stukas. But Stukas simply could not be over Scapa Flow.

Oberleutnant Franz Stenzel's bomber powered almost vertically out of the sky. His target, HMS *Rodney*, was dashing south toward the Sound of Hoxa and the open sea of the Pentland Firth, white water churning behind it. Stenzel had memorized the battleship's features. Three triple sixteen-inch turrets, all forward of a massive superstructure. Twelve six-inch guns, all aft. A peculiarly high freeboard.

"An ugly ship," he said into his mask.

His weapons officer, Sergeant Fritz Cohausz, replied over the engine's whine, "It's in my sights, ugly as it is."

Stenzel told me after the war that he was glad for the engine noise. It hid the tension and fear in his voice. The air in his mask smelled of engine oil. Engine vibration rattled Stenzel's teeth. He had a cramp in his buttocks.

The *oberleutnant* was posted to *Staffel* 4 of II StG (*Stukage-schwader*, or dive-bombing wing) of *Luftflotten* 5 (Air Fleet 5), stationed at Herdla. Stenzel knew as well as the sailors he was falling toward that a Stuka could not possibly be over Scapa Flow. That is, he knew his plane would not make it back. The small belt of flare-gun cartridges around his calf was little comfort. He was also wearing a cloth and leather flying jerkin, much easier to take off than a flight suit, should his uniform become water-logged and begin to pull him under.

His plane was of a masterful design, carefully balanced and a delight to fly. As he plummeted toward the *Rodney*, Stenzel changed trim, which automatically adjusted the air brakes. The Stuka produced an unnerving scream, the plane's hallmark. The dive-bomber's vertical approach was fairly slow, allowing for precise aiming. Stenzel glanced through the window in the floor of his cockpit, then at the lines inscribed on the canopy to gauge the angle of his dive. The *Rodney*'s multiple pompons hammered the air around him, but because of the steep dive, could not draw a bead. The battleship grew in front of him.

At the last possible instant before a pull-up would have been futile, Sergeant Cohausz released his 1,100-pound bomb from the cradle beneath the fuselage. Stenzel pulled back on the stick. He rolled the plane to starboard as he climbed, hoping to confuse the *Rodney*'s gunners.

The bomb soared into the forecastle, forward of the first sixteen-inch battery, tearing open the six-inch steel plating, mangling the decks below and setting them on fire. The *Rodney* would have survived the blow, had not the rest of *Staffel* 4 followed Stenzel in. The next two bombs hit midships between the tower and the funnel, almost tearing the battlewagon in two.

The fourth bomb missed aft. The pilot, with a Spitfire on his tail, probably lost concentration, and when he tried to pull up, he crossed into the Spitfire's tracers. The Stuka disappeared in a ball of flame, which quickly blew itself out, leaving parts of the wings and fuselage fluttering toward the sea.

Stenzel and Cohausz still had a 110-pound bomb under each wing. The pilot banked his Stuka south, thankful the British pilot had chased after someone else. A Stuka was almost helpless against a Spitfire. He skimmed over the water, turning in a tight circle. This time he came at the *Rodney* from sea level, at an angle toward her damaged foredeck where AA fire would be less. At three hundred yards he began firing his two 7.92mm machine guns in the wings.

The *Rodney*'s decks were blanketed with oil-fed black smoke from the blazes, and the ship was losing speed. Stenzel lifted the Stuka's nose, and Cohausz released both bombs. They detonated against the control tower and bridge, showering the deck below with fire and metal shards. Other Stukas followed Stenzel's plane as it cruised over the crippled ship and through the wall of smoke, then raced east. They left the *Rodney* a burning hulk.

Early that morning, *Oberleutnant* Stenzel had been assured by his wing commander that the genius of the plan would reveal itself to the pilots after they were safely rescued. Stenzel doubted it then, and he doubted it thirty minutes after his bombing run when he pancaked his plane into the sea. The Stuka was risky to ditch, since waves tended to catch the wings and flip the plane. Stenzel told me after the war that his successful water landing was due only to luck, as it wasn't a maneuver the Luftwaffe allowed one to practice. He and Cohausz quickly pushed themselves out of the cockpit and jumped into the water, knowing the plane would sink rapidly. Bobbing in the chop, they inflated life jackets, and Stenzel opened a dye packet he carried in his suit. The orange color spread over the water. By the time Stenzel looked over his shoulder, his plane had disappeared.

Unlike the RAF, the German air force had a dedicated sea-rescue service, the *Seenotflugkommondos*. Most of its float planes, Heinkel He 59s, had been moved to the Norwegian coast for this operation. Within ten minutes, Stenzel heard the drone of a Heinkel, sonorous compared to the wail of his Stuka engine. The plane landed nearby, and within moments Stenzel and Cohausz were lifted aboard, where they joined four other Stuka pilots and weapons officers.

His wing commander was a good judge of his pilots. Only then, safe in the belly of the Heinkel, did Stenzel fully appreciate the Luftwaffe's plan. To reach Scapa Flow, his *Staffel* had been sacrificed, but the maneuver caught the British completely unprepared. Stenzel laughed suddenly and shook Cohausz's hand.

U-502 led the pack through the Strait of Hoxa. Its commander, *Kapitänleutnant* Hans Fromm, had been assured that the submarine nets across the Strait would be removed at 1:30, but he was not told how or by whom. Sub nets conveniently disappearing? It didn't sound likely. He swung his periscope to starboard, then port. The sub was midway between Stranger Head and Hoxa Head. His U-boat would not be the first to enter the flow. During the night of October 13–14, 1939, Günther Prien and his U-47 slipped into the basin and sank the battleship HMS *Royal Oak*, a major blow to British prestige.

"Sub depth?" Fromm asked.

"Two meters, *Herr Kaleun*," the chief engineer answered, using the abbreviation for Fromm's rank.

"Prepare to surface."

A bell rang throughout the submarine. The stokers jumped to their diesel engines.

"Blow the tanks, Chief," Fromm ordered. He heard a long hiss of compressed air.

"We're up, sir."

"Horizon report."

His arms over the periscope handles, the second officer replied, "Land to the west, eight hundred meters. Some distance to the east. We're dead center, *Herr Kaleun*." A moment later, the officer exulted, "I've found the lights, sir."

"Open the hatch."

North Sea air spilled into the submarine. Fromm gulped it gratefully. First up the ladder were three lookouts. The commander followed them.

He stood forward on the bridge, leaning against the magnetic compass. The sky and sea in front of him were filled with what Fromm knew would be recorded as one of history's most ferocious battles. Luftwaffe planes—there must have been a hundred of them—filled the sky, diving in and out of curling black smoke. A few were being chased by Hurricanes and Spitfires. Tracers arced across the sky, and clouds of AA fire dappled it. The flow boiled with the battle.

"There they are, sir." A spotter pointed dead ahead.

Fromm allowed himself a smile. Two navigational lights floated on the surface of the sea, directing him. The *Kapitänleutnant* looked aft. Six submarines were following him in a precise line through the gap in the sub net.

Once through, Fromm and the spotters returned below. U-502 dove, but stayed near the surface, with the first officer directing them from his post at the periscope. The pack moved past Roan Head into the flow at periscope depth, then bore northwest in a line abreast.

Before departure from Narvik in northern Norway, Lieutenant Commander Fromm had been told only part of the battle plan. The *Führer der Unterseeboote* (flag officer commander for submarines), who had flown from Berlin for the briefing, had assured him that once the submarines were inside the flow, the Royal Navy would come to them. After twenty minutes in line abreast on the east side of the island called Flotta, the admiral was proven correct.

"Target, sir," the first officer called from the tower. "Enemy position off bow left. Angle forty, speed twelve knots, range three thousand meters."

Fromm climbed into the tower to relieve the first officer at the attack periscope. He sat astride the periscope saddle with his face hard against the rubber cup. His feet pressed pedals allowing him to spin the periscope and saddle left or right. A lever at his right hand could raise or lower the scope.

Fromm called out, "Stand by tubes one to four for surface firing."

The tubes were flooded. The first officer manned his position calculator, which was connected with the gyrocompass. He adjusted the torpedoes' steering mechanisms. When the submarine's course was altered, the new position was automatically changed for the torpedoes.

"Comparison, now," Fromm said. "Variation, zero. Open torpedo doors."

The first officer called, "Tubes one through four ready to fire."

"Connect tubes one and two."

"Aye, sir."

Fromm whispered, "My God, it's the *Nelson*."

In his sight was the *Rodney*'s sister ship, same silhouette, same battery of sixteen-inch guns, over 1,300 sailors aboard.

The chief engineer yelled from the sound room, "*Herr Kaleun*, I've got an earful here."

Fromm ignored him. His prize was too close. "Report angle."

The number came from the control room below.

The commander said, "Tubes one and two, fire."

"Fire, one and two," the first officer answered.

A blast of air propelled the torpedoes from the submarine.

"Starboard ten degrees," Fromm ordered. "Connect tubes three and four."

"Aye, sir," from several.

The chief engineer shouted, "*Herr Kaleun*, check ninety degrees to port. We've got something coming at us."

The periscope motor hummed. Fromm looked north for an instant, but kept what he saw to himself. He spun back to his prey.

"Give me the angle." He waited several seconds more. "Fire tubes three and four."

"They're off, sir."

Fromm called, "Flood. All hands forward. Let's get under."

But it was too late, both for the *Nelson* and U-502. As the first two torpedoes hit the battleship midships, the Royal Navy destroyer HMS *Garrity* plowed into the submarine's quarterdeck, its prow slashing into the engine room, lifting the submarine almost out of the water, then breaking it in two like a board snapped over a knee.

Fromm was pitched off the periscope saddle to the deck grating. He slapped the alarm button. The first officer climbed into the tower. "We're through. The aft section has vanished."

"Call the abandon ship."

Of the fifty-one officers and crewmen aboard U-502, nineteen, including Fromm, were eventually plucked from the waters of the flow. They spent the remainder of the war interred in Scotland.

Here, too, the trade-off worked to the Germans' advantage. A U-boat for a battlewagon. The *Nelson* cruised under its own power into the Pentland Firth south of the flow, but there it went down, smoke billowing from it until the tip of the ensign staff on the stern slipped below the surface.

The Battle of Scapa Flow was over in sixty minutes. The toll was dreadful. The battleships *Rodney* and *Nelson*, cruisers *Sussex* and *Norfolk*, six destroyers, four corvettes, and twelve other ships including mine-sweepers, net-layers, depot and repair ships, and an oiler were sunk or gutted. Four British submarines were also caught on the surface and destroyed.

The Luftwaffe lost every plane it sent, 123 dive-bombers. Nine U-boats also failed to return to Narvik, victims of Royal Navy destroyers or mines. But it was a cheap price to pay to break the Royal Navy's back.

Victoria Haselhurst was strolling through Eaton Park when the second destruction of Norwich began. The first had been by the Danes, who razed the town in 1004. Now it was the Germans' turn.

Not that the people of Norwich, in the county of Norfolk, had been complacent through the centuries. Norwich citizens had taken part in the Peasants' Revolt in 1381 and Kett's Rebellion in 1549. And an ancient poem pointed to their importance in any invasion: "He who would old England win / Must at Weybourn Hoop begin." Even so, this war had largely spared them.

Norwich was a town of less than a hundred thousand people in East Anglia, northeast of London, eighteen miles inland from the North Sea on the River Yare. Little in the town had interested the Luftwaffe, until the waves of Dorniers and Heinkels appeared over their town during the same hour that the Battle of Scapa Flow raged.

Haselhurst worked in a boot-manufacturing plant. She was a striking woman, with blond hair, cut short so it would not get caught in machinery, and blue-gray eyes that spoke of Viking ancestry. When the air raid sirens had begun ten minutes before, she had left the plant for the park, rather than descend into the factory's musty basement with all the old people and their smells and dull chatter. She preferred the park's oaks and elms. And most of the plant evacuations were false alarms anyway.

This one certainly was not. She had never imagined so many planes. She recognized the flying pencil shape of the Dorniers from the airplane recognition chart at work. Above them were escort fighters, dots against the blue sky.

It seemed to her the bombs would all miss the city, for they fell from the planes' bellies too early. Could the Germans be bombing the old manor house south of town? But as they fell, the bombs followed the planes forward, reaching for the town. They were tiny things, wiggling in the air, dropping in batches. They came by the thousands. She told me after the war that for a moment she was oddly pleased that the town had finally merited some attention. She was later ashamed by the thought.

Fascinated rather than fearful, she watched as the bombs, still appearing harmless, fell in tight patterns that opened as the bombs descended further. Several escort Messerschmitts banked out of formation to face approaching fighters, although she could not see the RAF planes.

The bombs hit with a peculiar bubbling noise, nothing like she expected, splats rather than blasts. Waves of flame flickered from rooftops. They were incendiaries, designed to set the town on fire. Each bomb was a gray cylinder, a little over a foot long and weighing two pounds. The first clusters hit along Cecil and Townclose roads, then worked their way north into the ancient neighborhoods of crow-stepped gabled buildings and half-timbered houses, made to burn. Victoria watched silently, raising her hand to shade her eyes. There was nothing she could do.

George Reed's experience during the Norwich fire raid was more immediate. He was a member of Norwich's Auxiliary Fire Service, and when the warning siren sounded, he was filling sand bags from a mound of dirt a lorry had left earlier in the day. He descended to the ARP building basement carrying his shovel.

He waited patiently for the all-clear, picking at a callus on his hand, glancing at the air raid warden sitting across the room, envious of his uniform. The sirens forced the people of Norwich into the cellars several times a week, and it always came to nothing.

Reed had once been in London during a fire-bomb raid. He stood quickly when he recognized the fluid sound of an incendiary hitting the stones of the street. A man and a shovel could usually put out the fire caused by one of these cylinders. He ran up the stairs toward the street.

A fire was burning fiercely in the center of the road. The blackened canister was off to one side. Reed dug his shovel into the dirt and ran to the fire. A dozen shovels' worth might extinguish it. Just as he tossed the dirt, another canister ripped through the ceiling of the nearby chemist's shop. Fire flashed through the first floor, billowing out the windows.

Reed changed direction, thinking the street fire would burn itself out in several moments. He carried the shovel toward the chemist's. A third canister landed near a fruit vendor's cart half a block away, setting it on fire. Another hit the roof of the ARP post. In quick succession, small bombs landed in a weedy lot at the end of the block, on the roofs of the solicitor's office and a pensioner's hotel, and in the flatbed of a truck parked across from the ARP post. Then a cylinder splashed onto the cobblestones four feet from Reed.

Fire crawled up his pants. "Believe it or not, we AFS volunteers had been trained for just this situation," he recalled. "I dropped to the street and rolled around, suffocating the fire, then kicked my pants off as fast as I could."

He suffered severe burns on his right leg, and the purple scar was still vivid when I spoke with him after the war. He rose unsteadily to find that fires were growing rapidly all along the street. Forgetting his leg, he ran to the post's basement door and yelled a warning to the ARP warden. Then George Reed joined a growing stream of people abandoning their town.

Incendiaries rained down on Portersfield and Whitehall roads and crossed Earlham Road, and at least two dozen found Heigham Hall, setting all parts of the old mansion ablaze. The next run of planes came in closer to the center of town, and the clusters landed on Victoria Station, the Norwich Hospital, and city hall. The Lutyens War Memorial and the Guildhall, dating from 1407, were caught by the bombs, as were hundreds of common-walled homes. The skyline in Norwich was quickly topped by fire. Only Norwich Cathedral, with the second tallest spire in all of England, rose above the flames.

Victoria Haselhurst had been raised in Ipswich, forty miles south, so she felt shamefully unconnected to the roaring fires. But, after all, her parents were safely south. The loss was not hers, not really.

She would learn later that the loss was indeed hers. Ipswich, the chief town of Suffolk, was receiving the same rough treatment from the German bombers. The canisters fell across it, too, in a swath to the west of the town center.

In both Norwich and Ipswich, the westerly winds worked for the Luftwaffe, prodding the flames across narrow streets and onto more and more buildings. Victoria's parents fled the approaching firestorm, but her home, in her father's family for two hundred years, was consumed. As Victoria watched the Norwich fire, she did not know that the Ipswich fire had reduced her and her family's possessions to the clothes on their backs.

Eighty percent of the buildings in both towns were destroyed. Fires burned for a week. Because the canisters produced no concussion, casualties were surprisingly light, 1,554 for both Norwich and Ipswich. Most people ran ahead of the flames. To appalled English citizens, the destruction of those lovely towns seemed senseless.

The Defense Committee understood the Germans' tactic, however, which was to flood the area with refugees fleeing the conflagrations. Homeless, frightened, confused people choked the roads of Norfolk and Suffolk. The task of reinforcing

British troops along the coastlines of those counties had suddenly become much more difficult.

Victoria Haselhurst watched the bombers recede. With Norwich engulfed in fire, she began walking south along Blue Bell Road, skirting the town. She heard the steady singing of the all-clear behind her.

Forty miles was a long way to walk, but she hoped to inveigle a ride, her usual method of traveling home. Hitchhiking was virtually unknown in England before the war, but it had become common. She paused for a last look at the town. A band of orange flame rose above it, and higher yet was a vast plume of black smoke. Due to the melee of S-Day, she would not see her parents again for two months.

7

"If I ever write a report about you, I'm going to put this in it," General Clay grumbled as he levered himself out of the jeep and walked toward a cottage that had a thatched roof, a narrow wood door with a rough iron bolt, and small, leaded windows. "The Hun might be hours away, and I'm more lost in the goddamn Sussex countryside than the Wehrmacht divisions ever will be, thanks to you."

The general routinely accused me of causing all the snafus in his war effort, everything from coffee that was cold to delays in merchant marine convoys, sometimes charging that a particular blunder had "set out the red carpet for Hitler." I had nothing to do with any of them, and he never failed to grin. He did so then, as he pushed aside a gate and walked toward the cottage at the side of the lane.

After meeting with the prime minister, we had flown toward an airfield eight miles north of Brighton. Our destination was II Corps' headquarters at Adisham, between Deal on the channel coast and Canterbury, but from the air we discovered that Luftwaffe bombs had just pockmarked the dirt runway. Engineers with dump trucks and a grader were filling in the holes as we flew over.

Captain Norman searched for a few moments before finding

an oat field long enough to land on and with furrows running lengthwise. He touched the Cub down gently. Our British driver was back at Adisham, so the general and I commandeered a jeep from the 127th Field Artillery Regiment and began toward corps headquarters. I drove, the general gave directions, and five minutes later we were lost.

Before he could knock on the door, a boy wearing a striped shirt and shoes two sizes too large appeared from behind a corner of the cottage. He frowned at the general and stepped back in retreat.

"Hold on there, son," Clay ordered. "Can you tell me where Adisham is? It can't be far from here."

The boy was about seven. He squinted up at the general. "I could, but I daren't."

"You daren't?"

The boy scratched his head. "Mummy and the reverend say not to tell strangers where they are." His hand remained in his mass of unruly brown hair, apparently forgotten. "You could be a German."

"Look, kid—" Clay checked himself. He knelt down and continued sweetly, "Lookee here, lad, I'm wearing the uniform of a general in the United States Army. Do I look like a German to you?"

"It could be a 'sguise," he said.

"Holy Christ," Clay blurted. "Kid, I'm going to hand you over to G2, and then we'll see how quickly you talk."

The boy lifted his chin defiantly. "Mummy does not allow naughty words around here."

The cottage door opened a few inches. The boy's mother leaned out hesitantly. Her eyes widened when she recognized the visitor. "Why, you're General Clay."

"Could be a German, Mum," the boy cautioned her.

Clay touched his cap. "Afternoon, ma'am. My driver here, who will be reduced to second lieutenant as soon as I can push the papers through, has gotten us lost. I'd appreciate directions to Adisham."

"Of course." She stepped from the doorway and raised a hand to gesture, but paused. "Would you care for a bite to eat first?"

129

I was surprised when the general said he'd be pleased to. He told me to use the jeep's radio to alert HQ Adisham where we were and to tell Gene Girard, commander of II Corps, to meet with him as soon as possible. The woman informed me of our location, an intersection near Shepherd's Close. I went back to the jeep and lifted the radio handset from its pocket. Using that day's code names, I relayed the general's instructions.

When I returned to the cottage, the boy opened the door for me. A table was at one end of the sitting room, and the general was already cutting into a small piece of beef. Several slices of bread were also on his plate. An apple and an orange, a cup of strawberry jam and another of butter, and two biscuits were on another plate. The woman was in the small kitchen scrambling several eggs.

She was undoubtedly serving her honored guest every carefully hoarded morsel in her kitchen. Standard fare for the English was dried eggs from America, powdered skimmed milk, which was called Household Milk and tasted like cardboard, bread made from gray wholemeal flour and with the texture of plaster, called the National Loaf, and the nearly indigestible Woolton Pie. Sugar, fruit, meat, coffee, and tea were only occasionally available.

Homemakers improvised. They made a jam resembling chutney from carrots, used cheese rind for flavoring, added corn flour to stretch dried eggs, filled sandwiches with potato crisps, replaced cooking fat with glycerin and paraffin. The green dye that marked meat unfit for human consumption was often cut out before the meat went into the pot. Rather than waste an old joint, cooks scraped away any maggots, and the meat was roasted again. Bananas were so rare that children, unfamiliar with them, often tried to bite through the skin. Not only humans endured the shortages. Dogs were fed potatoes, and a new law forbade giving bread crumbs to wild birds.

And here was General Clay gobbling down her entire larder while the boy stared steadily at the biscuits. She stepped in from the kitchen with the eggs and a slice of bread on a plate. "I'm low on meat today, I'm afraid, Colonel. I hope these eggs will do."

She pulled out a chair opposite the general. Distressed, I sat down and lifted a fork. She nodded encouragement. I chewed slowly, trying to appear grateful. General Clay continued to eat with gusto, apparently oblivious that he was devouring a week's food.

If this home were typical, food would not be the only privation. German propaganda leaflets were used as toilet paper. No photographic film was available, so an entire generation of British children was not being recorded. Jam jars were used as glasses, and spoons were so scarce restaurants had taken to chaining them to their tables. Only newly married couples were given priority dockets to purchase bedding, and even then a pair of sheets might cost nine guineas. To save fuel, citizens were urged to remove bulbs from all but essential sockets, to fill the tub only to five inches, and not to heat food. Many homes tried cooking with a hay box, where heat was generated from decomposing hay or grass. The list of unobtainable items was endless.

"What's your name, ma'am?" General Clay asked around a mouthful.

"Evelyn Blaine," she said as she sat in the third chair at the table. "My husband is Lieutenant Jeffrey Blaine of the Royal Navy."

She said it confidently, as if Clay might have known him. The general did not pick up on it. He reached for the orange and peeled it carelessly, letting drops of juice fall to his plate. She was a striking woman, unhampered by the lack of lipstick or other cosmetics, which had almost disappeared earlier in the war. Perfume had vanished, but she had the scent of roses about her. Her face resembled one on a Victorian brooch. Her skin was the pale color of milk glass, but her peaked lips were a youthful red. She had fine, even teeth. Mrs. Blaine apparently disdained the Victory Roll hair style, because her hair swept across her forehead in the Veronica Lake fashion. She wore a pinafore that might have been made from black-out cloth and was tied around her waist with a strip of cloth. Elastic had disappeared.

"He's on the *Argyle*," she said. "Would you know of the ship, or where it is or what has happened to it?"

Clay shook his head. "I'm sorry, no. But if it'd been sunk, I'd have heard of it."

She brightened and returned to the kitchen for a coffee pot. She emptied it, pouring each of us half a cup. The general blew on it for a moment, then drank half her weekly ration in several quick swallows. Longingly, she watched it go.

"If you're a general, why aren't you fighting with your soldiers?" the boy asked.

"Thomas," his mother warned.

"Generals don't really fight," Clay replied, lowering the cup.

"Well," Thomas persisted, "shouldn't you be in front of them, leading them?"

The general pushed his empty plate away. Normally he would have used such a question to dredge up minutiae from his inexhaustible repertoire of military history. But this time his audience was a child. I thought we'd be spared. I was wrong.

"You bring up one of the great dilemmas for any military commander, Thomas. Where should he be during battle? At a rear headquarters, where he is able to best communicate with line and reserve troops, and where he can maintain contact with his superiors? Or at the front, where, leading in person, his presence will lend courage and stamina to his soldiers and he can make instant decisions?"

"But he might get killed," the boy said. On a cupboard behind Thomas were his gas mask cannister and air raid tin, which, if it were like the tins of other English children, contained several comics, a sweet or two, and a favorite toy to keep him busy during a raid.

"It can happen, all right. Gustavus Adolphus was mortally wounded leading troops on a rescue mission to his hard-pressed left at Lützen in 1632. But these days, generals don't lead the charge into battle or engage in hand-to-hand fighting. Vendôme at Oudenaarde in 1708 and Charles XII at Poltava in 1709 fought in person and were the last to do so."

I couldn't help myself. "What about Marshal Ney at Waterloo?"

He glowered at me. "Ney was deranged at the time. He doesn't count."

"Washington visited the front lines at the Battle of Princeton," I ventured.

"I'm talking about Europeans," he argued. "Washington doesn't count, either."

"What about La Marchant at Salamanca? He fought like a common soldier."

"La Marchant was Wellington's subordinate, not the commander, so you get no points on him either."

"And George II at Dettington," Evelyn Blaine joined in. "He was the last British monarch to lead troops into battle. And didn't General Cardigan himself lead the charge of the Light Brigade?"

Clay threw up his hands. He turned to the boy and said solemnly, "Thomas, let this be a lesson to you. Your mother and Sergeant Royce have encircled my position, cut me off from reinforcements, and soundly whipped me."

Mrs. Blaine laughed. Her son joined in, if only because of Clay's scowl of defeat. She pushed the biscuits toward the general. He finished one in two bites.

She looked at him with a perplexed and affectionate expression. In the previous months, the Americans had swarmed over the British Isles, leaving wide swaths of candy and nylons and cigarettes and casting forth goodwill and optimism. The young American soldiers with their brazen exuberance and sheer cockiness seemed the incarnation of Hollywood films. To the English, accustomed to doing without and making do and scarcely complaining at missing husbands and lovers, the Americans were bigger than life. American troops, who were paid four times as much as their British counterparts, arrived on English soil laboring under heavy loads of money and luxuries and all too willing to part with them, grinning wonderful prewar grins all the while.

Who could blame English families for inviting American soldiers into their homes for something to eat, knowing that more often than not the soldier would reciprocate with a plump carton of Camels or Lucky Strikes? Who could blame English girls for not refusing invitations into American service clubs, with their rich ice cream, sugar-coated doughnuts, and intoxicatingly aromatic coffee? And the Americans didn't mind if the girls put a few extra pastries into a handbag for the family. Americans even looked taller, healthier, and they smelled better. These exotic cousins from overseas were to be stared at and wondered about, and Mrs. Blaine could not help herself.

I heard the sound of a jeep, and a moment later a knock at the door. Major General David Lorenzo did not wait for an answer, but pushed open the door and strode quickly toward the table.

The G2 asked abruptly, "Have you heard, General?"

Clay stared at him, perhaps unwilling to admit he was not the first to know anything. Lorenzo leaned over the table and spoke in a low voice, too agitated and hurried to exclude Mrs. Blaine. More vehicles rolled up outside.

Clay interrupted, "Gone? The *Queen Mary*? Our troops?"

Lorenzo nodded and went on, telling him also of Ipswich and Norwich and Scapa Flow. He did not yet know the full damage, but could tell the general enough to shake him. Clay gripped the edge of the table. Mrs. Blaine's face turned ashen.

He was still talking when Gene Girard walked into the cottage, followed by his executive officer, Major General Felix Arden, who was carrying a map that flowed behind him and a cardboard map tube. I heard yet more jeeps and maybe a few trucks. Arden tacked the map to a wall while Girard joined Clay and Lorenzo.

The door pushed open again, and Major General John Hammond, commander of the 35th Infantry Division, entered the room, followed by a short parade; Hammond's deputy, Major General Mark Keyes; Hammond's chief of staff, Colonel Henry Culligan; and Colonel Walter Pelovik, his G4. They crowded around the table. Arden pulled a larger scale map from the tube and laid it over the table, dishes and all.

Thomas and I were squeezed out of the circle, so we left our chairs and retreated to the fireplace. Mrs. Blaine held her own, though, and nodded wisely at several comments by the officers. The boy's face reflected his amazement and gratitude. His age would not keep him out of the war after all.

Next into the room was the 35th Division's signal officer, Colonel William Brice, and two men from his signal company.

134

One carried a portable telephone pack, and another a wire roll. In the past ten minutes, they had strung a wire, laying it loosely along the roadside and guarding it with Signal Corps troops the entire mile to the nearest telephone poles. Ground communication was much more secure than wireless transmissions.

I'd seen all this before. General Clay was a low pressure zone, creating weather systems of men and machinery wherever he went. His subordinates collected around him, posting him on developments and seeking his instructions. AEF's advanced command post was wherever its commander happened to be.

Lorenzo repeated his news, and the group was silent for a moment. Lieutenant General Girard's eyes blinked rapidly. He was a reed of a man, so thin he appeared ill. The skin on his face was stretched tightly over flaring, spatulate cheekbones, and with his severe mouth and notched jaw, his head reminded me of a skull. Despite his appearance, Girard was known for his fondness for Spanish sherry and sophomoric pranks, an odd combination.

Hammond was roughly handsome, with brown hair streaked with gray, and a thick build. He was one of those go-getters Clay put into the battle slots. His restless eyes, forward stance, and rapid gestures broadcast an eagerness to enter the fray, much like a Staffordshire terrier at the end of a taut leash. I once overheard him tell General Clay that he'd leave England a hero or in a box. I had expected Clay to instruct Hammond that he would best serve his men alive and that the AEF could not afford to lose him. Instead, Clay said, "Good for you."

The 35th Infantry was comprised of the 69th and 70th Infantry Brigades, each with two regiments. The division also contained the 60th Field Artillery Brigade and tank and tank destroyer regiments and battalions. But its core was the infantry, the dog soldiers, the vanguard of the army's combat capability. Clay was an artilleryman, but he well knew that a battle was not won until the disputed terrain was occupied by foot soldiers.

They got down to work. An argument quickly ensued, and from the sound of it, General Hammond feared he would receive neither his medal nor his box. Clay was proposing that certain regiments of the 35th be held back from the beach. As it was, the 35th was spread along the channel coast from Rye Bay to Hythe, and included the stony cape of Dungeness, which thrusts into the channel like a swelled appendage. Behind Dungeness were the Walland and Romney marshes, wind-blown and inhospitable, but lower than the cape and protected from the channel by sea-thrown shingle ridges.

After a moment, Clay said, "Then we are agreed." He glanced sharply at Hammond, who had agreed to nothing. Clay won all the arguments. "The 425th and 406th will not continue their reinforcement of the seawall, but will remain here and here." He punched the table map with a finger, to tank battalions, which, with the rest of the 35th Infantry, had disembarked at Gourock only a week before and were still moving into place.

Disposition of Allied troops would have been an easy matter had there been sufficient numbers of them. Just build an im-pregnable wall of men and equipment. Trouble was, despite the flow of American men and material into Great Britain, scarcities were still ominous. Units that looked strong on paper were in fact undermanned, underequipped, and green.

In spite of the meeting at the war cabinet room hours before, where the unconquerable seawall was reapproved, General Clay continued to hold many of his units away from the channel beaches. He was aware of the gamble. But no one knew better, because the brutal dynamism of the German blitz attack, known in the German manuals as *Flächen und Lückentaktic* (tactics of space and gap) had never been defeated.

Clay stood from his chair and motioned General Keyes to follow him from the table. Clay whispered a few words to the 35th's deputy commander and returned to the group with a small smile. Keyes lifted the portable telephone and spoke into it for a moment, then returned to the discussion. David Lor-enzo made small marks on the hanging map as the maneuvers were decided.

"General Clay," one of the signalmen said, "Highbrow has been patched through."

Clay walked to the phone. Highbrow was General Alexander, Clay's superior. I supposed the code name came from Alexander's rising eyebrows.

"Yes, sir," Clay said into the phone.

The commander of the Joint Chiefs of Staff spoke for a moment. Clay responded, "You know my position on that."

Another pause, then Clay said, "All right. In light of that, I agree. But only one, correct? . . . Good."

He passed the telephone back to the signalman. "Because of the Scapa Flow raid and the bombings of the East Anglia towns," he announced, "ACCSS had decided to release the British XI Corps to the east to reinforce the Suffolk and Norfolk North Sea coast."

"Are we dancing to the German tune, sir?" Hammond asked.

"Christ on a crutch, John, if I knew that, they'd crown me king, and I wouldn't have to put up with this crap." Clay calmed himself with the comfortable motions of lighting a Pall Mall. "We must act on our best information, which is that the German is softening up the east coast with a purpose in mind."

"And we've still got the Canadians in reserve near London," General Arden pointed out.

"So I agreed to the release, not that my vote makes any difference anyway." He inhaled gratefully on the cigarette. "Is that all? Good. Everyone is to be there tonight, all divisional commanders. I want them to hear me."

They rose from the table and began to file out of the cottage. Clay might have nodded to Mrs. Blaine, but I wasn't sure. He stepped outside. Precious little thanks, I thought, for eating them out of house and home. Trying to compensate, I thanked Mrs. Blaine profusely and bade her good-bye.

The peaceful country lane had been turned into a staging area. A number of jeeps, two AA trailers towed behind scout cars, several three-quarter-ton Dodge trucks, and a signal corps mobile post crowded the road. A massive 2.5-ton 6×6 rolled around the parked equipment, leaving a deep rut in the pasture next to the road. The truck stopped in front of the cottage.

While General Clay had a few more words with Girard and Hammond, several soldiers began unloading provisions from

137

the 6×6. With his thumb, Clay directed them to Mrs. Blaine's cottage and continued with his conversation. This enormous vehicle belonged to the 110th Quartermaster Regiment, which fed and clothed the 35th Division. The driver leaped down from the cab to grab a wood case and follow the others into Mrs. Blaine's home. They repeated the trip a number of times.

I heard General Hammond ask, "So you don't think its wise to tell the chiefs about the Rangers?"

"Hell, no. They'd just worry it to death."

"I asked for that command, and didn't get it," Hammond said.

Girard said lightly, "Take the dagger out of your teeth, Mark."

"They're tough enough without you," Clay added.

Hammond responded with a rare smile. "I'm off then. See you in a few hours." He and Girard climbed into jeeps and sped away. Several vehicles followed their commanders, churning up dust trails.

The last of the quartermaster's troops left the cottage. Clay waved his appreciation, then knocked on Mrs. Blaine's door. He pushed it open.

Astonished, she was standing next to a mountain of supplies that almost covered her sitting room floor. There were boxes and bags and cans, all of them containing food: tins of ham and turkey, crates of oranges and apples and potatoes, cans of peaches and pears, boxes of cookies and candy; flour, sugar, baking soda, syrup; fruitcakes, pound cakes, marble cakes, honey cakes; sausages, a crate of eggs, beef jerky, and cases of beer; hard rolls, hardtack, and headcheese. Thomas was already digging wildly into a sack of Hershey bars.

General Clay smiled. "Try to save a little for my next visit, Mrs. Blaine."

So that's what he had requested of General Keyes. Clay climbed into the jeep, and I got behind the wheel again. Behind us, the signal company was rerolling the telephone wire. Because Girard and the others had come to us, we no longer needed to visit II Corps' headquarters. We pulled away from Mrs. Blaine's cottage, heading back to our plane.

138

After a while, General Clay growled at me, "Enough of your idiot grinning already."

Across eastern and southern England that afternoon, soldiers and civilians waited.

Arnie Fowler always had a crowd around him. He was the pitcher who had led Cincinnati to a hundred wins in 1940. He could have turned his flat feet into a 4-F like some other baseball players, but thought it undignified. He was as much a celebrity in the 23rd Infantry Regiment as he had been in Ohio.

He took on all challengers at dummy grenade throwing, five dollars a throw for a chance to best his distance. His arm was so strong he could launch it overhand like a baseball, rather than put it like a shot, the army technique. He'd collected over three hundred dollars in his week in England. He didn't feel like he was taking advantage of his unit, because he didn't charge for autographs or for standing arm in arm with some hick while a snapshot was taken. On that day, their lieutenant had banned the contest because of the invasion alert.

Fowler remembers spending the time trying to convince fellow soldiers that he had pulled a muscle in his arm, hoping they'd lay down more money on the grenade toss when the alert was lifted. He also remembers their not buying his story.

Geoffrey Hurst was a guerrilla, that is, if a short course at Osterly Park, home of the Earl of Jersey, taught by, among others, three Spaniards, made one a guerrilla. And if reading T. E. Lawrence's passages about guerrilla warfare in *Seven Pillars of Wisdom* made one a guerrilla. Both of which Hurst doubted. Hurst was a British Army captain, head of an auxiliary unit, under the aegis of GHQ Home Forces. In theory, the auxiliary units would emerge from hiding after the invasion to inflict as much damage as possible on the Germans before returning underground or, more probably, being killed. He had twenty men under him chosen from the Worthing Home Guard. Hurst was a veteran of Africa. His troops were overeager and woefully ignorant of what might come.

The captain thought the guerrilla force was an unproven

caprice of General Stedman, commander in chief, Home Forces. Guerrillas have little effect on an advancing army, so Hurst viewed his possible role as secondary, even cowardly. He knew the British Isles had a long tradition of guerrilla warfare. English guerrilla bands had operated from fenlands and forests after the Norman victory at Hastings. The Welsh carried out a long guerrilla war after the Edwardian conquest. The Scots became masters of the art in the centuries after Robert Bruce's triumph over the forces of Edward II at Bannockburn in 1314. And the British had been reminded anew of the potency of guerrilla tactics by the Boers. Still, Captain Hurst thought there was something distasteful about it all.

He was doing his best. Members of his cell had been selected for their resourcefulness, their abilities in fieldcraft, and their knowledge of the terrain near Worthing. Initially they had trained on weekends, but now, with increasing invasion alerts, they gathered each day near Highdown Hill, two miles inland from the channel.

At first, his unit's weapons were limited to Great War bolt-action rifles, coshes made of lengths of ribbed garden hose with a few inches of lead piping in the ends, iron pikes that appeared to date from medieval times, and bizarre homemade booby traps, an insulting mishmash of arms. One of Hurst's so-called guerrillas, sixty-five-year-old Roger Leeds, was president of the Worthing Archery Club and insisted on appearing at each training session with a homemade longbow, and not even Hurst's laughing in the archer's face kept the bow at home. "We were so short-handed, I even had a woman in my unit. Adrienne proved herself, though, bless her memory."

At least Hurst had not had to maintain a straight face, as had the auxiliary unit captain at Nottinghamshire, when the proud workers of the London Midland and Scottish Railway presented the unit with an enormous catapult capable of hurling a four-gallon Molotov cocktail a hundred yards. The catapult had been dubbed "Larwood," after the Nottinghamshire fast bowler. All was not hopeless, though, because lately Hurst's auxiliary unit had been issued high explosives. Perhaps the auxiliary units were finally being taken seriously.

That afternoon Captain Hurst's unit was training with a

Flame Fougasse, saving their explosives. The Fougasse was a forty-gallon barrel containing tar, lime, and petrol. A small charge propelled filings into the drum, igniting the mix, which shot out of the barrel in a molten, sticky liquid. Hurst's unit had installed four of these weapons, which his men had happily called a battery, at a bottleneck on a road. The barrels were dug into the roadside banks and camouflaged with branches.

Hurst stepped from behind a tree, gave a short blast on a whistle, and ran to the barrels. His Home Guard troops emerged from the woods to join him, propelled by pathetic eagerness to inflict mischief on the enemy. That's all those weapons would do against a Panzer. Warm things up a little. Create a nuisance.

His men pretended to yank cords that would ignite the weapons. One actually shouted out, "Whoom!" then waved his hands imitating the flaming mass that would erupt from the drums. A child at play. Hurst rubbed his chin sorrowfully. No, these fellows had never seen a panzer. He waved them back into the woods to do it again.

There was no eagerness or enthusiasm in the bunker above Minsmere Beach. Private Kevin Kenway of the 140th Infantry Brigade, 47th (London) Division, thought his eyeballs might fall out of his head if he had to stare one more minute through the binoculars. His view was of the North Sea off the Suffolk coast, a "particularly large expanse of nothing," he told me after the war. The beach was firm, with only a slight grade to it, perfect for amphibious operations. Maybe this would be like last month, where the stand down came after four days.

Kenway's post was forty feet above the waterline on a hill that rose abruptly from the sand. His elbows rested on a wall of sandbags as he kept the binoculars in place. Vickers machine guns were on both sides of him. The beach was criss-crossed with concrete and wood obstacles. Barbed wire followed the high-tide mark. Below him, engineers worked furiously to add to the beach defenses.

He lowered the binoculars to rub his eyes. A mistake.

"Hold there." The lieutenant walked purposely along the sandbags toward Kenway. "Private, have I not set out your duty with some precision?"

"Yes, sir," Kenway replied.

"Have I not instructed you on the use of those binoculars?"

"Yes, sir."

"What makes you think this is a summer holiday?"

"Nothing, sir."

"Then you keep those binoculars at your eyes, sweeping the horizon until I relieve you. Do I make myself clear?"

"Yes, sir."

The lieutenant walked away.

"Cheeky bastard," the machine gunner to Kenway's left said quietly. "I hope he never finds himself in my field of fire. I'd be tempted."

Kenway nodded his thanks for the support, then brought up the binoculars. Nothing but North Sea.

Private Douglas Stubbs had also stared at the water much of the afternoon. His view was of the English Channel from a fortified dugout just above the high tide line at Pett Level. Near Hastings, cliffs bar easy access to the interior, but at Pett Level, seven miles up the channel from Hastings, the cliffs are inland, inside the shingle and marsh. Just like Private Kenway's area 110 miles to the northeast, Stubbs's beach also seemed designed to invite the invasion. Pett Level rose gently from the channel waters. Here, too, the beach was jammed with menacing boat traps and dannert wire. Stubbs squinted at the blue horizon.

"Clear your barrel, Stubbs," his sergeant ordered.

"Ready?" Stubbs asked Private Rupert Mitchum, his belt feeder.

"Go," Mitchum answered.

Stubbs was the squadron machine gunner. His weapon was a .30-06 Browning M 1919. The cylindrical barrel jacket with the circular cooling holes, the flash hider, and the long butt with the pistol grip and carrying handle gave the weapon a more deadly appearance than the Browning M 1917 with its water cooling mechanism, the parent design. But Stubbs' weapon was awkward. Americans did not have a light machine gun of much merit and would not get one at any time during the war.

Stubbs respected the machine, nevertheless. He was frightened day and night, but during those seconds when the sergeant ordered him to clear his barrel he felt transcendent. The power of the Browning flowed two ways, out the barrel as bullets and out the grip and into his body as a manic energy.

He looked left and right, along the lines of soldiers of the Third Platoon, Able Company, 2nd Battalion, 9th Infantry Regiment. "Firing now."

He raised the barrel and loosed a two-second burst. The belt of shells was sucked through Mitchum's hands into the gun and the nozzle flash was visible even in the afternoon sun. The gun bucked in his hands. He released the trigger.

Two or three times a day the sergeant called for firing along the line. He used it as an antidote to fear. It worked every time for Stubbs. He let go of the grip, still shaking from the Browning's power. He grinned. He was invincible.

Perhaps Corporal Jamie Shaw should have had better reason to feel invincible. He was, after all, the driver of one of the new M4 Sherman tanks. Fifteen inches lower than its predecessor, thirty-three tons, with a power-operated traverse and a maximum armor thickness of three inches. Road speed of twenty-four miles per hour. Three machine guns and a cannon. His tank, parked under trees on the outskirts of Cuckfield, near the road between Brighton and London, was an iron womb, offering him hope for the days to come. His crew had christened the tank Cock of the Walk, which was painted on both sides of the hull.

Shaw was with the 69th Armored Regiment. He would have joined the infantry, but his father had insisted on armor. James Shaw, Sr., had served with the 1st Light Tank Brigade in the Great War and thought it an upright calling for his son. Passing time plays those tricks on old people.

And, truth to tell, the close, dank belly of a Sherman was a fine place to be, until it started moving. And Shaw started puking. Jamie Shaw suffered motion sickness every time he engaged the Sherman's gears. He kept a waxed bag between the dual clutch pedals, and within ten minutes of any outing, he would be jettisoning his lunch. The other four crewmen had not caught on, because he could vomit and drive at the same time (quite an accomplishment in a Sherman, he assured me after the war) and because the Chrysler engine's scream, the tread's metallic clanking, and the vehement cursing that goes on in all tanks every moment they are in motion drowned out his retching. At the end of each training exercise or convoy, he stuffed the vomit bag into his uniform pants and snuck it outside.

On that afternoon, prepared for the invasion, Shaw had carefully placed three bags near the clutch pedals. Three bags will outlast the goddamn Nazis, no matter how tough they are, he figured.

Second Lieutenant Del Mason had stood in the mess line for an hour, a long, dusty, winding procession inching toward the pots, which were so hot they steamed even in the afternoon sun. Mason's company always had a little extra space in line because other soldiers hesitated to get too close. Mason was with Company C, 66th Chemical Mortar Battalion, attached to the 8th Infantry Regiment, 4th Motorized Division.

All Allied and German divisions had chemical companies. Even though use of chemical and biological weapons was forbidden by a 1925 Geneva agreement, production of such weapons was allowed.

The mess was in a field east of Royal Tunbridge Wells, midway between Hastings and London. The pasture was crowded with soldiers, but they always stood apart from troops of the chemical companies, lest their mysterious weapons were contagious. Chemical Warfare Service officers were easy to spot. The design on their collar badges consisted of crossed laboratory retorts.

Not that Mason disliked the chemical service. It had an honorable history. Germ warfare dated back to the fourteenth century, when the Tartars catapulted rotting corpses of plague victims into the besieged Crimean city of Kappa to spread the disease. There was a professionalism to the service Mason appreciated, and always the sense that a mistake might be his last, which lent an air of importance even to training. He appreciated the amount of equipment he had to master: eyeshields and gas masks, M1A1 collective protectors (which drew contaminated air from outside a gasproofed shelter to purify it for circulation within), dust respirators, protective covers and ointments, water-testing kits, and medical supplies. And, of course, the gas itself.

The 66th was provided with two chemical weapons. Phosgene shells were proven by the Germans at Flanders in December 1915. When exposed to the air, phosgene becomes an extremely toxic cloud that smells of green corn or newly mown hay. The other chemical was tabun, a colorless, odorless nerve gas that frightened even Mason. Mason was an expert in the delivery system, the 4.2-inch rifled mortar which could also be used for high explosive shells. All divisions had chemical battalions, and like them all, the 66th was also versed in smokescreens and flamethrowers. Quite an arsenal, Mason thought approvingly.

When he reached the first mess table, Mason playfully slapped the shoulder of the officer in line next to him, his friend Lew Tunney, then said to the ladler, "Private, will you get me a tin of flour?"

"All I've got are beans, sir." He threw a ladleful into Mason's kit.

Mason smiled winningly. "What I'm asking is that you take a few steps into the tent and find me a small amount of flour. It won't break the quartermaster."

The private shrugged and handed the ladle to another private on kitchen patrol, then disappeared into the mess tent. He had returned by the time Mason and Tunney were taking their bread from the pile. He handed the lieutenant a pound of white flour.

"Come on, Lew, let's put them on their ears."

Mason and Tunney grinned broadly as they walked across the field, dodging groups of soldiers eating their late meal. Mason joined one of his CWS squadrons. Most had finished the food and were smoking and talking. Two played mumblety-peg with a knife. Mason put his kit on the ground. He and Tunney passed around handfuls of flour, and gave instructions.

The squad was alert, waiting for the signal. "Now," he called.

Mason and Tunney and the twelve others threw the flour

into the air with quick motions, then loudly began coughing and gagging. Mason stood unsteadily, clutched his throat, then dropped to one knee, his tongue extruding between his teeth. Tunney screamed, tore at his hair, then fell to the ground. Others groaned and shrieked, rolled their eyes, sank to their hands and knees, then collapsed. Above them, the flour was a cloud of fine, malevolent-looking powder slowly drifting away. Their uniforms were dusted with it.

"I might as well have yelled, 'Fire!' in a crowded theater," Mason told me after the war. "I've never seen so many people move so fast in my life. Those guys eating next to our platoon knew we were CWS, and they jumped and ran like they had turpentine on their butts. Elbows and assholes flew. They left behind rifles and packs, spilling their mess kits, shouting warnings."

That day, the lieutenant lasted only thirty seconds before he broke into maniacal laughter, joined instantly by the rest of the CWS platoon. They rolled with it, slapping each other, this time choking in earnest, with laughter.

"No one else got the joke, though," he recalled. "It took the other troops half a minute to understand what we'd done, and then they started calling us assholes and shitheads and jerkoffs and everything else they could think of. I mean, they were pissed. In fact, my unit, Company C, was known as Shithead Company for the rest of the war. Ask anybody from the 4th Motorized—they'd know who the Shithead Company was."

Later I did, and they did.

Mason ended his story on a sober note. "Lew Tunney and I must have laughed for another hour solid. But then, we didn't know what was coming, not really."

Neither did others waiting for the invasion. RAF Lieutenant Richard Ormsby tried to nap for a while that afternoon under his Spitfire at Digby, as he did many afternoons. His squadron was being held in reserve for the invasion. All sixteen planes were hidden under camouflage nets a hundred yards from the runway. Just the week before he had completed his course at the Operational Training Unit, and been assigned to 46 Squad-

146

ron. Because of the ammunition shortage, he had never fired live rounds. It worried him.

Allen Lewes had deserted his Northumberland coal mine once before to enlist. He had been tracked down and forcibly returned to the mine. That afternoon he deserted again, heading south. He'd be damned if he'd have to explain to his children why he hadn't fought the Germans, how the Essential Work Order had kept him digging coal. Some army unit, desperate for soldiers, would take him, he was sure.

Shirley Parker was a Wren, a plotter at Fighter Command headquarters at Stanmore, twelve miles northwest of the City. Her station was the plotting table in the filter room. The information sent to the filter room was gathered from CHL stations and Observer Corps posts via the Observer Corps Center at Horsham. Parker wore a headset, and she moved markers representing aircraft, red for enemy, black for friendly, with numerals to show estimated height, arrows to indicate direction, and a reference number displaying the plane's particular formation. Above her on a balcony, officers watched the table. They determined which planes were friendly, hostile, or doubtful. Their conclusions, the filtered information, was relayed to the Fighter Command operations room, and to group operations rooms and sector operations rooms of affected RAF sectors. More clearly than anything else that day, Shirley Parker remembered that the Luftwaffe was allowing her a respite. Unbelievably, she had time to remove her headset and sit for a while. Better than anything else that day, she recalled how pampered she felt to have time to rub her aching feet.

U.S. Army Captain Jonathan Goodrich's troops manned two 9.2-inch guns dubbed Winnie and Pooh. They were stationed east of Hastings, in a bunker of two-foot thick reinforced concrete atop fifty-foot cliffs that dropped straight down to the beach. Again and again he ordered the drills, timing his men as they loaded the gun. It was back-breaking training for these troops of the 15th Field Artillery Battalion, 2nd Division, and his gun crew had begun to gripe. He kept them at it, stopwatch in hand.

Doctor Sylvia Hathan was an anesthesiologist at the tiny hospital in Kirkwall, on Mainland Island in the Orkneys. When the raid on Scapa Flow began, she had been monitoring a Royal Navy sailor whose right tibia had been shattered in a fall from a gangway, a noncombat injury that had occurred that morning. The fracture had required a plate, and by the time the surgery was completed, the dive-bombers were gone. She rose from her stool to walk into the hallway. She had been concentrating and had not heard the delivery of the wounded. She was startled to see the hall jammed with broken and bleeding sailors and airmen, and litter bearers bringing in even more. "I remember that moment vividly," she told me. "It seemed like such a terrible beginning."

At Little Common, near Bexhill on the channel, Father Rafael Rodriguez took part in an enormous holy communion in a sheep pasture. He was not surprised at the turnout of American soldiers, because the same lines had occurred last month during the alert, and probably would again next month, if this one turned out to be another false alarm. Communion wafers were in short supply. Father Rodriguez had to snap them into quarters. Nobody complained.

Many recalled that day as long and lingering, as if the daylight were afraid to fade. The heat held until late in the afternoon, and despite a few high clouds, the air over much of England was magnificently clear, making distant landscapes seem closer. The sunshine, the droning insects, the idle breeze, it was a day to lull the senses, a day for long walks and casual reflections.

But not for the million Allied servicemen and women tensely waiting for the enemy horde.

"These guys are the hardest on the planet," General Clay told me as we walked from the Cub across the grass runway near Margate, at the tip of the Thames estuary, an area called the Isle of Thanet. "Don't accidentally piss off one of them, or not even I'll be able to save you."

He strode ahead of me and called out, "Colonel Yates, good to see you again."

Don Yates saluted smartly and extended his hand to the general. His men had been leaning against their packs and parachutes, hovering in small groups. They wore night field uniforms, black pants and jerseys, and many had already applied burned cork to their faces. They quickly closed around us. The Rangers seemed loathe to part with their weapons, and they brought them as they gathered. They were draped in British sten guns, ammunition belts, knives strapped to legs, BARs and heavier machine guns, grenades, 60mm mortars, the works. I even saw a sawed-off shotgun across one Ranger's stomach.

These were the soldiers of the 1st Ranger (Infantry) Battalion, formed recently at Carrickfergus in Northern Ireland. They were all triple volunteers: first for the army, then for parachute training, finally for the Rangers. They did nothing but train. Cliff-climbing, demolitions, small arms, unarmed combat, ambush techniques, signal, parachuting, camouflage, all grueling. The dropout rate was high. Those who remained were reduced to human sledgehammers.

I once saw Joe Louis rise from a sofa and walk across a hotel lobby in San Diego. I'll never forget the economy and vitality and utter confidence of even those simple movements. The Rangers were the same. There was a lupine air to them, a trace of mocking in their smiles, and a boisterous strength derived from their competence. One glance at these soldiers, and you knew they were unbreakable.

General Clay had considered using OSS operatives for the mission. The OSS was trained in behind-the-line insurgency, while the Rangers were typically to be in front of the enemy. But Clay insisted on Rangers when he found he could not assure himself full operational control over the OSS. "Too murky an outfit for my tastes," he had told me.

Parked near the runway were three transport airplanes, usually called C-47s. The model began service in 1935 as Douglas Sleeper Transport and was known to the British as the Dakota and to the Americans as the Skytrain. Flown commercially, it was called the DC-3, a remarkably durable, well-designed transport. When altered to carry paratroopers, as these three were, the planes were christened C-53 Skytroopers. They were powered by 1200hp Pratt and Whitney Twin Wasp radials. The planes could take an enormous amount of punishment, and new pilots were advised, "Fly the largest piece back."

"We weren't expecting you," Colonel Yates said. "We'd have prepared a salute or something."

"Horse manure," Clay replied loudly. "You Rangers don't have time for that. Leave the parade ground crapola to others."

There was nodding all around from the 120 soldiers in the group.

General Clay rose to his full height and locked his hands behind his back. "Colonel Yates has fully briefed you men. I don't have to tell you that you're in for a hell of a night. Everything you've learned and all your guts are going to be called into play in the next few hours."

The Rangers were rapt. General Clay's presence meant their assignment, code named Green Thumb, was urgent and critical, not just a fancy of an anonymous, dilettante major general somewhere up the chart.

Clay continued, "You men have gone through hellish training. You're going to have the chance shortly to use all of it."

The general took a few steps along the line of Rangers, looking at them right in the eyes, one after another. He roughly grabbed one Ranger's shoulder, then another, as if testing their mettle. "You soldiers are the best we've got, the best in history. I wouldn't send you in if I didn't know you will get what I want and come back out. You won't let me down."

Clay cleared his throat. "I want you to know how proud I am of you, and that my thoughts and prayers will be with you."

That was enough. He turned to go, but was stopped by a question yelled from the back of the group.

"Sir, we're scheduled to jump at four hundred feet. Can we use our parachutes?"

The Rangers roared.

Clay didn't miss a beat. He faced them again and with a poker face said, "Soldier, with the shortages back in the States, you'd consider wasting all that silk? And here I thought you guys had iron balls."

They laughed and whistled and applauded. I learned later

that the question came from Ranger Sergeant Aaron Hirschorn, whom I interviewed after the war.

The general and I walked back to the Cub. I asked in a flattering way, "Sir, do you wish you were going with them?"

"Not on your goddamn life."

8

General Clay met with his commanders as a group every other day. For security reasons, the location was changed each time. That evening's assembly was held at a manor house called Bilswell, near Storrington, fifty miles south of London in Sussex. The house was of the Lutyens style, with diamond-paned windows and numerous tall brick chimneys. Around the house were orchards and farmland.

Corps and division commanders and AEFHQ staff crowded the sitting room. Most had arrived early for informal meetings. General Clay worked the room, speaking with each of his commanders, prodding and encouraging. Voices were surprisingly loud, and I heard a few laughs. Several congratulated him on single-handedly bringing down the Messerschmitt. At the meeting four days before, and again two days before, when the tides had been propitious for a southern invasion, the tension had been more apparent, and the meeting more subdued.

General Clay finally took his place near the east wall, and the room fell silent. I stood to his right, notebook in hand. On his other side was an AEFHQ secretary who would take down verbatim everything said. In a chair near the stairway was British Army Brigadier Arnold Graves, the AACCS liaison officer.

Clay began without prelude, "You've received briefings regarding events today, which the prime minister called the Three Blows. In a telephone conversation with him less than an hour ago, he told me that historians will regard this afternoon's disasters as the ebb tide in the Allies' war. He said that our fortunes have turned, and the worst is now behind us. Mr. Churchill may be an optimist, but I agree that it is unlikely we'll hear worse news than today's."

There were several nods in the room. In an overstuffed chair on Clay's left near the secretary was Lieutenant General Alex Hargrave, commander of I Corps. He tamped his pipe with a finger. Hargrave was small-boned, with fine, almost delicate features. He had been one of Clay's classmates at West Point. His first words to me after I had been introduced as Clay's aide were, "The stories I could tell about Wilson."

In the Great War, Hargrave had been an infantry captain and was taken prisoner during the second battle of the Marne. Some said those few months' exposure to the German military as a POW made him a bit of a Prussian. He was supremely confident in his own abilities, while often affecting a put-upon attitude with his subordinates. He was fastidious in his personal appearance, and his words were clipped. "Damn near a German accent," Clay once told me. "I'm surprised he doesn't wear a dueling scar."

Near Hargrave were his division commanders. The 2nd Infantry head, Burt Jones, sat stiffly, as if uncomfortable in a chair, where his shoe platforms could not help.

The 4th Motorized's Major General Horace Singleman was next to Jones. Singleman had a structural engineering degree from Texas A&M and once told me he "was a born bridge builder." He enjoyed complaining that his military career had prevented him from constructing a bridge or anything else. Singleman was an exception to General Clay's rule that a commander should not carry more weight than his troops. Singleman's belly comfortably sagged over his belt.

The final I Corps divisional commander in the room was Major General Roger Franks of the 1st Armored. Almost seventy years old, Franks had been a brigadier during the first war. Clay had twisted arms at the War Department to bring Franks back to active duty, saying the AEF needed at least one commander with war experience as a general officer. Franks walked and gestured with a younger man's energy, he grinned quickly, and he wore an expensive wig, all designed to belie his age.

General Clay said, "I conferred a short while ago with David Lorenzo regarding the latest on when and where." For several moments he relayed what was known about the Wehrmacht's 8th and 28th Divisions, believed to be moving north into Belgium, then added, "A report came in tonight that a unit of the XII Waffen SS, which had been in Westphalia on the Rhine, is marching, or has marched, northwest toward the Hague or Amsterdam." Clay motioned toward Lorenzo.

The G2 filled in, "The XII Waffen SS is made up of the *Walküre* panzer and the *Westland* panzer grenadier divisions. We have fairly reliable ground reports only on the *Walküre*'s march, but we assume OKW is not detaching divisions, and that the entire XII Corps is moving toward the North Sea coast."

General Clay then told them of the midget submarine and the German agent who was killed and the other who escaped on the east coast. He went on, "A lot of you hope deep down in your bones that the Germans will hit our channel beaches, but it is looking less likely, as you can see with these new German troops movements. More likely, several of our divisions will be called on to join the Canadian and British corps in reserve and patch up failing lines in East Anglia or further north."

The general paced. "Irrespective of where the German lands, he will try to isolate London immediately. So you, Hal and Roger, are to be prepared to move north quickly when you're released to Arthur Stedman's Home Forces. Stedman is good. You can rely on him."

Clay spoke a while longer on preparations to move north, noting problems that would be caused by refugees clogging the roads and the destroyed bridges and the Luftwaffe overhead. I made notes as he issued orders. Hal was Brigadier Hal Larsen, commander of the 2nd Armored, who had replaced Major General Richard Duvall, killed one week before when Duvall's jeep had tried a U-turn in a mined pasture. Larsen had been Duvall's deputy. He was stocky, with a high forehead and a suggestion of blond hair. He wore tortoise shell glasses.

Sitting near Larsen were the other II Corps division commanders, John Hammond of the 35th, whom we had met with at Evelyn Blaine's home, and Major General Roderick Carsen, commander of the 5th Infantry. Their superior, II Corps commander Gene Girard, was perched on a folding chair near the fireplace.

Cigarette and pipe smoke hung heavily in the air. A fan had been placed near a door that opened to a garden and rose trellis. I could hear chatter from AA personnel, who had been posted on the manor house's drive and on nearby Merrywood Lane.

"What's the chance they'll come tonight?" Hammond asked Clay.

"Churchill and General Barclay put it at fifty-fifty."

"That's what they said last month," General Carsen said. He was the tallest man in the room, over six feet four, and as thin as a plank. He and Hammond wore .45s on their hips. For a hundred years, general officers had eschewed personal weapons. The style was reversing.

Clay said, "Some Defense Committee and Combined Intelligence people think the landing will be next month. June's weather is more reliable than May's. And they argue that the most critical German shortage is of dedicated landing craft. CIC maintains the Kriegsmarine is producing only about ten of them a week, and that if the Germans come tonight or tomorrow they'll still have to rely on canal barges for amphibious operations. Barges aren't seaworthy and offer little protection from shore fire. Yes, another month would give them a better landing capacity. But I still think it'll be within forty-eight hours."

Clay rubbed his jaw. "And yes, the Germans may be selling me a bill of goods, just like last month, when they made us think they were coming. It's the same tactic Alexander used at the Battle of Hydaspes."

Gene Girard moaned loudly, which was followed by soft laughter from others in the room.

"As you all undoubtedly recall, Porus, with his chariots, cavalry, elephants, and infantry, had a strong defensive position behind the River Jhelum. But Alexander crossed the fast-flowing river nightly, simulating amphibious attacks by noisy demonstrations all along the river bank. Eventually Porus tired of policing these diversions. And you all know what happened next."

No one in the room said anything. Several seconds elapsed. I saw my duty and I did it. "I don't recall what happened next, sir."

Mark Hammond mouthed a word at me. I think it was "toady."

"Alexander poured five thousand cavalry and six thousand infantry over the river onto an undefended landing place eighteen miles upstream from Porus' main position. Undefended because Porus simply got tired of challenging Alexander's feints. That's not going to happen this time."

That probably put me back up to captain or so.

"They're coming," Mark Hammond said. "The Scapa Flow disaster tells us that more clearly than if they'd written us a letter. It was no noisy diversion."

Clay nodded. "The Home Fleet's mission was to cut off reinforcements and supplies for the German wave, giving time for Allied ground forces to confront the first Germans ashore. Because the Fleet was largely destroyed this afternoon, we'll no longer be able to burn the German sea bridge. So I think the Germans' surprise attack on the Orkneys, with all the risks they took, means they are coming tonight or tomorrow night. Never have things looked better for them."

Clay stopped his pacing and drew himself up in front of his commanders. "Now I want you to remember a couple of things. Despite all our education and training, we won't know what in hell hit us when the German comes. We'll be faced with developments we aren't prepared for, maybe haven't even thought about. So above all, avoid rigidity. Our army has a tendency for stasis in doctrine and execution, a legacy of the German Baron von Steuben, who shaped our American revolutionary army. Throw out this German's thinking and we'll throw out the Germans. The secret of the blitzkrieg is not German material superiority, but their enemy's tactical inferiority. With the Wehrmacht, shock predominates over fire. Shock can only be met with flexibility. Improvise, think on your feet, don't get locked up by doctrine. This will be your tactical advantage."

Clay inhaled slowly, then said, "And take risks. You must have the spirit to gamble. There is an inexorable law in war that he who will not risk cannot win."

He lifted his spectacles from a pocket, examined them, and dropped them back. "By selecting your battalion and regimental leaders, you've already done much of your job. We should learn from the German army's troubles at the Somme in 1916, where their major problem was telephonitis, too much use of telephones to interfere on the battle line. Trust your judgment in your choices, and let your commanders do their work."

Clay took two steps, then squared himself again. "And go with your instincts. When the German war machine arrives, the time for study and reflection will have passed. Act, don't delay. Doing nothing is standard for an army. Acting is the exception. Move into a breach. Exploit a weakness. Move now, not later. A good plan ferociously executed right now is better than a perfect plan executed next week."

Hammond nodded fiercely.

"We are a newly assembled team," the general said. "Most of you have not waged war with me before. You will find that I can excuse mistakes and I can live with quirks of command style." Clay's voice rose. "But I will not tolerate a hesitation to engage the enemy, to inflict mortal damage on him. I demand savagery. You are to be as fired up as the foot soldier reduced to using his bayonet."

For a moment I thought I'd hear a chorus of "amens." But the room was silent. Even so, the commanders' faces reflected a renewed confidence.

The general concluded, "Your strength and stamina and aggressiveness will rub off on your men, and will make up for whatever they lack in experience and material. Remember, there are no poor soldiers, only poor commanders." The general's gaze swept the room like a scythe. "I don't think there's a poor commander in this room."

Clay adjourned the meeting with, "That's all, gentlemen. God willing, we'll all meet again in two days."

The men rose quickly. Some lingered for a few more words with General Clay, but most were anxious to return to their units. The speech worked. Although the officers had been shaken by news of the Three Blows, they left the meeting reinvigorated.

But God was not willing, and this group would never meet again.

Years may pass before the full story of Green Thumb can be told, before all the documents and the eye-witness accounts are collected and assayed, and before the darkness and confusion can be pared away from that night. Some things have been buried, and may remain there forever.

The U.S. Army General Staff School taught that surprise was the deadliest of all weapons. Clausewitz wrote that surprise was the most important element of victory, and noted that Napoleon, Gustavus Adolphus, Caesar, Hannibal, and Alexander owed the brightest rays of their fame to swift surprise. General Clay wanted to follow their shining lights.

For months the Allies had cowered behind the North Sea and English Channel, waiting at the Germans' leisure, reacting rather than acting, putting out fires rather than starting them. General Clay's turn had come. His operation, Green Thumb, was to be a stab at the Wehrmacht heart.

Ranger Sergeant Aaron Hirschorn's bravura got him into the C-53 Skytrooper, but it did not help him during the crossing. "I swear," he told me later, "I had to pee the entire trip."

Big talkers and big laughers, the Rangers in Hirschorn's plane were silent. The sergeant was loaded with weapons and equipment. Normally a parachute landing is the equivalent of a ten-foot fall. Carrying the extra weight, the drop would seem like twenty feet. Colonel Yates had confided to Clay that ten or twenty percent of the Rangers would suffer ankle or leg injuries from the fall.

"My mouth was dry the whole trip," Hirschorn remembered. "I couldn't have spit if I had wanted to."

Green Thumb's target was OKW's forward command head-quarters near Zottegem, in Flanders, Belgium, one hundred miles east-by-southeast of the Isle of Thanet airfield. Excited with his plans of the operation, General Clay had asked me, "Jack, do you know who said, 'Always attempt the unexpected'?"

I thought carefully, then replied, "Charlie Chaplin?"

"Jack, goddamn it, it was Frederick the Great. Sometimes I think you are headed for the loony bin."

The Rangers' mission was to destroy the German invasion command post and to bring back plans detailing the time and place of the invasion. With success, the Rangers would force the Germans to postpone their operation, giving the Allies more time to prepare.

Lieutenant Ronald Betts remembers being thankful the engines filled the Skytrooper's cabin with a loud roar. Otherwise his platoon would have heard his knees knocking together. Betts was the tallest man in his unit, and on training jumps the jumpmaster always put his hand on the lieutenant's helmet to make sure he didn't coldcock himself on the way through the hatch.

Private George Lukowski sat next to Betts on the two-by-eight plank. In long shadows cast by pale red overhead lights in the cabin, the soldiers, with their camouflage paint and gear, were hardly recognizable. He felt a quick jolt of fear. Maybe these men weren't his mates. They were as alien as Martians. Then Private Howard Lance leaned onto one cheek, crowding the entire line of Rangers, and loosed one of his patented farts, louder than the Pratt and Whitneys. Lance was rewarded with raucous, tension-cracking laughter. Yeah, this was Lukowski's crew.

To reduce the mission's radar profile, the three Skytroopers were unescorted. They flew fifty feet above the water, one of the Green Thumb's riskiest maneuvers. Moonlight strained through high clouds to illuminate the waves. To avoid spotters on land, the route was direct, with no diversionary zigzags south over Artois or north over the Schelde estuaries. Undetected, the Skytroopers breasted land at Ostend, forty-five miles from Zottegem. Fifteen minutes later, the light on the forward bulkhead came on. The jumpmaster barked orders to stand and attach static lines.

Just as the jumpmaster pushed open the hatch, an AA shell burst near the starboard wing, then another, higher but closer. The plane lurched. Rangers toppled against the cabin wall, but quickly regained their feet. A number of them made a point of grinning broadly. Most grabbed a hand rail above their heads. Lukowski was reminded of a crammed subway car in Manhattan, his hometown. There was no further antiaircraft fire.

The Skytroopers had been guided to Zottegem by a navigational beam system similar to the Luftwaffe's dog leg. The beams were accurate to within miles, not yards, so the pilots depended on the Belgian resistance to set four bonfires, a rectangle marking the landing zone. The pilots had been accurate. Ahead was a rectangle. Because the Germans enforced blackout regulations, no other lights were visible.

"Check lines," the jumpmaster called over the engine nose.

Lieutenant Betts yanked his static line. He also glanced for the final time over his shoulder at his parachute pack. His constant fear was that his pack would open as he fell, and, instead of the chute, out would come a couple of sandwiches, a canteen, tent staves, and a sleeping bag. No, this was his chute pack.

The line of paratroopers crowded together. Betts was first, Lukowski behind him. The jumpmaster wore a headset. He palmed Betts' helmet, then yelled, "Go!"

The stick sailed out the hatch. Night jumps are instantly disorienting. Lukowski told me after the war that he couldn't tell if he was cartwheeling head over heels or dropping in a perfect spread eagle. He felt his harness's tug as the silk opened above him. The sky was filled with chutes.

Sergeant Aaron Hirschorn dropped from the second Skytrooper. He swung lazily under his chute, feeling motionlessness, unable to find the horizon. Then he saw the first plane's Rangers below him. He was immeasurably reassured. He finally saw the bonfires. He swore he'd someday shake that pilot's hand. The sergeant lifted his submachine gun into his hands, prepared to fire back at muzzle flashes on the ground.

160

Betts landed in a pasture thirty yards from Lukowski. The lieutenant dragged his chute to the row of trees at the edge of the field. There was no time to bury them. The platoon formed up around him. Lukowski's knee had rapped his chin on landing, and he had bitten deeply into his tongue, filling his mouth with blood. Even so, he was better off than two of the platoon. Emil Johanson's leg had snapped, and Dennis Smythe had severely twisted an ankle on the field's furrows. They were helped to the trees. Johanson refused morphine. He and Smythe would join other Rangers assigned to the pasture's perimeter. The Skytroopers would be returning in forty-five minutes.

Two Belgians ran up to the Rangers. They may have been a father and son, and they gestured wildly. "New Germans" was apparently all the father could say in English. He whispered it over and over again, fiercely, making a huge circle with his arms.

Colonel Yates appeared out of darkness. He questioned the resistance fighters in halting French. Words poured from both father and son. Yates' mouth turned down. He stabbed at his map, demanding information. The father stared at the colonel as if Yates were daft. The Belgian exhaled loudly, shook his head, then pointed east. The Rangers hastily began toward the low rise to the east, toward OKW's advance headquarters at Viscount Henri Le Marten's chateau, and toward disaster.

More so than day operations, night attacks require a limited objective and particularly accurate daylight reconnaissance. Certainly the destruction of the chateau was a modest goal, but the last successful recon flight had been two days before.

During the intervening time, the 44th Panzer Regiment had moved into the Zottegem area. The Rangers were expecting a Wehrmacht guard company at the chateau. They were not anticipating three tank battalions, each with two companies of Type III battle tanks and a company of short-gunned Type IVs, and assorted self-propelled antitank guns and PZ II flame-throwing tanks. The Rangers had tripped over a wasps' nest of 120 armored vehicles.

An investigation by a U.S. Army commission after the war determined that the 44th Panzer was in transit and had just happened to bivouac that evening near the chateau. They settled in the cattle pastures east and north of the viscount's residence not by plan, but only because Zottegem was as far as they had been able to move that day.

"The Rangers' luck just plain ran out," Private Lukowski concluded later.

. The drop zone was five hundred yards west of the chateau, across several pastures and a barley field that straddled a hill. Yates knew the chateau was surrounded by formal gardens and that a forested area was to the south. The Rangers split up. Two platoons broke into squadrons and fanned out toward the hill. A third platoon, forty-eight men, including Betts and Lukowski, marched southeast, skirting the hill to come at the building from the south.

The Rangers knew they would not be able to land and move toward the chateau undetected. Too much noise overhead, too many Wehrmacht sentries on the ground. Speed was to compensate for lack of surprise during the approach to the headquarters. The soldiers loped along, some carrying almost a hundred pounds of equipment.

Just before the lead platoon crested the hill, small arms fire sounded from the north. Clumps of dirt jumped near them. Five Rangers branched off to deal with it, running at an angle to the sound.

Viscount Le Marten's home was an eighteenth-century stone structure at the end of a long courtyard. Two other sides of the courtyard were framed by unadorned annexes, built at right angles to the main wing. At the end of the northerly annex was a chapel, with stained glass in the small windows. At the head of the courtyard was a drawbridge lodge that had a lantern turret atop a rounded roof. The moat had been filled in at the turn of the century. Several outbuildings—an apple press house, stables, tool sheds—were arranged to the west of the main compound.

Colonel Yates and his soldiers gained the hilltop for their first view of the chateau, now only a hundred yards in front of them. Despite the blackout, yellow light shone through several windows. In the darkness, they could see the dim outlines of three trucks and several *Kübelwagens*, the Wehrmacht's equivalent of the jeep. In the courtyard were a number of black sedans, almost invisible in the darkness. Two of the automobiles were racing across the lowered drawbridge. Their headlights off, they turned south on the Gent road. Sounds of a firefight came from the north, several rifle shots followed by the stammer of a submachine gun. Hirschorn tripped over a rock and pitched forward. He rose quickly and wiped dirt off his Bren gun.

Lieutenant Betts and Private Lukowski's platoon entered the southern woods without incident. The ash and oak trees had been planted there a hundred years before by a prior viscount to give his bedroom windows a view. Betts kept an arm in front of him to ward off low branches. He high-stepped over exposed roots. Someone cursed behind him. After a moment they could see several lights of the chateau through the trees.

That is when the sound began, the unmistakable clanking and growling of a tank. Then another, and finally a chorus of them, hidden somewhere in the darkness ahead. Betts called it a "cold-to-the-bone" sound.

One of the tank's drawbacks is that it cannot do anything silently. Its engine roars, its gearbox grinds, and its treads rattle. Branches crack underneath, hatches slam, the turret whines. The machine blows smoke and kicks up dust. The massed tanks of the 44th Panzer began doing all this at that moment.

Lukowski had been assigned to set up a machine gun post at the edge of the woods to cover the Rangers' retreat. He did not trust the American Johnsons, so was carrying a .303-inch Bren light machine gun, with its drum rear sight and angled grip beneath the butt, fitted with a bipod.

Lukowski was stocky, almost six feet, two inches, and weighed close to 220. "I'm a big Pole, and the army figured I must be dumb as an ox. So they made me a machine gunner. They didn't think I knew that the average life expectancy of a machine gunner in the Great War after he first pulled the trigger was fourteen seconds. I'm lucky I could read and write, or they'd have given me a flame-thrower. Those're the real dummies."

Lukowski lowered himself to the ground a hundred yards

south of the chateau. The Ranger behind him dropped several magazines and followed the others toward the building. "That was Timmy Bridges," Lukowski told me. "Last I ever saw of him."

The private had not been told of the topiary. When the moon broke through the clouds, a camel, two horses, an elephant, and an enormous goose took shape between Lukowski and the building. Even during the German occupation, the sculptured bushes had been carefully tended. Lukowski had never heard of such things. For a moment he wondered if that loud bray, which at first sounded like armored vehicles, might be these animals. He resisted an urge to loose a few shots into the camel. More Rangers ran past Lukowski.

Sergeant Hirschorn led his squad toward the chateau from the west, over a series of hedges. The throaty, ominous rumble of armored vehicles filled the night. He heard commands shouted in German. Several Wehrmacht sentries rounded the building's northwest corner and raised their rifles. They were brought down quickly without the Rangers breaking step. The soldiers had been told to keep moving, that to drop and dig in would be to die.

A four-wheeled scout car next appeared at the corner. It fired both its 2cm cannon and MG 22, tearing up the manicured lawn in front of the commandoes. A Ranger bazookaman launched his rocket-propelled projectile, the back-blast lighting the garden like a flashbulb. The scout car erupted with flame and fragments.

The Germans were all coming from that corner. Two more bazookamen kneeled to wait. A heavy machine gun, a *Maschinengewehr* 34, opened up from the chateau's flat roof. Fire was returned, but half a dozen Rangers fell before it was silenced with another bazooka round that entered the third-floor window and erupted skyward.

Lights went out in several of the chateau's rooms. Lieutenant Betts, who had reached the elephant, saw muzzle flashes from several windows. Another Ranger machine gunner opened up, holding the Bren against his hip, pouring bullets into one window, then the next. Ejected casings hit Betts' arm and cheek. The window flashes stopped.

164

Betts waved his troops forward again. Twenty yards separated them from the chateau when the 44th Panzer arrived in force.

So many tanks rolled across the Gent road and into the garden that their procession resembled a freight train. They came in a column and quickly dispersed into a north-south line, six of them at first, more crowded than they would be on a battlefield. The southerly tank, a Pzkw III with regimental HQ markings on its turret, began to spin clockwise when a bazooka round shattered a tread. Their MG 34s blazed, plowing up the grass and everyone on it.

The bazookamen fell. In a crouch, Betts ran toward their weapon, which was lying on the grass near their bodies, but the lieutenant was met with the snout of another tank, poking around the chateau's southwest corner. That tank, and the others behind it, meant only that Colonel Yates' two platoons coming from the west had already been torn apart. Betts turned a full circle. More Rangers were down than remained standing, and they continued to fall, powerless against the unexpected onslaught.

Betts called a retreat, but was unsure anyone heard him over the snarl of tank machine gun fire. He motioned back to the woods. Several Rangers near him sprinted south. The lieutenant waited another few seconds, hearing the snap of bullets streaking over him. He could see no other Americans still on their feet. He turned to run.

A bullet shattered his wrist, then another shot through the meat of his forearm. Yet another creased his side. The ground around him seemed to be in a mixer, tossing and rolling as bullets dug into it. The tanks did not deign to fire their cannons. Nothing in the garden was worthy of a German armor-piercing shell. His wounded arm flapping behind him, Betts sprinted between the topiary animals toward the woods.

George Lukowski saw him coming, a mad hurdler frantically jumping over hedges. Two other Rangers made it back as far as the elephant, then a spray of bullets caught them, throwing them against a hedge. Lukowski waited until his lieutenant reached his post, then opened up with his machine gun.

"I might as well have been pissing into the wind," he told me.

Betts slapped him on the helmet with his good hand and yelled, "Let's get out of here."

Lukowski abandoned his weapon. They ran blindly, bullets nipping at their heels like unruly terriers. The private collided squarely with a tree trunk, breaking his nose and jaw and lacerating a cheek. With his good hand, Betts helped Lukowski to his feet, and they staggered on.

In the pasture west of the chateau, Aaron Hirschorn felt his life seeping away through a wound in his back. He had no memory of how he had been wounded, only of waking and of hearing the pounding of automatic weapons and the cries of fallen men. He might have been out sixty seconds or thirty minutes or longer, he did not know. His back was hot. When he tried to reach around to feel for the wound, pain coursed up his arm. He tried to rise, and collapsed. Again he tried, and this time found his feet. He hobbled away, around the bodies of three Rangers piled like firewood.

Right on time, forty-five minutes after the drop, the Sky-troopers landed on the field, one after another. The marker fires were still blazing. Perhaps the pilots had seen the melee at the chateau and had come down anyway, hoping for sur-vivors. They had landed into the wind and had taxied the full length of the field to take off.

Not one Ranger met the planes. Instead, several Wehrmacht tanks rolled onto the hill and finally had a worthwhile use for their cannons. It was the work of a few seconds, an unfair match. The C-53s were ripped apart by the blasts. Fuel ignited in red and orange mushrooms. After a moment, not even the planes' skeletons remained, just pools of fire on the pasture and unrecognizable pieces of charred metal.

From the edge of the woods, Betts and Lukowski saw the planes disintegrate. Lukowski tied a bootlace around the lieu-tenant's wounded arm to stanch the bleeding. They returned to the woods.

They walked south all night, first through the woods, then across pastures and bogs. Sirens sounded behind them. A dozen times they threw themselves into ditches or ran into glades when vehicles passed on nearby roads. Betts began bab-bling, hallucinating, and at times Lukowski had to pull him along. At the first light of dawn, they entered a dilapidated barn and dug into a haystack. They ignored the yapping of a farm dog. Lukowski did not expect Betts to live another hour.

Nor did the private expect to be shaken awake by a man speaking Flemish. The farmer tried to clean Betts' wounds, and wrapped a length of cloth around Lukowski's head to prevent the private's fractured jaw from dangling. Several hours later, about noon, members of the Belgian Resistance arrived in a hay truck to take the Rangers to a safe house in Deinze.

Sergeant Hirschorn's story is shorter, because he knows little of it. His memory of that night is patchy. He stumbled along, he fell. He struggled to his feet and walked again, then fell. Over and over again. He has no recollection of being found by a Flemish dairyman, nor of being handed over to the underground. When I spoke with him twelve months after the war, he still carried pieces of shrapnel in the muscle tissue near his spine.

A number of Belgian farmers claim—and I believe them— to have seen eighteen or twenty Rangers being loaded into trucks near Viscount Le Marten's chateau. Most wore bandages, head dressings, or slings. The trucks turned toward Gent, and those Rangers disappeared. There is no record of them. No German I spoke with after the war knew of their fate or would admit to it.

Only Betts, Lukowski, and Hirschorn survived Green Thumb. One hundred twenty-three Rangers and pilots perished.

General Clay had told his commanders that the Three Blows was the worst news they would hear. Not so, not for Clay. I was with him later that night when he was told the Skytroopers had vanished. He seemed to shrink before me. Then his face contorted. He turned away and for a moment I thought he might weep. But that passed.

Never again, not through S-Day and the calamitous days that followed, would I see the general as stricken or as vulnerable.

9

General Clay and I walked across the garden to his trailer. Our last meeting had just broken up. It was 1:30 in the morning. At West Point, the general had suffered an ankle fracture falling from a horse. He still limped late at night or when he heard bad news. As we crossed the grass, the hitch in his gait was pronounced. He had been unable or unwilling to speak of the Rangers since we had learned of their fate.

He pushed aside the blackout curtain over the door, and we entered the caravan. He lowered himself onto the settee and removed his shoes. I made him a scotch and water, stood by while he threw it back, then got him another. This one he put on the floor while he rubbed his ankle. I sipped a scotch.

"Some day the goddamn army will issue a decent shoe," he said.

"There aren't any reporters here, sir," I chided. I was with him when he bought those brogans on Bond Street.

"Sorry. I forgot." He picked up his drink and slumped back in the settee. "Jack, you're a military historian. Someday you should do a study on what separates a brilliant commander from an adequate commander. What do you think?"

"Well, presumably there are—"

"Some say there are only two professions in the world where the amateur excels the professional. One is military strategy, and the other is prostitution."

He had asked, and I was determined to answer. "Many reasons—"

"But I don't buy that," he went on. His voice was just above a whisper, and it was tainted with sadness. He was searching for his own weaknesses. "I side with Marshal de Saxe, who said talent in war is like talent in painting, poetry, and music. But tell me, why was Stonewall Jackson able to throw a handful of troops between vastly superior forces and win a victory at Second Manassas, while Germany's von Kluck, using the same tactic at the Marne, was unable to duplicate Jackson's victory?"

Clay sipped his drink. "Jackson was a great soldier. Von Kluck only a good one. What is the difference?"

"Well, I think—"

Clay went on, "If I only knew I'd—"

He was interrupted by a knock at the door.

He scowled, then shouted, "If you aren't bringing me word of the invasion, go away, goddamn it. I've had enough for one day."

From outside the trailer came a tentative, "May I speak with you, General?"

We both recognized the voice. Clay slammed his glass onto his desk, stabbed his feet into his shoes, and jumped up from the settee. He brushed unseen crumbs from his pants. "Jesus," he whispered.

I also scrambled from my chair, then squared my necktie and cleared my throat.

General Clay opened the door and curtain. The king of Great Britain and Northern Ireland entered the caravan.

"It's late, I know," George VI said. He was carrying a leather valise. "I have been touring the forces, bucking them up and all."

We saluted smartly. The American Revolution was not as successful as George Washington may have hoped. Americans still feel an overwhelming urge to bow or curtsey before English

169

royalty. I stood awkwardly, shifting my feet, wondering what was proper. His majesty motioned us into chairs. He sat on the settee.

We had met the king a number of times at Buckingham Palace and at Lord Louis Mountbatten's ancestral estate. Clay was no more familiar with the formalities than I was and referred to the king only as "Sir." I think they were fond of each other.

His majesty withdrew a document from the valise. I could see "Top Secret" stamped across the top page. He stared at it glumly for a moment.

George VI endlessly visited British troops, being seen and lifting morale. His code name when he traveled usually was General Lyon, for Lion of the Empire, I suppose. As tactfully as possible, Churchill had asked the king to go to Canada to preserve the monarchy during the coming invasion. The king had countered by ordering Churchill to flee to Canada with the government at once when the Germans came. Both understood each other and had refused each other. George was a slight man, with a substantial nose and a lean face. He was wearing the uniform of a general of the British Army. Shy, with a stammer, George was well loved by his people.

"I have brought you a translation of several documents Churchill gave me this morning." The king passed the folder to General Clay. "I have never before seen anything as frightening."

Clay's eyes raced down the first page. It was titled "Orders Concerning the Organization and Function of Military Government in England." He turned to the second and said, "It's a blueprint for the occupation."

"The Germans have plans to install a *Reichskommissar* of Great Britain, probably Ribbentrop," the king said. "That document shows they will run England with brutal efficiency. It will be a war on our civilization. They plan to deport all able-bodied males between the ages of seventeen and forty-five to the Continent, where they will be interned in camps."

When Clay turned to the next document, the king said, "The Germans are going to establish a Military Economic Staff."

"The *Wehrwirtschaftsstab* England," the general said.

"It will have commands in London, Birmingham, Newcastle, Liverpool, and Glasgow. That organization will denude England. All stocks, such as food, petrol, automobiles, and lorries, even horses, which are not being used by the army of occupation, will be transported to Germany. Factories will be dismantled and sent into Germany. Research laboratories, cloth mills, mining equipment, all go, to be reconstructed in the Reich. There are even plans to cut down English forests, shipping the lumber to the Continent."

Clay said, "They want it all, don't they? Here are orders to transport to Germany all stones, cut or uncut, precious or semiprecious. But there is an exception for coal in household scuttles."

"In return, they will give us the Gestapo, which they are going to call the German Secret Police for Great Britain. The Gestapo has drawn up a list of 2,300 names and addresses of British citizens who will be hunted down and arrested—writers, trade unionists, industrialists, police officials, religious leaders, professors, and the nobility. They call it the Special Search List, G.B."

"I presume your name is on the list," Clay said lightly.

"Rest assured, it is." He smiled briefly. "And they are not overlooking anyone else. They have targeted Jews, freemasons, refugees, socialists, communists, and liberals, in which category they include Parliament. Glance down until you find the Boy Scouts, and read that."

It took the general a moment. Finally he read, " 'The Boy Scout movement represents a camouflaged but powerful instrument of British cultural propaganda and an excellent source of information for the British Intelligence Service. The liquidation of the Austrian Scout movement produced proof of, among other things, the link between the Scout movement and the British Secret Service.' "

"It would be laughable, were they not serious, General Clay. We already have experience with a German occupation, as you know. They have for several years occupied the Channel Islands. On orders from Whitehall, the islanders offered no resistance to the Germans. Still, all British citizens were deported to camps on the Continent. We know where most of them are,

171

but the Jews on the island, twenty of them, have disappeared. Our inquiries through the Swiss and Red Cross produce nothing." The king inhaled slowly. "The Germans plan not just to occupy us, but to end England, to bring to a conclusion our millennium of statehood."

We were silent for a moment. I finally asked, "Would you like something to drink, sir?"

"No, thank you."

The general reached for his glass.

The king then quickly said, "Unless you are having something."

I figured that after an adulthood of it, his majesty might be tired of single malt Scotch whiskey. I poured him Jim Beam, neat. He sipped it gingerly, as if he feared I had given him Kentucky moonshine. He nodded his approval and took a heartier drink.

"Do you know anything about the men who are coming? Von Rundstedt of Army Group A and Rommel of Group C?"

The general swirled his drink. "Von Rundstedt is a Prussian through and through. He excels in preparation, and his army is the most drilled and polished in German history. He is an odd combination of arrogance and pliability. He is thought to be susceptible to Hitler's persuasion. He was retired from the army after the Fritsch-Blomberg crisis, but was able to return. His Panzer spearhead broke through at Sedan and cut off the British Expeditionary Force. Von Rundstedt's mistake, as you know, was to persuade Hitler to halt the ground offensive, to leave the destruction of the BEF to the Luftwaffe, which never happened. Despite that error, there is every evidence he'll be a tough customer."

"And Rommel?"

"Rommel was seen three days ago in Amsterdam, at Army Group C headquarters. Since entering the German army in 1910, he has excelled at every level of command he has held, from platoon on up."

"I've read a translation of Rommel's textbook on infantry tactics he wrote between the wars. Have you had the chance?"

"Why, yes." Clay was surprised. George VI was the titular head of the British armed services, but was not known as a military theoretician. "In fact, I assigned it to my division commanders, so I hope Rommel will be surprised when he finds some of his own tactics used against him. The most telling insight into his character is that he commands from the lead tank. His command of the 7th Panzer in the sweep across France was brilliant, using some of those tactics you read about."

The king said wearily, "I suppose we can expect no less from him in England."

"He'll do the unexpected," Clay replied. "He'll drive his troops, and, above all, he'll be fast. His plan will be to hit the beach running and not stop until he gets to the Irish Sea."

"The German people believe Rommel is invincible," his majesty said. "Is he?"

"I know better, and so does Rommel. His invincibility is a creation of the German propaganda machine, with assistance from the British and American press. He is a fine general, and that's all."

"Better than our Allied commanders?" The king plainly wanted reassurance.

"Erwin Rommel has his talents. On the battlefield, he seems to know precisely which second to commit himself. He is persistent, a talent in itself. And he has what Frederick called the *coup d'oeil*, the ability to grasp salient features and advantages of terrain at a quick glance."

"This doesn't sound promising for us, General."

"Rommel has another gift, sir," Clay said gloomily. "His men will follow him anywhere."

"Surely any general insists on no less."

"There's more to it than just ordering the troops. A mysterious charisma is involved, and I've tried to understand it and tried to develop it in myself, if I may admit. Our General Grant was a brilliant tactician, but Union soldiers didn't love him, as they did Pap Thomas. Ludendorff was an effective chess player with his units, but German soldiers worshipped Hindenberg. Confederates respected Longstreet, but they would have followed Lee into hell. Rommel has what Lee and the others had. Their devotion to him will cost us, I'm afraid."

The king seemed perturbed. "Then what are Churchill and Barclay and you and the others going to do about him?"

Clay smiled grimly. "General Rommel hasn't passed through this war invisibly, sir. He has left tracks, and I've studied them. It took Napoleon's enemies twenty years to learn his tactics. Rommel won't have that luxury." Clay glanced at the wall, and said in a low voice, as if to himself, "I know Erwin Rommel better than his mother does."

Now it was the king's turn to smile. "You speak with some confidence, General."

Clay retreated into modesty, an occasional ruse, dragged out with some effort. "Well, we'll do our damnedest, sir."

"I know you will, General." The king finished his drink and set the glass on the desk. He rose and stepped to the door. Deep lines of worry under his eyes seemed etched into the skin.

We stood also. Forgetting deference and tact, Clay asked, "Sir, you haven't said what you were doing in our neck of the woods tonight."

"Kings go anywhere they want, anytime they want. It's one of the better benefits of the position." He smiled quickly. "And the prime minister said you might need a boost, after news of the *Queen Mary* and all."

"Well, I'm grateful. It has been a boost."

"Good night, then, General." He nodded at me, then left the trailer. His driver, bodyguards, and other retainers had been waiting in the garden.

Clay undid his tie, pulled it through the collar, and said to me, "I thought monarchs were always preceded by trumpet fanfares, so they can't sneak up and startle us common folks."

He began with the buttons of his uniform blouse. "I'm hitting the hay, Jack. This'll be a long, nervous night for all of us. Let's hope tomorrow is a little brighter."

"It will be, sir," I answered without conviction.

I left him in the trailer. Because I had been summoned in the middle of the night many times before, I stood by on the gravel for a few minutes in case he remembered something else for my notebook. Only a slit of light was visible below the blackout curtain on the window of his bedroom. When the light blinked out, I started toward the manor house. It was two in the morning. I wondered if I'd sleep. The anxious waiting was grinding at me.

But our long wait was soon to end.

The largest armada in history had just set sail for the English shore.

PART TWO

War, "the business of barbarians."
—NAPOLEON

S-DAY

German First Wave Landings
May 28, 1942

LONDON

From Rotterdam
and Antwerp

Dover

Dunkirk

Folkstone

35 Div
17 Div

Calais

Hastings

XIII Corps

Brighton

Boulogne

Portsmouth

7 Div

1 Mtn Div

VII Corps

Lyme
Bay

Poole

34 Div

26 Div

XXXVIII Corps

Cherbourg

12
Div

32 Div

31 Div

II Corps

Le Havre

28 Div

8 Div

VIII Corps

30 Div

6 Mtn Div

X Corps

Researching this manuscript, I tried to find the first person in all of England who knew with certainty the invasion had begun. After the long, gnashing months of waiting, who received the dubious honor of knowing first?

It was Henry Hathaway, a dairyman and widower, who was asleep in the bedroom of his cottage that morning. "Double Summer Time was wicked on us dairy farmers, and we always need our sleep," he told me after the war. "I didn't get a right proper amount that night, I should tell you."

Hathaway awoke to a tearing sound coming from his garden. He bolted upright in bed, clutched the blanket to his chest, and leaned forward to peer out his window toward the pasture. It was too dark to see, but the commotion swiftly closed, a peculiar, muted rasping and splintering. "I had this sudden, dotty fear my milk cows were coming for me, to pay me back for my cold hands all those mornings."

The splintering grew to a roar, and then Hathaway's bedroom buckled inward. Stones and plaster flew in at the dairyman, bowling over his chest of drawers and coat rack, shattering his wash stand and its mirror, and sending a framed, yellowed print of Queen Victoria soaring across the room. The roof beams near the wall collapsed, showering Hathaway with dust and bits of wood. The dairyman's August Junghans pendulum clock dropped to the floor, stopping at 2:32.

"Quite on their own, my legs began working," Hathaway remembered, "and they pushed me up the headboard almost to standing, as an enormous metal nose slid through the rubble and into the room."

It was the prow of a Gigant glider, which, by the time it entered Henry Hathaway's sleeping quarters, was badly mangled. Sheets of the fuselage were twisted and bent, the windshield was ripped out, and the forward airframe was bent into sharp angles. The pilot and copilot were crushed against the cockpit bulkhead, and their legs dangled over Hathaway's bed, their controls and instruments a tangled knot in front of them.

"It's fortunate my wife Elizabeth was long dead, because this would have killed her."

An antilanding post in the pasture had already ripped off the Gigant's starboard wing, and Hathaway's raspberries, eight rows of old woody vines, had slowed the glider, saving him. Hathaway squinted through the dust and darkness. A German commando, "the most frightening rotter I've ever seen in my life," he said, "with his face painted black, coal scuttle helmet, stick grenades in his belt, and carrying a machine pistol," climbed out the aircraft's nose, crossed the room, and disappeared through the door. "He didn't even look at me."

Other German soldiers followed, clambering through the glider's wreckage, stepping over several stilled comrades who were pinned in the wreckage. Hathaway heard moaning from inside the glider, then heard shouted commands. The Gigant held over a hundred solders, and they poured out the midships hatch, carrying mortars and machine guns, filling the dairyman's garden. More pushed their way through the damaged prow and quickly left the bedroom.

"I raised my hands to surrender, but nobody was interested," Hathaway told me. "Hurt my feelings a bit, I don't mind telling you."

Moments later the glider was empty of the living. Wrapping

his blanket around himself, Hathaway tumbled off his bed and stepped over the rubble to look through the gap in his wall along the glider's fuselage. He narrowed his eyes, trying to see through the night. Wehrmacht troops were gathering at the edge of the pasture. One other Gigant had landed safely, but the third had slammed into a post head on, cleaving the glider lengthwise almost to its rudder. Only a few Germans were emerging from the metal carcass.

"They took off at a trot, the lot of them, leaving the wounded and their aircraft behind."

Using a crowbar and wire cutters, Hathaway spent the rest of the night freeing two injured Germans from the Gigant. He hauled them as carefully as he could out of the glider and lay them on his bed. One seemed grateful for the water and headache powder the dairyman gave him. The other was dead by the time Hathaway offered him the cup.

The dairyman recalled, "Only at dawn did I have time to wonder about the rest of England and what was to become of us all."

Or perhaps the first person to know England's hour had come was Jane Ridgeway, who early that morning was walking along the river near her farm, picking her way in the darkness along the path, knowing that in only five hours she would be trudging the opposite direction, along the same route, returning to her cows.

The work on the farm was endless, and she was a city girl, not accustomed to the hours or the toil. And worse, she had volunteered for it. She sighed, hitching the handles of her shoulder bag higher. She brushed her rough hands together. In moments of self-pity, she seized on the calluses that had grown across her hands in a broad array. Calluses on calluses. They would never go away, she thought angrily. She had always been proud of her graceful hands, with their slim fingers and long nails.

She laughed bitterly as she remembered all the time she had spent practicing her gestures in front of a mirror, trying to imitate Vivien Leigh, whom she had seen in *Gone With the Wind* three times at the Empire Cinema in London. Now her fingers looked little better than the tongs of a manure fork.

Jane stumbled over a stone on the path and quickly righted herself, once again adjusting the hand bag. To her left was an embankment, spotted with bushes and a few trees, which led down to the river. When the clouds parted for a moment, she could see yellow, fleeting ripples on the silent water. She walked along in the darkness and did not look toward the clouds when she heard the airplanes. They were always overhead, the RAF or the Luftwaffe. She hadn't been swept up in the plane-spotting rage early in the war and had never been able to tell the difference.

Jane Ridgeway was a member of the Women's Land Army. She had volunteered out of a sense of duty, unlike many girls on her assigned farm, who had joined to escape the textile mills of Lancashire and Yorkshire, and she received no little satisfaction from that fact. She had been given four weeks' training and was paid twenty-eight shillings a week, from which were deducted room and board, leaving her almost nothing. All day, from darkness to darkness, she milked cows and pitched hay, cleaned stalls and lifted milk tins. One of the few rewards of her service was her uniform: khaki breeches, a green jumper, and a hat with a broad brim. She was in livery, which was more than many of the girls at home could say.

She and six other Landgirls were billeted in a nearby cottage, and she was only a hundred yards from the house when she heard a distant splash, then another and another, reminding her of waves breaking against the shore, a sound she had grown to love during her family's holidays in Brighton before the war. She turned to the river and held her hand to her eyes as if shading them from sunlight. She saw nothing but the emptiness of night.

Again the splash came, and in the darkness she saw a gray haze hovering between banks of the river. She heard a man's cry.

Another rent in the clouds allowed the moonlight through. The haze took form as a parachute, and it plunged into the river. Four others already dappled the black water, spread over the surface like stains. An unseen man still struggled below one of them, turning and twisting the fabric, but soon was still.

182

The moonlight held, and the sky soon was filled with parachutes, descending along the waterway.

Another soldier hit the water and quickly sank from sight, the parachute floating on the water, marking his end. Then another, who disappeared just as quickly. The paratroopers' heavy packs and weaponry acted as anchors. Perhaps a few saw their fate in the sudden break of moonlight, because they furiously yanked at their lines. It was too late. One by one, they followed each other into the river, which allowed little struggle before taking them.

Jane Ridgeway counted twelve paratroopers, all drowned, before she started to run. Other soldiers may have landed in the field on the other side of the river, but she could not be sure because the night had closed in again. Breathless and holding her hands in front of her to ward off branches, she ran toward the cottage.

Or Elizabeth Cooper may have been the first to know. Early that morning she was nursing her three-month-old, John. She walked to and fro in her home, cooing to him and rocking him, kissing his bald head. John, she suspected, needed none of this affection. Food was his only concern. God, he was an eater. Because he regularly drained her and bawled for more, she kept an extra ration of milk in the cooler. Ten pounds, two ounces at birth, and he had been slapping on the weight since. Eat and sleep, give her a grin once in a while. He did little else. She loved him for it.

Mrs. Cooper knew of the danger that night, of the invasion alert. She had been preparing her home for it: hiding her mother's silver tea service under a floorboard in the barn; disabling her automobile by removing the rotor arm; storing a string of sausages—containing so little meat the British called them "breadcrumbs in battle dress"—in the Anderson shelter. Even little John had been swept up in the war. Instead of the Marmet pram he deserved, he had to make do with the government's utility pram, a fragile box perched on hard tires, with no springs or padding. She had paid ten pounds for the pram, and thought it utterly worthless, until a neighbor offered her fifteen. John would have to make do until his father, an RN officer stationed at Folkestone, could return on leave to improvise a proper one.

Mrs. Cooper told me after the war that she had no reason to walk to her parlor window, other than to move John about. She turned off the table lamp, then pulled aside the blackout curtain. She leaned an elbow against the middle pane for support. She gazed out, seeing nothing in the darkness, aware only of the warm comfort of the baby's sucking.

The room flashed white and just as abruptly returned to darkness, as if from a photographer's bulb. The light was followed by a sharp report that rattled the window against her elbow. She yanked the baby away from the glass and covered his face with her hand. A second blast illuminated the road in front of her home, followed by a series of other detonations.

She saw a telephone pole begin to topple, lit by flashes that made the falling pole appear jerky, like an old cinema. Other poles followed like dominoes, filling the road with wire. Five or six explosions, she could not be sure, and then it was over except for the ringing in her ears. John did not seem to notice and continued to empty his mother.

Mrs. Cooper rushed out of the room and grabbed a few blankets from the hall chest with her free hand. She pushed aside the blackout cloth, wrestled with the knob, then nudged the back door open with her hip. She quickly crossed the yard.

The Anderson shelter was a corrugated steel shell, six-by-six-by-four, buried to a depth of four feet in the yard behind the house and covered with two feet of soil. She shuddered when she stooped to enter the shelter, a seeping, insect-ridden tomb. Her slippers splashed in the mud. She hesitantly settled onto the plank seat, then draped the blankets over herself and the baby. The dank shelter smelled of earth and sausage.

She glanced again at her baby, still at her breast. A tear slid down her cheek, but she caught it before it dropped on John. Maybe the war would spare him. So far it had. In all the excitement, he hadn't missed a swallow.

184

Archibald Fair argued he was the first to know the invasion had begun. "And I came close to being the first dead, too."

Fair was a Home Guardsman, a pharmacist—"Chemist," he corrected me—who was assigned to guard a VP, a vulnerable point, a two-lane bridge near his home. XII Corps of the Home Guard—by then officially called the Local Defence Volunteers —had posted an entire platoon, over forty men, at the bridge. That early morning Fair was some fifty yards downstream from the bridge. It was an antiquated stone structure, but the Ministry of Works had determined it capable of the heaviest loads, and the span had endured many Allied armored convoys.

He had served his time in the Great War and still limped from a bullet that shot off much of his heel. He had doubted the Home Guard would take him. But the Guard's only requirement was that the volunteer "be capable of free movement." That he was, even if he hobbled.

Fair was stationed in tall grass and among bushes along the brook. The night was as black as he ever remembered a night, and he could not see the bridge, much less the fellow Guardsman he knew was a few paces up the stream.

An Invasion Alert No. 2. The Germans could come tonight, his lieutenant had warned. Judging from the drone of airplanes overhead, which had begun in earnest about midnight, the lieutenant might be right for once. Fair stroked the stock of his rifle, but was not reassured. The weapon dated from the Indian Mutiny, a relic removed from a display cabinet at the Imperial War Museum. German propaganda called the Home Guard *franc tireur*, a murder band, but at times like these, late on a lonely night, he felt more a member of a Broomstick Army, another German sobriquet.

He soothed himself by repeating over and over, "Those wretched rats are wrong and not soothing," the phrase he had been told any suspected German spy attempting to pass himself off as English would mangle in an interrogation.

Archibald Fair heard nothing but the planes. No movement in the grass, no tossing of branches, not even the whisper of the passing water. He had thought during the Great War that

185

he developed a sixth sense for imminent danger. It failed him that night.

A hand reached out of the darkness from behind Fair, cupped his chin, and yanked his head back. A knife blade slashed across his neck, and Fair toppled into the grass. Heavy boots stepped across him and disappeared along the embankment.

"The Lord pulled my number that night," he said after the war. "But the German commando bungled it."

Fair told me the German must have been holding the knife backward, so the blunt edge of the blade creased his neck.

I replied this was unlikely, given the probable caliber of the commando.

He then said perhaps the blade didn't touch him at all, but only the blade guard did.

Implausible, I said.

He replied with force, "Then you tell me how it happened." He added, "Cheeky colonials," under his breath.

I had no better explanation.

Fair was in the grass only a few seconds. He rose to his knees, lifted his weapon, said a short prayer to the saint of antique rifles, and squeezed the trigger. The German blew down and stayed down. Screaming an alarm, Fair dashed toward the bridge, almost tumbling over the commando's body.

A yellow flare was instantly launched from the east side of the span, and gunfire erupted from all directions. Fair fell again, this time with a bullet in his hip. He could recall only the beginning of the fierce firefight for his bridge, a fight the Home Guard lost, but for which his unit received the first LDV battle honor of the war.

Richard Richman had been called away from his vicarage after evensong to attend to a parishioner, Agnes Smathers, who had been dying, on and off, for much of the year. This had been another false alarm, but the old woman hadn't come around until after one in the morning, gasping and fanning herself with her hand and begging the vicar's pardon again. The vicar wondered whether the Church of England maintained records on which of its faithful had received the greatest number of last offices before finally expiring. Richman wanted to nominate Mrs. Smathers. The road to her small home was well worn by his Austin Twelve.

The war had not touched Richman yet, and he preferred it that way. He was sixty-four years old, a peaceable man, seldom driven to anger, always forgiving. He had been too old for the Great War, and he remembered being glad of it. Let the others do the fighting. He had not been engulfed by war fever then or now. He might even have called himself a pacifist, but not to anyone else.

He shifted the Austin into a lower gear and crested a small rise. He drove slowly, unable to see much beyond the auto's bonnet. The headlights had been covered with the official pattern mask, resembling a black coffee tin with three slits in the end.

His church had not sustained bomb damage, but his ministry had suffered nonetheless. The bells in the tower had been silenced, to be used only as alarms. And because his church hall was the largest room in the village, it had become a wet canteen, serving beer to servicemen, of all the shocking sacrileges. But he had forgiven the military authorities for that outrage, just as he would forgive the Germans once they came. Absolution was his business. And he would meet the German invaders with the dignity and forgiveness required by his station.

The Austin rounded a corner, paralleling a stone fence overgrown with ivy. He should have been able to see the church, another fifty yards along the road, had the windows not been covered. All of them were papered over, except his beloved rose window, the only stained glass in the chapel, which allowed little light through, and, as he told me, "God would have struck me dead had I covered it." Looking for the church, seeking comfort in its solid, familiar lines, he saw instead a German soldier jump from the fence to the road.

A German, no question, even when seen in the meager light of the Austin's lamps. Long-necked helmet, stick grenades, and a vicious little machine pistol. The commando may have been as surprised as the vicar, because the German tried to

187

do two things at once, raise his weapon and reclimb the stone fence.

"I had given myself over to God decades before," Richman told me, "and I think at that instant God gave me back. I have utterly no other explanation for the sudden fury that gripped me."

The vicar stamped on the accelerator. The Austin surged forward. Richman twisted the steering wheel, sending the auto toward the wall. The German managed to take two strides before the fender rammed him, bowling him against the wall. The Austin glanced the stones.

The good vicar, apparently as fearless as he was peaceable, craned his neck out the window to see the commando attempting to rise. The Schmeisser was on the ground, as were two grenades. His helmet was in the middle of the road, upside down and still spinning. Richman slapped the gearshift into reverse.

"I think it was the only time in all the years I owned that Austin Twelve that I actually kicked up gravel."

The car roared backward, again plowing into the German, who bounced away and collapsed at the foot of the stone fence.

"I was simply in a rage, a demonic fury at that German for daring to enter my parish."

I asked the vicar if it occurred to him that night that the German might not be traveling alone.

"Not until the next moment."

The next moment muzzle flashes lit the entire road. They came from atop the stone fence.

"My poor Austin," the vicar sighed.

A machine gun—from the results, I suspect it was a Spandau, which has a startling rate of fire of 1,200 rounds a minute— sliced the Vicar's auto cleanly in half, the boot from the bonnet.

"I may be old, but I'm not slow," Richman told me. He scrambled out the door and crawled to the trees opposite the fence. The Spandau roared again, peeling the top off the Austin. "That machine gunner was a bit upset, I could tell," the vicar told me. "I hate to think what would have happened had he seen me."

Richman hid for two hours, crawling deeper and deeper into the woods. Just before dawn he found his way to his vicarage. By then it was too late to ring the church's bells in warning.

Or Kenneth Wright may have been the first to know. Wright was a farmer, but he also ran a stable for Sir Harvey Lacewell, who rented Wright's barn. Sir Harvey had run horses at St. Leger and Oaks a few times, but his success had been limited. When he was in one of his moods after a loss, Sir Harvey would decry the common knowledge that every thoroughbred in the world was a direct descendant of Old Bald Peg, born about 1659 and the first mare listed in the *General Stud Book*. His horses, somehow, had missed their genetic inheritance.

Wright made the balance of his living from cattle and a few goats on his eighty acres. That night he awoke several times to airplanes overhead. Nothing unusual in that. He had always been a sound sleeper, and he quickly returned to sleep. But Wright was attuned to his land and the animals, and when frightened neighing came from the stables, his feet were on the floor before he was fully awake.

Grabbing his coat from the back of a chair, Wright sprinted through the blackout curtain and back door, ducked the clothes line, and dodged the ancient well. He smelled the pungent odor of burning hay, and turned toward his barn, where fire was curling through the plank siding. He heard the crack of a horse kicking against its stable gate.

"I was running as fast as my legs would carry me, and I didn't look left or right and saw nothing but the fire."

No, he affirmed to me after the war, he certainly did not see the company of Wehrmacht paratroopers that had landed in his pasture. The soldiers were of the 7th Parachute, under *Luftflotte* 2, whose mission was to clear Wright's pasture of antilanding posts before gliders of 22nd Air Landing Division appeared out of the black sky. The paratroopers were gathering the equipment from parachute harnesses and forming up. A shot kicked up dirt at Wright's feet.

Backlit by the growing fire were half a dozen German soldiers, all pointing their weapons at him. Wright obediently raised his hands, but did not break step. He was barefoot and barelegged, and his coat flapped around his bare buttocks. The Germans saw little threat from him, at least so he supposed after the war.

Ludicrously calling aloud, "Give me a moment, just a moment," he dashed through the paratroopers and into his barn. Their muzzles followed him.

Wright told me after the war that the fire was started by a bundle of signal flares that had crashed through the roof of his barn onto a stack of hay. One of them must have ignited accidentally. Fed by dry hay in the loft, the barn roof was rolling with fire, as was the north side of the building. Wright threw the latch on the first stable, rushed in alongside the bucking horse and slapped the animal's shoulder, backing it out of the pen. The thoroughbred left the stable, but then frantically danced in a circle, too frightened and disoriented to escape the conflagration.

Wright released the other gates, pushing and cajoling the frenzied horses from their stalls. But when he tried to pull them out of the barn to safety, they balked, bucking away from him, their eyes wide and wild. "I felt like sobbing, all those horses. And it was too hot for me to stay any longer. They would die where they were."

Wright heard a sharp whistle and turned to the barn door. Standing there was one of the paratroopers, waving excitedly at him. The German was wearing a rimless helmet and a camouflaged smock kilted up for jumping. A submachine gun hung across his stomach.

"And the blighter was holding one of my goats by the nape of its neck."

Wright had no idea what the German had in mind. The paratrooper dragged the bleating goat into the barn. Wright made way for him. The commando then whistled again several times, perhaps to alert the horses. He released the goat, which instantly sprinted out of the barn and away from the fire.

The horses followed, every one of them.

190

"I've never seen anything like it," Wright remembered. "The horses were crazed with fear, entirely confused in the smoke and flames. But when that goat bolted, they charged right after it. I later learned it's an old trick, to get a goat to lead horses from a burning barn, but I sure didn't know it then."

The paratrooper smiled and touched his hand to his helmet, then rejoined his comrades. The barn burned to the ground, lighting the pasture for the 22nd's ten gliders that used it that night.

"It was all for nought, though," Wright said. "My horses were pressed into the German army two days later, used as draft animals. Last I saw them, they were straining in harnesses, hauling a Wehrmacht howitzer. I doubt those beautiful creatures lasted long doing that."

Wright never saw the thoroughbreds again. Neither did Sir Harvey, who has never forgiven him for their loss.

Or Captain Richard Swarthmore may have been the first to know the invasion was at hand. The meteorologist admitted to me after the war, "It was nothing but intuition. I simply figured that the Germans, whose luck had held throughout their early adventures, would be lucky again."

Dr. Swarthmore had briefed the Defense Committee that a depression had formed between Newfoundland and Ireland, and that it might deepen and move east, leading to rising wind and water on the channel.

"In my office at Dunstable," he said, "I heard reports in the early morning of S-Day from Iceland and Ireland and from one of our weather boats that a low pressure zone was indeed deepening and moving toward us."

"So how did you know the Germans had arrived?" I asked.

"I didn't know, I just presumed. I figured it would be just their luck to beat the weather system here. And, sure enough, channel waves started churning, but the Wehrmacht was already on our soil."

* * *

Bertram Selwyn may have been the first to know. "If you don't count my cat," he added, "I was first."

Selwyn was an orchardist, mostly apples. He had woken to a distant explosion. He got out of bed, wiped his eyes, and ambled over to his window in time to see a bomber fall from the sky in flames. "I'd seen it before," he told me after the war. "This one was going down in spirals, leaving a pretty path of fire and sparks behind it."

Overhead was the murmur of airplanes. The local AA battery had opened up, their tracers bending across the black sky. Selwyn supposed this time the Germans were really coming. His wife, Sarah, was still sound asleep, and he saw no need to wake her, not until he knew for sure. Then she would expect him to know what to do. He didn't have a clue.

He heard a bell ringing near his tool shed, then a sound, perhaps a pruning saw falling from its hooks, and another sound, this time maybe his entire rack of tools crashing to the ground. He pulled on his pants and cursed the cat, who wore a bell on his collar and was endless trouble. If Selwyn had his way, the tom would be taken to the veterinarian to surgically remove a little of its rambunctiousness, but Sarah wouldn't think of it. "How would you like it if I took you to the veterinarian instead?" was her standard response, to which Selwyn had not found a rebuttal.

He heard the bell again as he made his way along a row of firewood behind his cottage. He paused when the ringing came again, this time from behind a pile of branch-bracing poles. That cat is faster than he looks, he thought. The orchardist changed direction, stepping off the path and along a row of apple trees toward the braces. Then the chiming came from yet another direction, the road in front of his cottage. He turned, but turned again when the bell sounded once more from the toolshed.

Selwyn thought maybe one of his neighbors had also belled a cat. He returned to the path. He could see nothing, not even the outline of his toolshed, but his feet knew the route well enough. He had been born on the orchard and had lived all his forty-six years there, save two in a trench in France.

He came to the shed. As he suspected, the door had been pried open by the cat.

He called its name, "Willard."

He was answered by the soft sound of the bell.

"Willard?"

He stepped inside, reached blindly, moved his hand along a shelf—which, to his surprise was still in place on the back wall—until his fingers found the fur of the cat.

The feline instantly began to purr, as it always did. He lifted Willard into his arms, scolded him a moment, and gently shook the cat's bell, ringing it, as if that might teach it a lesson. He chuckled, then, stepped out of the shed, and was met with the tinkling of a bell—a second bell—a few inches from his face.

A rifle barrel cracked against his teeth, chipping one of them. A German commando stepped out of the darkness close enough for Selwyn to see him, which was also close enough to smell his breath. "They really do eat sauerkraut," he told me. With his other hand, the German rang his bell. He said something in German, which Selwyn thinks might have been, "You sure as hell aren't my sergeant."

The paratroopers of the 7th Parachute had been given tin Christmas bells to identify themselves in the dark.

A second paratrooper appeared, then a third, cautiously ringing their bells. The crowd of German soldiers grew by the moment. Several tied Selwyn's hands behind his back, then his feet together. They lowered him to the floor of the toolshed. They ignored Willard, who watched dispassionately. Selwyn was joined shortly by Sarah, who must have struggled, because she was trussed at her ankles and knees, and her hands were bound to a cord around her waist.

Increasingly hungry and thirsty, the Selwyns remained on the shed floor for twenty hours, long after the paratroopers had left. Willard stayed with them much of the time, but left frequently to journey to his food bowl near the back door of the cottage. The tom always came back, licking his whiskers and making the Selwyns even hungrier, happily rubbing against their tethered ankles. Using a hoe blade, the orchardist finally severed the cord around his wrists. He patted the cat a long moment before untying his wife, which did nothing for her mood.

As Sarah struggled to stand, she snapped, "That cat goes to the veterinarian after all."

11

Even on the eve of battle, General Clay could sleep like a stone, a trait he shared with Alexander, Wellington, and Grant. I hammered on the caravan's door several times and called out his name, then waited a moment, using the time to tuck in my uniform shirt. The general had been in bed less than two hours. Tiny red glows from the cigarettes of two sentries rose and fell near the rose garden.

The Germans lost the First World War in part because their vast military bureaucracy reduced them to fighting *der Papier-krieg*, the paper war, rather than the Allies. Clay insisted on a lean command, with many officers having direct access to him. One exception was that I always decided whether he should be woken. He trusted my judgment on that.

I beat on the door again and finally heard him switch on his lamp, my cue to enter. I found him sitting on his bed, already tying his boot laces.

A prelude would have been cut short. My voice rose uncontrollably. "Sir, General Lorenzo reports Wehrmacht paratrooper sightings near Battle, inland from Hastings. Others have been seen near Lewes, on the river Ouse, five miles north of Brighton, and more near Peasemarsh, near Rye."

The general stood and quickly buttoned his uniform blouse.

He did not look at me and appeared absorbed in dressing. His fingers, working the buttons, did not tremble.

I went on. "German gliders have landed near Stanford, just inland from Folkestone, near the roadway to Ashford. Another glider sighting has come from the town of Sellindge, two miles further inland."

I wanted to shout that Sellindge was less than ten miles from where I was standing, watching the general calmly place his cap on his head. He pushed it into its distinctive angle.

He lifted his spectacles from the table and dropped them into his blouse pocket. "All in our sector, then?"

"Yes, sir, so far."

He thrust out his chest. His head swiveled to me, so much like a tank turret in its steadiness and purpose that I thought I heard the hydraulics. His eyes were startlingly green even in the dim lamp light. "Is this the invasion, Jack?"

That question, that instant, looms large in my memory of all that was to follow. I dearly wish I would have answered simply yes or no, an outright guess. A fifty-fifty chance of being entirely prescient, of being to General Clay as Adam Cardonnel was to Marlborough, or Eichel was to Frederick II, the indispensible, shrewd, knowing aide.

And I wouldn't have had to record myself here as a stammering bumbler. "Well, sir, I . . . I didn't really have time to ask around. I was awakened just few minutes ago, too, and—"

General Clay brushed by me and left the trailer. I didn't catch up until he rounded the rose garden. We ran along the veranda toward the French doors. From a hillock north across the pasture, a three-light searchlight section probed the sky, accompanied by a yellow crescent of tracer bullets from its companion M2 machine gun. When Clay reached the doors, he slowed to a measured walk before passing into the room.

At the time of Blenheim, a general acted as his own chief of staff, intelligence officer, and quartermaster, a solitary ordeal. In the subsequent two hundred years, the headquarters staff had evolved to a complex organization. Members of General Clay's staff poured into the billiard room, quickly filling it.

David Lorenzo appeared not to have slept that night. His uniform was rumpled, his dark hair unkempt, and his eyebrows wilder than usual. He was leaning over a map on the billiard table. His deputy stood next to him, as did Captain Richard Branch, AFEHQ's signal officer. In front of situation maps pinned to walls were General Girard and Clay's chief of staff, Major General Jay Pinkney. One of Clay's stenographers ran into the room, holding up his pants with one hand, his belt in the other. Lieutenant Mohandas Gupta hurried in. Gupta was a British Army signal officer from Calcutta, posted to AEFHQ, with whom I had eaten dinner a few times. Others rushed in, some donning articles of their uniforms as they ran.

Clay met General Girard at the signal station near my desk. Although most of Captain Branch's equipment was in an outbuilding surrounded by sandbags, a teletypewriter we called a TWX, two wireless radios, and several telephones in leather cases were in carrels, manned by the AEFHQ Signal Company.

When we reached the signal station, General Hargrave was hovering over a carrel, demanding of the wireless operator, "Anything from Jones yet, Corporal?"

"No, sir." The signalman's desk was covered with message logs and two code books.

"When was your last message from his 2nd Infantry?"

"Forty minutes ago, sir. Lieutenant Barkley of the 2nd HQ Company reported planes overhead. Haven't been able to get through to them since."

Hargrave stabbed his pipe at the corporal, "Try the radio."

"Sir, our security requirements—"

"To hell with that. Raise them over the air. And what about Singleman?"

"Last report from the 4th Motorized was at 0310, twenty-five minutes ago, and I've got nothing now but a dead line."

When agitated, Hargrave set his face in cement and gave away nothing. His lips barely moved as he said in a candied tone, "Tell me, Corporal, can you reach any of my divisional HQs?"

"Yes, sir." The signalman lifted another receiver and passed it to Hargrave. "Here's Colonel Sellers, 1st Armored's G2."

Hargrave spoke with the intelligence officer a moment, then was switched to Major General Franks, the 1st's CO. Hargrave put a finger in an ear to shut out the noise as more headquarters personnel flowed into the room and the TWX started to rattle. Clay and Girard waited nearby, discussing something I could not hear. Outside, an AA gun began its rolling peal, then another, nearer and more insistent. I stepped closer to Clay's circle.

Hargrave slipped the telephone into its case. "Franks says little is going on in his area. Luftwaffe fly-overs, nothing else reported."

"General Hargrave, I've got 2nd Infantry HQ on the radio, an unsecured line." The corporal reached for a pencil and a one-time pad.

Hargrave waved the signalman's encoding effort away. He again stopped his free ear. He said into the transmitter, "What's going on, Burt?" He was speaking with General Jones, commander of the 2nd Infantry. Hargrave frowned. He listened for a full minute without interrupting.

General Girard crossed the room, followed by his G2, Colonel George Dayton. They also gathered around the communications carrels, demanding connections from other signalmen. More radiomen from the HQ signal company sprinted through the French doors and manned their posts. Lorenzo joined them, a map trailing behind him. The hubbub around the carrels grew.

Clay stepped away from the signal station. He wandered back to his desk, his hands clasped behind him. I followed. He scanned the room, then pulled a Pall Mall from the pack in his pocket. He tapped the cigarette against his thumbnail before lighting the other end. He appeared disengaged from the growing commotion at his command.

I ventured, "You don't seem concerned, sir."

He exhaled a cloud of smoke. "The higher the rank, the less an officer should have to do, Jack. Remember that."

"Well—"

"And Darius's defeat at Gaugamela was at least partly due to his inability to delegate. Remember that, too."

"Yes, sir."

"I tell you, Jack, this ceaseless grooming of you for higher rank can be tiring."

I was impressed. This could have been the invasion—on the south coast of England, proving that the Defense Committee had been disastrously wrong—and General Clay had the time and inclination to be sarcastic with his aide.

We made our way slowly to his desk in the center of the billiard room. His secretary and two stenographers stood by, glancing anxiously at him. Clay stubbed out his cigarette in his ashtray, a cut-down howitzer shell. The AA battery fell silent.

His corps commanders soon joined us. General Hargrave began, "There is occurring in East Sussex an attempt to disrupt our communications. Lines are down between the 2nd and the 4th's headquarters, although we can raise by radio a number of their units—the 8th and 12th regiments—and we're working on others. There have also been a number of firefights tonight in my sector prompted by more dummy paratroopers."

"Anything at all from those divisional HQs?" Clay asked. "Are you in contact with them?"

Hargrave shook his head. "And several bridges over the River Ouse, a few miles inland from Newhaven on the channel, have been seized by Wehrmacht paratroopers. Firefighters are reported at other bridges, and the road between Hastings and Battle apparently has been disrupted, held by enemy troops at least at one point. But much of the reported small arms fire has turned out to be firecrackers again. The 8th Regiment has suffered six casualties, all inflicted by its own troops, startled by the noisemakers."

Clay turned to Gene Girard, who reported, "We don't know much yet. There have been several sightings—we think legitimate sightings—of paratroopers in Romney Marsh, behind Dymchurch on the channel. But there have also been reports of paratrooper scarecrows, like last month."

Girard was interrupted by Colonel Dayton who pushed a report into his hand. The general glanced at it. "And we've got more sightings by the moment. Wehrmacht paratroopers, they think."

"Who else would they be?" Hargrave asked testily.

Girard smiled tightly. "There's a lot of night out there, Alex, and it's hard to tell whom you're fighting when the only light is from the enemy's muzzle flashes."

Dayton handed Girard another sheet of paper. After a moment Girard said, "The 134th Infantry Regiment behind Folkestone is engaged in a firefight with Wehrmacht paratroopers."

David Lorenzo joined us. "A Home Guard unit at Tenterden, fifteen miles west of here, reports that a telephone exchange in the city has been destroyed. Another exchange in Canterbury has also been knocked out. Ground action in both cases, not air strikes. Telephone communications in Kent and East Sussex are scrambled."

General Clay turned to a stenographer. "Order Captain Branch to dispense with first level security to corps and divisional units. Notify all divisional signal headquarters not to waste time trying to patch through over telephone lines. Use wireless. Eliminate radio codes until 0500."

I made notes along with the stenographer. One of my duties was to push orders down the line. Apparently Clay believed it more important to rapidly determine the situation in southern England than to have units take the additional time to code and encode messages.

Twenty minutes elapsed. Clay stood at his desk with Hargrave and Girard. General Pinkney and AEFHQ's deputy commander, Lieutenant General Patrick Neil, gathered around Clay. It had taken Neil a while to get to the manor, because Clay insisted that his deputy not live in the same building, nor ever travel in the same plane or jeep. Neil was billeted in a farmhouse a mile north.

Ninety-nine percent of incoming information about a battle disappears without a trace. The commanders sifted through the messages reaching Eastwell, searching for patterns, digging for clues, trying to wave aside the smokescreens they knew were being laid.

General Clay was immensely calm, issuing orders dispassionately. Those who did not know him well may not have noticed that his hand was bunched in his trousers' pocket, the only indication he was doing anything other than chatting idly about the weather for a picnic. He had once referred me to Corinthians 1:14: "If the trumpet produces an uncertain sound, who will prepare himself for battle?"

At four in the morning, Clay polled his corps commanders, his deputy, and his G2. There was agreement only on what they did not know. The green phone was out, so he and I walked to the signal carrels. He said to the corporal, "Put me through to the prime minister."

Lieutenant Gupta quickly joined us. Clay received the handset from the corporal and passed it to Gupta. Sixty seconds later, Gupta said, "I have Lieutenant Handi, sir. The prime minister is standing next to him."

General Clay ordered, "Jack, take down every word the lieutenant here says, as a matter of courtesy."

Courtesy was a polite phrase for protecting the record and guarding one's place in history. Churchill would be doing the same, and both men knew it. I brought up my trusty notebook.

Clay said to Lieutenant Gupta, "Give the prime minister my greetings in as short a manner as your incomprehensible Hindu customs will allow."

The lieutenant said a few words into the telephone.

The general went on, "Tell Mr. Churchill that apparently extensive German glider and paratrooper operations have begun in East Sussex and in Kent, but that much of the activity also appears to be with mock units and equipment, as in the false alarms in days past."

Gupta relayed these words in Hindustani. The prime minister had reserved this protection against German radio interceptors for this moment, and this was Gupta's first official act as translator. At Churchill's insistence, Indian translators had recently been posted to all Allied forward headquarters.

There was a short wait while the Hindu at Churchill's end did his work. Then Gupta said, "The prime minister says, and I quote, 'I want to know one thing. Is this the invasion or simply another German stratagem.' "

Clay responded, "It is too early to know. However, the German rarely used complex ruses in the Great War."

More translating. His eyes politely averted, Gupta said, "The prime minister wishes to remind you the Germans successfully baited an elaborate trap for the Russians at Tannenberg in 1914."

Clay said in a choleric tone, "I already knew that."

The lieutenant said, "The prime minister wishes to know your estimate of the disposition of Rommel's Army Group C."

AACCS commanders, including General Clay, as recently as twelve hours before had agreed that Army Group C was leading the invasion from embarkation points in Holland and other points north.

"Mr. Prime Minister, I still believe Rommel's army group is poised for the invasion across the North Sea," Clay answered, as if speaking directly to Churchill. "I have seen nothing to indicate otherwise."

The Indian spoke into the receiver, listened, then asked, "Is there anything we can be certain of at this time?"

"I am afraid not."

The Indian waited, then spoke again, "Mr. Churchill says that no Briton or American will think it wrong of him if he proclaims to you, General Clay, that to have the United States at Great Britain's side is to him a source of great joy and comfort."

"Thank you."

"The prime minister says that he cannot foretell the course of events and does not pretend to have measured accurately the martial might of those arrayed against us, but England will live, Britain will live, the Commonwealth of Nations and the Empire will live."

"Yes, yes, of course," General Clay said, making a small circle with his fingers, indicating he wanted Churchill to hurry.

Lieutenant Gupta looked helplessly at the general, but continued bravely, "The prime minister says that once again in

202

our long island history we shall emerge, however mauled and mutilated, safe and victorious."

Clay said in an aside to me, "Winnie has a maudlin streak in him, doesn't he?"

A faithful recorder, I report here General Clay's impudence with the greatest reluctance.

Gupta concluded, "The prime minister asks that you call him again in one hour."

"Of course."

The Indian placed the handset in the cradle. General Clay surveyed his headquarters. The intelligence officers and corps commanders were still huddled around Clay's desk. Several dozen more maps had been hastily posted on walls, leaving little of the wood paneling showing. Colored pins were quickly appearing on the maps. General Clay walked across the room to the French doors. I followed and held aside the blackout curtain for him.

As we stepped onto the veranda, the antiaircraft gun across the pasture erupted again. The yellow beams of the nearby searchlights swept grandly across the night sky. The lights changed directions quickly, guided by a radar control called "Elsie," searching for Luftwaffe planes.

General Clay breathed the cool air deeply. "You think I was indecisive in there, not calling this the invasion?"

"No, sir."

"I simply don't have enough intelligence yet."

"I fully realize that, sir." I also realized he was arguing with himself, not me.

"You know what happens to uncertain generals, don't you?"

"Yes, sir."

"They become laughingstocks."

"Yes, sir."

"Because of his indecision and lack of resolve during the oer War, the British public began calling General Sir Redvers uller a new name, Sir Reverse. I know dozens of other ex- mples of this from history." He looked at me and pointed to is skull. "Every disgraced general in recorded history, com- mitted to my memory."

"Yes, sir."

"Hell, the press will start calling me General Clay Feet."

"Yes, sir."

"Or General Clay Pigeon, a target to be shot at."

"Yes, sir."

"I'm going to tell Churchill in one hour whether this is the invasion. Tell him without equivocation. I'll know by then. The only uncertainty will be how well the Germans froze us."

He stared at the somber sky for a moment. "It's easy to be strong during the day, Jack. At night, it's more difficult." He looked at me. "Don't put that in your journal. Don't even remember it."

"Yes, sir."

At that moment, one of the searchlight beams fell out of the sky like a toppled tree. The light was a sixty-incher. It rested a moment, the beacon lying over the top of the ground. Then the beam swept madly across the pasture, spotting for fleeting instants a nearby farmhouse, then a grove of trees, then several small outbuildings and a cottage, sweeping toward us like the raging crest of a wave.

We learned later that the Elsie had malfunctioned due to a burned out tube. But at that moment it seemed like the sun had risen and was searching us out. When the beam reached us, it suddenly ceased its travels, and we were ablaze with light so intense and white I thought it must be entering my eye sockets and boring out the back of my head to continue on its journey.

I raised my hand to ward it off, to no effect. The light seemed to have weight, pushing me back on the veranda. With difficulty, I turned toward the general. He stood with his hands at his side, the light soaring over and around him as if it were flowing water. The blast of light seemed to set off sparks from his clothes and hair that slipped away toward the manor. And it reduced him to two dimensions, to a facade. I could see nothing behind his shimmering face and chest but black. All else was lost in the contrast.

General Clay seemed unaware of the searchlight. He turned to walk back into the billiard room. Behind me, the manor was illuminated as if it were midday. Then, abruptly, the light was gone, and the night suffocated us under total blackness.

As he walked by me, he said, "The fog of war covers the enemy, too, Jack. Remember that."

Since the war ended, I have been besieged by historians and journalists demanding information about the general. Some of them have impressed me more as assassins than accurate chroniclers of the war, yearning to validate hostile rumors, anxious to print innuendo as fact, inquiring of the general's record according to their own predispositions.

I want to set certain things straight while I have the chance, a preemptive strike before the ruinous hearsay gains its own momentum. In light of General Clay's actions following the invasion, I view this as my obligation to history.

One of the most damaging and persistent falsifications about General Clay was that he was callous about casualties. One might even expect such from a commander who witnessed many battles. Clausewitz said that an officer becomes indifferent to all suffering around him after thirty minutes. To the contrary, Clay spoke with me evening after evening about the tragedy of the losses. He felt deeply for his soldiers, and perhaps even for the enemy, for the injuries and loss of life, and he felt for the grieving in the homes of those soldiers whose families would learn of their fate, for the heartache of those parents whose sons would simply disappear forever in the chaos of battle.

He said once that the only reason he regretted leaving artillery to become an infantry commander was that the infantry reaps most of the combat agony. It is flatly untrue, as reported by *Time*, that the general ever said, "Death in war is incidental to victory."

In fact, as odd as it sounds for a man in his profession, General Clay was revolted by the sight of blood. Whether it was an atrocious battlefield injury or the drawing of his own blood during an examination by his physician, he always lost several shades of color at the sight of it.

Another rumor, this one grotesque, was that the general suffered a deathwish, that he pursued with single-minded dedication a glorious demise. This slander was a complete inversion of the simple truth that Clay was fearless. Maurice de Saxe wrote, "The first of all qualities is courage." General Clay went beyond this, with the indifference to danger of a man who disbelieved his own mortality.

Clay scoffed at the Great War's chateau generals, and at Napoleon and Caesar, noted for their aversion to exposure in battle. Rather, he revered Washington, who rode within thirty yards of the British line at the Battle of Princeton, and Seigneur de Bayard (whom history has labeled *le chevalier sans peur et sans reproche*, the knight without fear or blame), who had three horses killed under him at the Battle of Garigliano in 1503. When I once offered that a hero is a coward who got cornered, Clay's scowl would have felled a lesser man.

Perhaps the general's bravest moment was his flight at dawn of S-Day in Captain Norman's plane, which I'll describe later. But the act of daring for which Clay was best known among his troops was his evening at the 7th Engineering Battalion's bivouac near Dover, ten days before S-Day. A rumor had swept the 5th Infantry Division, assigned to defend England's southeast corner, that the German SS had planted an assassin at one of the division's units, the 7th Engineers. The supposed assassin spoke perfect American English, had been sent to the United States to join the army, and had been ordered to lay in wait, looking for the first chance to murder the AEF's commander, a suicide mission.

It was an absurd, laughable story but it refused to go away, despite the best efforts of 5th's General Carson and the 7th Engineering Battalion commander, Lieutenant Colonel Henry Johnson. Neither Axis Sally nor Lord Haw Haw discussed the assassin on their radio programs, which confirmed the rumor as fact for many of the soldiers. The tale was creating tension in the ranks.

So General Clay flew to Dover. He ordered all officers and men of the 7th, about 650 of them, to line up outside a tent. Inside, Clay sat with his back to a table. He told me to place my .45 pistol on the table, then leave. One by one, the men of the 7th Engineers were ordered to enter the tent. There, alone with the general, each soldier was given the opportunity to murder him. Three hours later, after the last of the men left the tent, General Clay emerged to thunderous applause.

On the flight back to headquarters, Clay said, "There better not have been bullets in that pistol, Jack."

Another odd theory that has gained some currency of late is that the soldiers' devotion to General Clay was largely due to his appearance. This disparages the general, because it is a backhanded way of saying that nothing else Clay did could possibly have generated this adoration. Clay approached being handsome, with his red-gray hair, even teeth, and pronounced cheekbones. His eyes could be glacial or warmly avuncular, often switching instantly from one to the other, depending on the news he was receiving. With his Irishman's red complexion, his face looked as if all the capillaries were trying to surface. He had a powerful physique, with a strong, corded neck and sloped shoulders. The Pall Malls had colored his teeth, and he once told me he would have tried Broadway if his nose hadn't resembled Wallace Beery's, with freckles on it to boot. Clay did nothing to trade on his appearance.

One commentator has even gone so far as to say that General Clay's rapid rise in rank and his soldiers' willingness to follow him depended solely on his appealing appearance and that history shows homely men do not become generals. Malarkey. Prince Eugene of Savoy, with his pockmarked face, short stature, and slouching manner, and Frederick, who was stooped and sway-backed, were worshipped by their soldiers. No, to understand the soldiers' love of General Clay, look to his actions as a commander. Even today, after all that has passed, after all the controversy regarding his conduct in the battle for England, AEF veterans still honor the man.

I defend the general, but he did have his peculiarities. I'll list a few here.

I rarely saw him angry, but he would later fume to me when an American at the dinner table ate with an upside-down fork. He called it an elitist affectation. If an Englishman did it, he'd later say, "What can you expect?"

He ate rice at least once a day and would go to extraordinary lengths to procure it, once sending Captain Norman in his plane to Glasgow. His commanders knew of this predilection and would have their kitchens prepare elaborate rice dishes: Risotto alla Milanese, jambalaya, pilaf, and others. For months, I ate what the general ate. I'll never eat rice again in any form.

Clay had, to my mind, an inordinate affection for cats. He occasionally lobbied Churchill to repeal the wartime law forbidding feeding them fresh milk. The prime minister would blame his intransigent parliament and deftly change the subject.

The general loathed hunting and found the British practice of running a fox to ground with a dog pack particularly abhorrent. Despite enjoying fish at a meal, he was not a fisherman, and I once asked him why not. He replied, "I let someone else kill my fish."

Also—and this I found truly peculiar—rather than swat at flies buzzing in his caravan, he would trap them with a glass and a piece of paper, then release them out the door.

He disliked French toast, French dressing, French perfume, French cuffs, and the French themselves, "though they're hellish fighters, if you give them some rifles and are tolerant enough to train them." Charles DeGaulle wore on Clay like a hair shirt. Clay had picked up President Roosevelt's habit of calling DeGaulle "Joan of Arc."

He had other peeves.

Bagpipes set him off: "They sound too much like my last root canal."

Know-it-alls upset him: "I don't like them interrupting me."

Use the term "kill two birds with one stone," and your request would be denied, whatever it was.

The general's quick mind and memory are legendary. He never forgot a face or a name. I saw him recognize a fellow, an artillery sergeant, he drank one beer with in Paris twenty-four years before and had not seen before or since. Another time, when he ran into one of his soldiers from the Great War, an army lifer he had not seen in all the intervening years, Clay asked out of the blue, "And how's your wife Emily?" The general claimed to know by name every unit commander above a company, meaning he knew every lieutenant colonel and up in the AEF. I believed him.

I once saw him do the *Observer* crossword puzzle in eleven minutes. Putting the newspaper down, he said, "I could've done it faster, but there were a dozen of those pissant British words we Americans kicked out of our language centuries ago."

He also told me he was cursed with never forgetting a phone number. I laughed aloud. He turned his gunsight eyes on me and demanded, "Ask me." I thought for a moment, then said, "Tell me the telephone number of your high school in Davenport." He immediately gave me a number. I wrote it down. After the war I checked it and was astonished that Clay had remembered it.

He took ten dollars off me one day when he said he could remember, in order, all the cards I dealt from a shuffled deck. I was quick to make the wager, and I lay down the cards, one by one on top of each other as fast as I could deal them. I turned the deck over to check him. He recited them in order, all fifty-two, and I gave him the money, accompanied by a particularly grating laugh from him.

The general needed all his mental prowess for his arguments with the prime minister. They seldom quarreled over anything of substance, as they generally agreed on the conduct of the war. Instead, they would burn their combined intellectual gifts squabbling about trifles, like an old couple that has lived together for sixty years. Churchill once snorted when Clay used the word "sick" to mean something other than nausea. They argued over the word for an hour and a half. They debated Churchill's plan to move British clocks ahead fifteen minutes after the war, so England would have its own time and to spite the French in the bargain. They argued over whether the steering wheel should be on the left or right side of an automobile. They argued over modifications of the rules for rat-baiting, should that sport ever come back into vogue.

I listened to these discussions, dismayed at the genius abused, the wit wasted, and the time these great men consumed. Such was the caliber of the intellects being squandered and such was the inanity of the subjects that these discussions can fairly be compared to bringing in two bulldozers to remove a dandelion from a lawn.

General Clay never got the best of the prime minister, so he always editorialized to me later, "Winnie can be a bonehead, Jack, which you've just seen for yourself," or, "Who does the prime minister think he is, anyway?" I've said this before, but I think the two truly enjoyed each other.

Another fabrication cherished by the general's detractors is that he became wealthy during his tenure as AEF commander. The truth is that Clay's game was high-stakes poker, and he was good at it. Once a week he organized a game. I may sound like a prig, but, along with his picayune arguments with the prime minister, cards were the other profligate waste of Clay's intellectual might. He was a consistent winner, scooping up the chips and leaving the table with most of the money. I credit applied brilliance to his success.

Clay's poker table was a hot ticket, and he allowed anyone to join the game "as long as he can pay the freight." Not many soldiers could afford the ten-dollar ante and the raises that put five hundred dollars in the pot many times a night. But few could resist the challenge. So AEF battalions would pool money and send their best poker player to Clay's table. A typical game would include a sergeant major who ran a brigade motor pool, a corporal from a rifle company, an AA loader, a nobleman from one of the nearby manors, a surgeon from a divisional HQ, a major general from an AEF division, and Clay. The guests usually left the table at three or four in the morning, baffled and broke.

I wish I could report that Clay did something virtuous with his winnings, donated it to some good cause. Instead, he wired it to his wife in the States. By my estimate, the general was sending home a thousand dollars a week before the invasion.

I have had a good chuckle at the military historians' attempt to determine the origin of a peculiar battle flag shared by two AEF battalions. They were white pennants with an ace of spades embroidered on them, carried as a sort of armorial banner by the 81st Reconnaissance and the 5th Quartermaster battalions. Another of the pennants flew over Breathed Manor near Deal, placed there in triumph by Sir Robert Squires. The pennant was created by the 81st when its player became the first to beat General Clay at poker. Clay learned of the flag,

and allowed it, although he claimed that Sir Robert was undoubtedly a ringer, brought in by his enemies. "They found
some cardsharp from Chicago and taught him a British accent." The ace of spades pennants were highly prized, and
when Clay inspected the 81st and 5th, they were exhibited
prominently and tauntingly.

I have recently read another calumnious story about the
general, the writer trying to draw broad personality conclusions from it. The story dates from Clay's days at West Point.
I doubt it is true. During hazing, Clay and five other plebes
were assigned by senior cadets to capture the Naval Academy's
mascot, a goat named Captain. The team was to return by
midnight the following day. Kidnap attempts were regularly
made on the goat, which was well guarded by midshipmen.
On those few occasions the goat was successfully stolen, it was
returned after a week, dressed in a tailored West Point cadet's
uniform

Clay's team, minus Clay, appeared at the appointed hour
before the senior cadets. They had failed, and their dressing-
down was well underway when Wilson Clay appeared in the
hall, dressed as a farmer and rolling a manure-filled wheelbarrow in front of him. He dug his hand into the wheelbarrow
and pulled out Captain, its eyes rolled back in the sockets and
its throat cut.

General Hargrave scoffed at this story. He said that he was
on Clay's plebe team, that Clay was also duly berated for having
failed, and that Clay did nothing of the kind. But Jerome
Carleigh, Clay's quartermaster general, told me he saw Clay
that night driving through West Point in a pick-up truck with
a wheelbarrow in the back. I've mentioned Clay's aversion to
blood, so the story is unlikely. Yet gardening was not taught
at the academy, so I don't know why Clay would have had a
wheelbarrow that night.

I return here to Lady Anne Percival, perhaps confirming
some rumors and, with luck, killing others. Hargrave once
called me Clay's chaperon. I argued that I acted instinctively,

211

like a grizzly sensing danger to her cub. He laughed uproariously and said, "Jack, you were an old maid, clucking and fretting and patrolling, as if guarding the virginity of your young ward."

I should have been offended, were there not some truth to Hargrave's comment. Lady Anne was a raptor, making me want to protect General Clay. I did so without much subtlety, I'm afraid.

One evening at Haldon House, long after the earl had retired, I wearied of amusing conversation and excused myself. Lady Anne and the general didn't hear me. I walked through the long hallway, then through the massive door and passed a yew hedge. I wandered over to the two bodyguards in the jeep behind the general's. They were riflemen happy for this soft assignment.

One of the bodyguards was slumped back in the seat with a knee across the steering wheel. His M1 was on the passenger seat. He spoke with a street accent. "I got a look at the lady. Quite a looker, heh, Colonel?" He gestured vulgarly with his hands, approximating a woman's bosom.

"You will do both of us a favor, Corporal, if you keep your comments to yourself."

He raised an eyebrow at the other guard, a private standing near a rear wheelwell and leaning on the two-way. The private grinned knowingly.

"Yes, sir," the corporal answered. "I mean, I thought all English babes were skinny. But the general's girlfriend has a body that would sweat paint off a Chevrolet."

"Corporal, did I not make myself clear?"

The private straightened and renewed his smile. "Looks like the general is doing pretty well for an old guy, don't it? Take a look."

I turned to the house. I didn't notice anything amiss.

The private said, "Someone just turned off the light in that room there." He pointed to the windows of the reception room off the main hallway. Where there once had been a slice of light below the blackout curtain, there was now only darkness.

The corporal said, "I remember the first time I tried that with my girl back home. Snuck my arm around her shoulder

212

and switched off the lamp. She was ready for that kiss, I'll tell you. She almost sucked my lips off."

The library blackout curtain had a number of pinholes in it, through which lights glinted. These suddenly went out. I held up my hand for silence, but sexual drivel, like smallpox, is hard to contain once loosed.

"Yeah?" the private asked. "My girlfriend back in North Chicago, first time I kissed her, she stuck her tongue so far down my throat I gagged. Christ, it was like an eel loose between my teeth. I coughed and spit, pretty much killing the mood. Then I learned she'd been going out with one sailor after another from the Great Lakes navy training center before she met me."

The hall light was visible through a slight gap in the circular window above the doorway. It was extinguished. I said, "Please, quiet."

"Milt, goddamn it," the corporal lectured, "no tongue that's ever been in a sailor's mouth will ever go into mine, I'll tell you that much. You got to have some standards in this life."

In the south wing, a light was turned off. The ground floor of the manor was now black. I was seized with alarm. Lady Anne Percival was going to work her will on the unsuspecting and, compared to her, innocent general.

I turned to the private. "I want you to call 16th Engineers and tell them General Clay's temporary HQ has lost power."

We were in the 1st Armored's sector, and the 16th was its engineer battalion.

"What, sir?"

"Do it now, Private, or you'll be dredging latrines for the duration."

The corporal brought his knee off the wheel. "Hell, Colonel Royce, the general deserves a little nookie more than most folks in this war."

I pointed at the private. "Get on the phone."

He shrugged and lifted the handset. I peered up at the second floor. Slits of light could be seen below the blackout cloths. One room abruptly went dark. The private spoke into the phone.

Alex Hargrave laughed when I told him this story. "Jack, you were having a jealous fit."

I only knew my general needed help.

Another light was doused. I ordered the private, "Tell them this is a priority one. If a company of engineers isn't here within five minutes, General Clay will have their asses."

"Yes, sir," the private answered uncertainly. He plugged an ear with a finger and continued talking into the phone.

I waited anxiously, drumming the jeep's hood, glancing at my wristwatch, and watching the second floor lights go out one by one. Finally the enormous house was dark. Wilson Clay of Davenport, Washington, was in a darkened mansion with a diabolical European seductress. I was not thinking like an adult, I concede.

The 16th Engineers must have gotten my message, because eight minutes later half a dozen four-ton GM trucks roared out of the night and screeched to a stop near our jeeps. A captain leaped down from the passenger seat of the lead vehicle and ran up to me.

"Colonel, we got here as soon as we could. Tell me the problem."

Other soldiers spilled out of the trucks, many carrying tool boxes and spools of wire.

"We've had a power failure here. General Clay wants it fixed right now. I don't know exactly what the problem is."

All soldiers in the AEF were eager to be of personal service to the general. The captain said, "We'll find it, don't worry."

He issued orders. The soldiers quickly spread out. Some pushed open the manor house's door and rushed inside. Others circled the building. Still others pointed flashlight beams up at the power lines. One engineer donned climbing spurs and started toward a power pole.

A room at a time, lights came on. I could hear the engineers' heavy boots on the hardwood floors. Instructions and questions were called out. Their commotion was gratifying.

The corporal said from his jeep, "Colonel, I don't really want to be here when General Clay comes out of that house."

I replied, "Neither do I."

It didn't take long.

Clay appeared at the door, backlit by the hall light. The house was now ablaze in light. He walked toward the jeep. His uniform was rumpled. His face might have been smudged with lipstick, but it was too dark near the jeep to tell.

"Jack, do you know anything about this?" His voice was bitter with lost opportunity. Or perhaps he tried to make it sound that way for the benefit of his young bodyguards.

"Sir?"

"Do you know why the goddamn 16th Engineers would show up at Earl Selden's home just now, crashing into the house, running up and down the stairs, barging into rooms, pointing their goddamn flashlights into every corner, hollering and carrying on?"

"The 16th Engineers?" I'm not too good at thinking on my feet.

He climbed into the jeep. "Jack, I want you to investigate this and hang whoever did it. And if it was you, you hang yourself, and do it so you suffer."

"Yes, sir."

This was indeed a mild reproach for my brazen and juvenile act. The reason was found in Clay's voice. His tone was of relief. He never mentioned this little episode again, but I suspect he viewed it as a narrow escape.

I started the jeep's engine, and we pulled away from Haldon House. I heard Lady Anne's voice. It was several octaves above the level that passes as polite in English society. She was gutting the 16th's captain. I pitied him.

Lady Anne's pekinese was burdened with the registered name Wallingford Warmspring's Lady, but went by the nickname Wee Wee. To see the elegant, haughty daughter of an earl, dressed in silk and diamonds, wander through her manor house calling out, "Wee Wee, Wee Wee, here Wee Wee," almost made the war worthwhile for me. A higher-strung and more worthless cur cannot be imagined. The peke, not Lady Anne.

One afternoon during a session with Earl Selden, General Clay approached me. "Jack, Lady Anne's goddamn dog has been missing since yesterday."

"Sir?"

"I want to do her a favor and find it."

I waited, not picking up my cue. Finally, I said, "Go ahead, sir."

"Jack, a four star general in the United States Army doesn't have time to look for a useless pekinese."

"No, sir."

"But a lieutenant colonel does."

"Aw, goddamn it, sir."

"You go find that flea bag and give it to me so I can hand it over to Lady Anne. Got it?"

"Yes, sir."

It seemed to me that the more eyes that searched for Wee Wee, the more quickly it would be found. I telephoned Lieutenant Colonel Al Fantine of the 19th Ordnance Battalion.

I said into the telephone, "Al, this is Jack Royce, General Clay's ADC."

"Sure, Jack. What's going on?"

General Clay's name always pricked up ears. I seldom used the authority of his name, but this time I did. I knew, however, that while no battalion commander would order his men to scour the land looking for an English noblewoman's dog, they would cheerfully search for the AEF commander's animal.

I lied, "General Clay's dog is missing. Your battalion is posted near Haldon House."

"You bet," Colonel Fantine said. "We're right down the lane. I'm looking at the mansion right now."

"Well, could you have your men look for it?"

"Of course. Only too happy to oblige General Clay. I'll send six hundred men into the field two minutes from right now. What are we looking for?"

My voice was steady. "A pekinese named Wee Wee."

A long pause. "General Clay has a pekinese named Wee Wee?"

"Bring it over to Haldon House as soon as you find it, will you, Al?"

"A pekinese named Wee Wee?"

I lowered the phone back to its cradle. Colonel Fantine's entire battalion put aside their ammo boxes and belts, abandoned their trucks and tractors, and began a stone to stone, bush to bush search for the dog. They found it less than an hour later, locked in a grain bin near one of the earl's wheat fields. One of the farmhands had not looked around before locking up.

Colonel Fantine and twelve of his men drove to Haldon House in a flatbed. I notified General Clay, who hurried out to the road, thanked the colonel, and grabbed the dog.

A master sergeant who must have weighed 250 pounds, with none of it fat, called from the bed of the truck, "General, I hope you didn't miss Wee Wee too bad."

They tried, but the soldiers couldn't keep it in. Their laughter rocked the truck. Colonel Fantine tried to wave them to silence, but his men were buckled over with laughter.

Master sergeants can get away with almost anything. This one knew it. He said, "General, you'd better follow Wee Wee next time she goes out for a pee pee."

The laughter might have been heard as far away as London.

General Clay held this panting bundle of hair with as much dignity as the situation would allow, which was almost none.

He said between clenched teeth. "Colonel Royce, may I speak with you a moment?"

I followed him inside the manor, our departure hailed with another round of convulsions. Safely inside the hallway, he turned to me and said, "George Patton owns a bull terrier named Willie, as rough-and-tumble a dog as exists. Patton is famous for it. And now, Christ on a crutch, every one of my soldiers is going to think I've got a pekinese named Wee Wee."

"Perhaps I didn't think this through sufficiently, sir."

"Jack, just as soon as you can push through the paperwork, I want you to bust yourself down to about private first class, and assign yourself the worst duty in the AEF."

"Yes, sir."

"I don't mean just KP. I mean something truly awful. Maybe bomb disposal."

"Yes, sir."

He walked into the library to present Wee Wee to Lady Anne.

The general must have been forgetful, because I reappeared

at AEFHQ the following morning still wearing my silver oak leaves and carrying my notebook, and he did not say anything about it.

General Clay had bigger things on his mind, the defense of England. We return now to the beaches.

12

Private Ray Chase had been dozing about twenty minutes, lying across his pack with his feet on a box of rations, when a blast dropped a lump of cement and a yard of dirt into his trench. He leaped up, coughing against the dust and trying to swat it away with his hands. Immediately another explosion tumbled the earth above him, rippling the walls of the trench and shaking Chase's insides.

He sank to his pack, spitting sand and dirt, hearing his sergeant call over the ringing in his ears. Chase yelled out, "I'm OK, Sarge."

The concrete had smashed a canister of M2 HB machine gun ammunition. Bullets in their belts covered the duckboards on the trench floor. Chase thought of repacking them, but then another round screamed into the ground above, and more debris dropped on him. He would sit right there.

More rounds, each seemingly closer than the last. The trench filled with dust. The earthen wall vibrated against the private's back, pushing him off balance. He righted himself. He tried to look skyward, to his post at the machine gun, but pebbles rained on him. The sound was of the sky splitting and the earth opening. He wanted only to burrow deeper into his hole.

He held his hand to his helmet lid and peered to his right.

Tom Osborne was crouched there, gripping his M1, his head buried in his chest and his eyes squeezed tightly closed.

"You with us, Tom?" Chase bellowed. He could not hear his own voice above the bombardment. He tried again. Still not a distinguishable sound. There were half a dozen other soldiers along his portion of the trench, but it was a traversed system, a zigzag designed to prevent an enemy who jumped into it from shooting its entire length and to contain explosive bursts. So he could see only a few of his fellows. Chase slumped lower, wishing the trench were fifty feet deep instead of twelve.

His dugout was just off the beach and had been on the receiving end of explosives before, but nothing like this. The private did not know if these were lobbed by German ships or dropped by planes. The sound alone crushed him inward, sucking the air out of his lungs. He lowered his helmet to the bridge of his nose. He drew his legs closer, so his knees were against his chin.

Good Christ, he wanted out of the trench. There was a time a week or so ago when he considered going SIW, self-inflicted wound, a comfortable one in his leg or foot. He once read somewhere that nineteenth-century Russian serfs knocked out their own front teeth so they would not be able to bite a musket cartridge and thus avoid conscription. He laughed at the serfs' cowardice at the time. Not now.

He opened his eyes to a slit, and they found his new green stripe below his chevrons. All Allied combat troops—British, Canadians, Americans, Poles, Free French, the lot, but only combat forces—had been awarded the stripe two days before. It didn't make him feel better.

It should not have been possible, but the roar of bombs escalated, bucking the walls of the trench and dropping football-size dirt clods on him. Ray Chase was frightened to his core, not so much of the bombardment, but of the silence that would come momentarily if this were the invasion. The last bomb would hit. The walking barrage up the beach would end. For a moment, serenity would come to the FEBA (another acronym from the staff college dolts, short for forward edge of battle area).

This deadly calm would begin the race to the parapets, the

fortified top edge of the trench. If the German invaders rushing up the beach behind the barrage arrived first, Chase and his friends would die. If Chase got there first, the Germans would be obliterated. His machine gun would see to that.

Chase thought he heard his sergeant again. He brought his head up. Instead it was the corpsman, waving at him. A blanket of sand fell between them, but the medic appeared again, still waving. Cursing, the machine gunner rose to his knees and crawled north on the planks. The din was unceasing.

The corpsman yelled into Chase's ear, "I need your help. Some wounded ahead."

The private followed him around a bend in the trench. Sitting on the planks, motionless as if asleep, were three of his buddies, their legs ranged out in front of them and their rifles across their laps. Their eyes were open.

The corpsman bent over them, taking pulses, shining his flashlight into their eyes. He turned to Chase. "I won't need your help after all. They're dead."

"Dead?" Chase yelled above the storm of bombs retorts. "They're not dead. Just look at them."

The corpsman didn't have the time. He moved along the trench. Chase knelt to his friends. They were still and unseeing. And dead. "Jesus."

Chase could not have known, but a bomb blast above them had created an instant vacuum in his friends' body organs, hemorrhaging their brains and spinal cords. Otherwise, they were untouched.

Chase crawled back around the corner to his post under his weapon. He sat on his pack and clutched his legs, forming himself into a ball. He shuddered under the crack and thunder of the explosives.

God, he wanted out of the trench. He closed his eyes so tightly they hurt. Anywhere, God, anywhere in the world but here.

William Barber's grandfather had once told him the Barber family came from a long and distinguished line of poachers, so William came by his disregard of warnings honestly. He had been advised to move inland, but he had claimed, rightfully, that he was an essential worker. He had also been warned to stay on shore this early morning, but, truth be told, the American sentries had not seemed too concerned about his casting off. One of them had growled, "It's your ass, pal."

Too much profit to be made to stay on shore. The mongers had never paid so much for fresh fish, not in his life. Thank the war for that. Barber and his three brothers owned two beach-luggers, clinker-built boats, thirty and thirty-five feet long. The boats had wide beams, and their shallow bilge keels limited their heel when they were winched onto the beach over baulks of timber. Lately their beach moorage had been hemmed by land mines.

The four Barber brothers fished for anything they could get: cod, skate, hake, conger eels, mackerel. That morning they were out for dogfish. Harold and Timothy were in the longer lugger, fishing a half mile west of William and Arthur. It was an hour before the first glints of dawn. The brothers had already spent an hour rigging their lines, each of which had several hundred hooks and would be left in the water for hours. William had quickly lost sight of the other boat.

William and Arthur were two miles out, but could not be sure precisely how far because there were no shore lights. Planes were overhead, as always. William had seen so many fighters and bombers over the past weeks that he had lost interest in whose they were. An unusually patchy fog had settled over the water, a haze that tasted slightly of smoke. Fog covered the channel one day in five this time of year, but the Barbers were accomplished boatmen.

Just as they began to lower their lines, a burst of fire erupted on the beach. The explosion was made soft by the haze and distance. Another ball of flame shot up, then a series of them. The sound of marshaled airplanes grew above the shoreline. Then more explosions, which quickly grew to a steady knell. The fog hid the land from Barber, so it seemed the bomb flashes were suspended at eye-level in the distance. Soon the entire length of the shoreline was speckled with red bursts. So many bombs were hitting the beach that the night sky above glowed orange, as if from the lights of a distant city.

William turned to his brother. "We might have taken one too many chances, eh, Arthur? I mean, we were told they might be coming this morning, and here we are anyway, eh?"

His brother, a taciturn man good with lines and nets and pots, quickly hauled in his gear, not taking his eyes from the roaring shore.

"Where we going to winch out, I wonder?" William asked.

A moment passed, then his brother deigned to say, "I would argue you are a dunce."

"We fished during last month's Alert Number Two," William protested, "and you didn't mind our fifty quid profit." He lifted his line hand over hand. "And, besides, this may be just more German dodgery."

Arthur exclaimed, "God, William." His voice constricted. "Look."

A form congealed out of the black haze, first just an indistinct smudge emerging from the fog like a spirit, black on black, then gaining size and shape as it closed. It was a *Räumboote*, a motor minesweeper, and it bore down on the brothers, its prow pushing aside a white wash.

"Take us astern," William yelled.

Arthur scrambled for the rudder, but it would have been too late, had not the minesweeper's helmsman spotted them. The R-boat changed course only a few degrees, brushing by the beach lugger. The R-boat was 140 feet long, cruising at seventeen knots. Added to its complement of thirty-four crewmen were fifty engineers.

"I'll never forget them," William remembered after the war. "They were lining the rail, all in black rubber suits, with burnt cork on their faces, masks raised to their foreheads, many readying rafts to lower over the side. Each of them must have been carrying a forty-pound pack."

The R-boat was ferrying engineers to the surf, and the packs contained explosives. The ship's armament was limited to 20mm and 37mm AA guns, and, installed for this mission, MG 34s on AA mountings on the foredeck. One of the heavy machine guns swiveled toward the brothers, the gunner peering over the barrel at the fishermen.

"That machine gunner was our Jack Ketch, no question

about it," William told me, using slang for an executioner. "But another German, must have been an officer, held up his hand, and the gunner raised the barrel. The ship slipped by, as black as tar, leaving us bobbing like a cork in its wake."

As soon as the first R-boat disappeared into the haze, a second emerged, following the white water of the first, long and dark, its twin diesel engines rumbling. It was also full of engineers, and they too ignored the brothers as the minesweeper sailed by. The R-boat was so close William could make out the blue collars of the sailors' pullover shirts. The collars were worn outside their blue pea jackets.

His hands over his head, Arthur said, "No mistake, you are a dunce, William, bringing me out here this morning."

"Where are we going to land?"

When he found a theme, Arthur was a dog with a bone. "A dunce. Harold and Timothy will readily agree, when I tell them what we've just been through."

The second motor minesweeper vanished into the murk toward the shore fusillade.

Wiping his palms on his pants, William said, "Our brothers won't believe it, not a bit of it."

The brothers would never learn of it. Harold and Timothy Barber were never heard from again. Neither their bodies nor their beach-lugger was ever found.

After having towed the midget submarine into port, the *Pettibone* returned to station off Benacre Broad. The sub's ensign had been run up the foretopmast. The ship was patrolling, on watch. Its store of mines had been exhausted days before, and there were no more in all of England.

Uncomfortable in a uniform on loan from the captain and hoping none of the crew would notice the extra piping, Lieutenant Keyes leaned over an aft rail, a pair of binoculars at his eyes. He looked east, to the first traces of false dawn, purple trails low in the sky. The danger would come from the east, from Holland and northern Germany, from Army Group C and its commander, Erwin Rommel.

"See anything, sir?" asked a warrant officer.

"Not a thing."

"I thought they might be coming this morning, sir. Felt sure they would be sailing right at us."

"So did I."

But before them was an empty North Sea, rocking gently in the predawn.

In a weary voice, Lieutenant Keyes said again, "So did I."

The surf pitched Erich Rogge forward, skimming him along the sea bottom, which raked his wet suit and tore at his legs. He could see nothing through his mask but churning bubbles. When he was tumbled by the next breaker, he lost his bearings and had no idea which way was up or which way was toward shore. The surf pulled him back, then rushed him forward again. The weight of the plastic explosives pulled him toward the ocean floor. Another frogman's leg smashed into Rogge's ear, stunning him. He shook his head and kicked, his fins digging into the water.

The water receded, bouncing him on the bottom. He struggled to his feet, pulled off his fins, and began laboring up the beach. The next wave bowled him over, spinning him along the sand. His head dragged on the bottom, tearing his mask away. He spit saltwater and sand, and tried to stabilize his legs under him. He waded ahead.

To his left and right, other frogmen emerged from the water. The nearest engineer wagged a thumb at him. It was Kummetz, his sergeant. The morning was still too dark to see the short hill Rogge knew rose behind the beach, and the ferocious defenses he knew to be there, despite their captain's scoffing at them. Endless explosions were ripping the beach apart.

He found his first obstacle, a tripod made of steel, half in and half out of the water, designed to tear out the bottom of landing craft. He pulled a charge from his pack and strapped it onto one of the obstacle's legs. Trailing a wire, Rogge high-stepped to the next one.

* * *

Jim Goldschmidt had never liked small spaces. His sandbag bunker surrounded him and his belt feeder on all sides, except for the narrow aperture facing the water through which his machine gun barrel protruded, and a small exit to the rear. The chamber gave him the heebie-jeebies. He would have hated it in there, were it not for the barrage overhead, which made him grudgingly grateful for the place.

The blasts rippled the sandbags, showering him with dust. The explosions were so loud they sounded like they were inside his head, pushing out his eyeballs. He squeezed the grip of his weapon, as if it might save him from the high explosives walking up and down the beach.

His feeder, Ron Mott, tapped his helmet and pointed out the dugout along the barrel. He yelled, "I think I see something out there, out in the surf."

Goldschmidt had to open his eyes. He looked over the gunsight. He saw nothing but the faint line of surf, almost lost in the haze and night. He shook his head.

Mott squinted. Again he put his lips to the gunner's ear. "Jim, I swear I'm seeing something move out near those boat traps."

Mott was hollering as loudly as he could, but Goldschmidt was picking up only a few words. The rest were lost in the pounding. Mott bellowed, "I'm going to ask Sarge to flare it."

Goldschmidt nodded, still seeing nothing. Mott slid away. The sky might have been lighter than a few moments before, but he could not be sure. Dawn was coming, and it had never been slower. He had slept only two hours that night, on his stomach, the butt of his Browning stabbing at his chest. He ached from his helmet to his boots.

Mott returned. He shouted, "We'll see if I'm right soon enough."

A pinpoint of light opened high in the night sky, quickly expanding to a radiant globe, descending by parachute. Out in the surf, a quarter mile away, caught in the white light and seemingly paralyzed by it, were several dark gaps in the surf.

226

They might have been beach obstacles or men dressed in black. Goldschmidt could not tell. But anything out there was fair game.

"Ready?" Goldschmidt demanded.

He didn't wait for a response. He squeezed the trigger. The Browning bounced. The belt flew into the breech. The machine gun's roar hardly registered against the barrage all around. Muzzle flashes reached for the black figures.

Erich Rogge had wired five dragon's teeth. One more to go for a set. He plunged ahead, the water swirling between his knees and the backtow pulling sand out from under him. Kummetz worked parallel to him thirty feet higher on the beach, strapping explosives to metal-tipped wooden stakes. Other engineers, just visible along the surf-line, worked on the obstacles as swiftly as the darkness and surging water would allow.

The engineers were abruptly cast in a stark white light, making the surf pearl white. The saw-toothed boat traps loomed larger in the flat light, and there were so many of them. Rogge kept moving.

Behind Kummetz, the water bubbled angrily, popping and spitting, more than just surf. The churning moved to him. Kummetz screamed. Rogge turned in time to see his friend torn open, from knee to shoulder, then along his ribcage. Kummetz was quartered before he slid under the surf, his blood tainting the roiling water for only a few seconds. Slapping into the water, the bullets searched for Rogge.

He threw himself behind a concrete cone. Bullets chipped away at it, then moved on. The body of another engineer brushed his leg, then was carried away by the receding surf. Rogge pulled a package of plastic from his pack.

The engineers had been told that if they could stay alive for those forty minutes, they would have a lot of company on that beach. Rogge intended to stay alive. He stuck his head out from behind the cone. The beach was suffering blasts so incessantly that the Luftwaffe planes could not be heard. When the flare sputtered and died, Rogge dashed for the next cone, unraveling wire from the spool.

Safely behind it, he threw the switch. The sound of his detonations was lost in the shore bombing and the surf, but the explosives worked well enough. The concrete cones and metal stakes he had wired toppled into the surf. He lifted another charge from his pack.

Being assigned to fly the Owlet would have been an insufferable humiliation to RAF Lieutenant Sidney Baxter, were it not that many of his fellow pilots had no plane at all. The Owlet was a two-seat training monoplane with a 150-horsepower Cirrus-Major engine and an open cockpit, as far removed from a Spitfire as Cheapside was from Windsor Castle.

Baxter was posted to 48 Squadron, Number 15 Group, Coastal Command, stationed at Thorney Island. He was to fly a figure eight reconnaissance sortie, covering fifty miles of water, and he was to be in position at dawn. He was two minutes into the air when the Luftwaffe found him. The enemy must have been looking for scouts from his base.

A stream of machine gun bullets ripped into the empty student's cockpit in front of Baxter. Tracer bullets seemed to dust his flight jacket. He pushed on the stick, trying to muscle the Owlet from the sky. It might have worked with a Spitfire. The trainer responded slowly, letting another Me 109 find the range. A portion of the port rudder ripped away. Baxter fought to control the Owlet as it began to roll. The German fighter flashed by, then another appeared off his starboard wing. The RAF pilot twisted the Owlet toward the water.

Twenty seconds later, Baxter brought the trainer under control. He anxiously glanced over one shoulder then the other. He had lost the German fighters in the darkness. His altimeter read two hundred feet. He pulled back on the stick and the Owlet gained altitude. The first pale rays of dawn lit the water below. He had come out of the dive heading north, and the beach passed under him. The port rudder was jammed. He brought the right wing up, intent on finding his base.

A stream of oil splashed across his windshield and his gog-

228

gles. He tried to wipe it away with his sleeve. The engine fluttered, then froze, the dry pistons glued to the cylinders. The plane began to sink and spin.

The lieutenant threw off his safety harness. The ground below seemed to turn on the axis of his fuselage to appear above him as the trainer rolled. Using the windscreen frame for leverage, he climbed out of the cockpit. The wind fought him, pushing him back. He found the ripcord, then jumped free of the plane.

Not quite free. The ragged rudder caught his parachute pack as it passed, violently twisting him. Baxter heard his pack rip. As he plummeted toward earth, he yanked the ripcord.

The white chute played out above him, but the rudder had done its damage, and several of the lines fouled. Baxter felt a tug as the chute caught the air, but only part of it opened. The rest flapped wildly like a flag.

Before he hit the ground, he plummeted through the branches of a tree, then a large rhododendron, then onto a moss-covered stream bank.

He told me after the war, "It's not the fall that kills you. It's the sudden stop."

He broke both arms, six ribs, his right femur, his right clavicle, four bones in his right hand, eight in his left foot, his nose, and his jaw.

Picking up his tone, I asked levelly, "Did it hurt?"

He grinned over his pint of ale. "A Yank would have thought it hurt, I dare say."

The lieutenant lay on the ground twelve hours before he was found.

I tell Lieutenant Baxter's story because it is a fair representation of the intelligence regarding the invasion available to the Defense Committee that morning.

Captain Jonathan Goodrich's spotter called, "Sir, I've got something."

Standing between the barrels of Winnie and Pooh, Goodrich raised his binoculars. The darkness and fog hid whatever was out there below the cliffs. "Locate it for me, Lieutenant."

"I've lost it, sir." A moment passed. "There it is. One o'clock."

The captain lifted the pack telephone, spoke a few words, then announced, "If there's a ship out there, it's not one of ours. We've got permission to fire."

In the concrete room behind the guns, another lieutenant was preparing a firing chart pinned to the plotting board, marking the position of the illusive target. Yet another lieutenant, the Plans and Training Officer, was speaking into a telephone.

"I see it, a ship," Goodrich said, his field glasses at his eyes. Again he lifted the telephone.

An electric bell rang and thirty seconds later sounded again. At each ring, an observer trained his telescope on the ship and from the scope's dials read aloud the compass bearing of the line of sight.

In the chart room, a soldier wearing earphones immediately plotted the same compass bearing in a straight line on his chart. He placed a ruler along the line.

A mile away in an observation post, another soldier repeated the process with his telescope when his bell sounded. A fourth soldier in the chart room plotted the second line of sight. The intersecting lines showed the ship's position.

A fifth artilleryman threw down a calibrated pointer. One end was attached to Winnie and Pooh's map location. "Fifteen hundred yards, sir."

There were ten other soldiers in the plotting room, each a specialist, factoring the ship's course, the wind, the curvature of the earth, and much else. Some read scales, others traced coordinates, another worked with logarithms. Adjustments were made. Ninety seconds had elapsed from the first sighting. The bell rang again, and all measurements were retaken, tracing the ship as it slipped in and out of the haze.

A row of pin holes appeared on the chart, the ship's course at thirty second intervals. The final pin hole, the set-forward point, was placed on the map, the target location. Hydraulic engines hummed, and the barrels lifted and swiveled. The guns would fire the next time the bell rang, fifteen seconds away.

"Number one ready," reported the gun commander. "Number two ready."

Gunners held the lanyards, ready to yank them on command. The gunroom was silent, everyone waiting for the bell. Ten seconds.

A burst of submachine gun fire came from cliffside, an impossibility, as there was nothing there but a sheer precipice down to the water-washed boulders.

Goodrich called, "Sentries report. Hold steady, gunner."

A concussion grenade flipped into the gunroom, with a delay just long enough for the artillerymen to find it with their eyes. The blast blacked out Goodrich on his feet.

He awoke later bleeding from his mouth and ears, and with his hands bound behind him. A Wehrmacht commando guarded him and two other gunners who had survived the grenades and automatic weapons' fire. Everyone else in the captain's crew was dead.

I have been unable to locate any of the German commandos who took part in the raid on Goodrich's coastal battery. We know they were the *Adler* (Eagle) Regiment of the 1st Mountain Division, and we know they arrived by inflatable rafts, scaled the cliffs below the battery using ropes and grappling hooks, thought an impossible feat. We also know they blind-sided the sentries, getting close enough to use knives.

Winnie and Pooh played no other part in the invasion, never loosed a single shot at the invaders. Up and down the beach, other coastal guns were meeting similar ends.

The motor antisubmarine boat had been built by British Power Boat in 1938, but had found few Kriegsmarine submarines in coastal waters, so had been converted to a motor gunboat in 1940. Then its primary mission had been to draw the fire of enemy *Schnellboots* while RN motor torpedo boats rushed in for the attack.

All that was in the past, however, when the Royal Navy had the equipment to put up a fight. Now, in the early morning Lieutenant Neville Sanders' boat was on patrol, watching and waiting for the invasion, cruising three miles off the coast, its three Napier Sealion engines pushing it along at seventeen knots, half speed. Two of his six-man crew had binoculars to their eyes. Two other sailors manned the Lewis guns.

The night was lessening its grip, and the lieutenant judged he had two hundred yards of visibility. Fog was drifting toward the coast. Sanders was acutely aware that his mission was only to report and flee. This passive role ran against his grain.

After the war, Sanders told me that the Luftwaffe and Kriegsmarine must have had little else to do but gang up on his ship, not much of a war prize by naval standards. From the German standpoint, the attack must have been quite boring.

It began with a strafing run by an entire squadron of ME 110c's, eleven planes in all. "Not their best fighter," Sanders said, "but good enough for this job, I'll tell you."

Five came out of the darkness aft of the gunboat, one after another at over 320 miles an hour, two Oerlikon guns and four Rheinmetall Borsig machine guns spitting metal from each fuselage. Then six more of the fighters roared in from off midships, yellow tracers preceding each of them.

"I don't think our Lewis guns found a single fighter," Sanders recalled. "They came too low and too fast."

Sanders' most vivid memory was of the slivers of his boat filling the air, dug out by the streams of bullets. The lieutenant rushed from the bridge and found one of his spotters lying on the port gangway, bleeding from a ragged tear in his leg. Sanders dragged him to the edge of the boat, which by then was almost cut in two. He called the abandon ship. An AA gunner dove overboard, followed by another spotter. The wounded crewman's life jacket was secure, so the lieutenant dropped him overboard.

Sanders was running along the torn up deck toward the engine compartment looking for the oiler when he saw a periscope off the beam. "My only thought then was how silly all this was, a whole squadron of fighters and a submarine, all for my little sixty-footer."

The U-boat commander may not have seen the Luftwaffe fighters and how well they were doing their job. He launched

232

a torpedo at the gunboat. At that range, it was a dead shot. The torpedo coursed into the gunboat's aft quarter, which erupted skyward. The blast sent a foot-long wood splinter into Sanders' thigh and another into his scalp, lifting a hand-sized flap of hair and skin from his head. He collapsed to the deck, and, finding he could crawl to the gunwale, dropped himself over the side.

Little remained of his gunboat, "not enough to sink, really, just enough for us to cling to as we bobbed in the water."

Sanders and two others in the crew were picked up by a German patrol boat an hour later. Sanders was almost dead from exposure and loss of blood. He never again saw the wounded spotter he had helped overboard or any of the rest of his crew.

The long night had done nothing to lessen Private Douglas Stubbs' fear. His sergeant had not allowed barrel-clearing of his Browning during the night, and Stubbs had nothing else with which to treat his fright. He had spoken only a few words with his mates of the 3rd Platoon at Pett Level that night. He was not alone in his fear, but that didn't help.

The Luftwaffe's bombardment, which must have lasted three hours, had left him partly deaf and gasping for breath, but otherwise unhurt. The beach and the hill behind it were crater-pocked expanses. Amazingly, no one in Stubbs' platoon had been hurt.

He had released the grip of his machine gun only twice that night, each time to urinate. His hand was so cold he could not tell where his fingers ended and the machine gun began. And he had to pee again. Stubbs had an enormous fear that the next time he left the fortification to urinate, the Germans would be on them, and he would be without his weapon.

And, goddamn, he was tired of squinting out at the channel. He yearned for a view of anything that wasn't interrupted by a machine gun sight or framed in barbed wire. Nothing but water and waves and darkness and fog all night. And the cold. He was sick of it.

Thank God it was getting lighter. The black had turned to

purple, and now streaks of blue were lightening the channel. He could see beyond the crashing waves.

"You awake, Stubbs?" the staff sergeant yelled for the twentieth time.

"Yeah, Sarge, I'm still here and awake, goddamn it to hell."

"Where would you rather be, Stubbs? With Mommy and Daddy at home in—where you from, Stubbs? Boise? That's right, Boise—with your radio on and a tuna casserole in front of your face? That where you'd rather be, Stubbs, rather than out here having a fine old time with your new friends in the U.S. Army?"

The sarge might be an idiot, but he was a good guy. This razzing would have to do instead of clearing the Browning's barrel. "You got that right, Sarge."

"Me, too, Stubbs. Even if it was your mommy and daddy and even if it was in Boise goddamn Idaho." He pronounced it "Eye-day-ho."

Rupert Mitchum, Stubbs' feeder, laughed, and the squad joined him.

They appeared as if by sleight of hand out of the fog, all at once, covering the water up and down the English Channel as far as the eye could see.

It must have been every ship in the German navy. And they were all headed for Private Douglas Stubbs.

He could not say a word, nor could anyone else in the platoon.

Finally, Stubbs muttered, "Aw, goddamn it."

The fog—surely it was a smokescreen—was suddenly lifted by the wind. More than he could count, ships of all sizes, led by tiny, buzzing landing craft skipping across the waves toward his platoon. Hundreds of these craft, already close enough for him to make out the individual Wehrmacht soldiers who crowded them.

So many ships Stubbs wondered why the German soldiers just didn't walk across the channel on them, ship to ship, like a pontoon bridge. Every square yard of water seemed occupied by a German vessel.

Then the Kriegsmarine battleships and cruisers began their shore bombardment, their barrel flashes hurrying the light of morning. Stubbs heard the whistle of the shells, then the molar-rattling roar as they detonated. He tried to dig in lower in the sand to wait. His machine gun seemed to shrink. It was impossibly small, a toothpick. He hoped someone along the line had thought to notify headquarters. He mouthed good-byes to his parents and his kid brother.

"Aw, goddamnit," he said again.

13

Wilson Clay's hour was up, and he had promised to call the prime minister. The billiard room was still in a state of controlled tumult, but many eyes were on the general.

"I still don't know, Jack," he said as he lifted the green phone. "I thought I would, and I don't, goddamn the German anyway. Winnie is going to chew my ass."

As he put the receiver to his ear, the lights in the room snapped off, dropping us into darkness. With curtains over the windows and French doors, no moonlight entered the room, and other than a few black shadows, I could see nothing.

"Captain Branch, I've lost the phone connection," Clay called out. "Get me through."

"Yes, sir."

The dogs barked. They were in their normal frenzy, howling and yipping.

A sulphur match sputtered. An oil lamp with a glass flume was lit by a signalman near his station, its wick flaring brightly until he replaced the flume. The lamp's glow meagerly lightened that end of the room, but left the rest of us in murk.

Clay ordered, "Captain Swain, will you kindly see what is going on."

Gordon Swain was commander of headquarters company.

A sentry at the veranda doors answered, "He's already gone to check into it, sir."

Clay left his desk for the north doors, his hands in front of him to ward off unseen people and officers. I walked after him. He pulled aside the curtains and stepped onto the cobblestones.

The sky was filled with slivers of ice, flashing and dancing in the silver moonlight. It was late spring, and I was astonished. It couldn't be ice. Yet this ice or snow or confetti filled the air, drifting and rolling, so thick it blocked my view of the stone rail around the veranda. The stuff sparkled and glinted, rushing with wind currents, landing on the porch stones and swirling into soft mounds. I felt I was in one of those water-filled glass balls that you shake to obliterate Santa with snow. It landed on our shoulders and hair, our eyelashes and ears.

"Chaff," Clay observed.

"Pardon?"

"Antiradar. Strips of aluminum foil dumped overhead, probably by the Luftwaffe."

I had never heard of this defense. If it disoriented me this well, it must have been excellent against radar. The chaff diminished the world to the general and me, insulating us, and surrounding us with a sparkling gaiety I didn't feel. I swatted at it.

I returned with the general to his desk inside. He had ribbons of aluminum in his hair, which caught the lamp's yellow light, making his head appear to have serpent's scales.

Clay lifted the phone and said again, "Signal, put me through—"

The dogs abruptly halted their insane barking. It had never before been completely silent at the manor. I had thought no force on earth could stop those miserable dogs from yammering.

I was spooked, but Clay looked at me and shrugged.

He resumed, "Signal, get me—"

The pounding of a machine gun came from the garden. The blackout curtain over the French doors billowed into the room, suddenly stitched with holes, and the plaster above my desk shattered and fell to the floor, snapping off the cue chalk holder. We threw ourselves onto the floor, except for the general, who gazed disdainfully at the damage.

"Get down, everybody," Alex Hargrave yelled unnecessarily. Several M1s returned fire outside.

General Clay said, "I'm just trying to make a phone call."

I felt foolish, looking up at him. Three HQ company soldiers ran into the billiard room, bumping into desks in the darkness. Two were carrying Thompson submachine guns, the other an M1. They surrounded General Clay and pushed him to the floor.

"Excuse us, General," one of them said. "Orders."

Clay landed on his rump. "Orders from whom, goddamn it? I give all the orders around here."

"We've got to keep you safe, General," one explained.

Clay tried to rise, but one of the bodyguards put a hand on his shoulder. "Please, sir. Just for a minute, until we figure out what's going on."

From the roof came a crash, then a splintering sound, and another crash.

Clay said, "Go see what that is, Jack. It doesn't sound good."

No, it didn't. I didn't complain I was not a combat soldier, that I was an academician, and not a brave one at that. I crawled away from the desk on all fours, passing other HQ personnel crouching behind desk and cabinets, out the door into the hallway. I rose to my feet and ran up the broad stairway to the second floor, hoping I didn't bump into anyone coming down. I couldn't see a thing.

General Clay's physician, Colonel William Strothers, joined me as I climbed the narrow stairs up to the servant's quarters on the third floor. He was carrying a flashlight and a .45. I hadn't thought to arm myself.

He shook his head. "Terrific," he whispered, "a pediatrician and a historian in search of heavily armed, crack German commandos."

"You're a baby doctor?" I exclaimed in a whisper. "I thought you were a surgeon."

"I lied to get into the service."

I nodded toward his pistol. "You ever fired that thing?"

"It went off once by accident when I was trying on the holster. Does that count?"

"Jesus."

We searched room to room on the third floor, opening each door and flashing the beam in, until we found the cause of sound. A canister the size of a thirty-gallon barrel filled with German rations had fallen through the manor's roof and the ceiling to land on the floor. It had broken open. Tins resembling our C-rations were scattered across the room. Parachute lines dangled from the hole in the ceiling.

"Chute must have failed," Strothers said.

I gathered up several cans and returned to the billiard room, leaving Strothers upstairs. I kneeled next to Clay. He extended his hand and I gave him a tin. He opened it. I couldn't see what was in it.

After a moment of chewing he said, "Sausage. Could use more garlic, but not bad."

The wall east of the veranda doors buckled, then blew inward with a flash of an explosion. Stones and plaster and wood tumbled to the floor. The bodyguards above us raised their weapons. Shouting came from the porch, then automatic gunfire followed by a smattering of rifle shots. Then silence.

I saw General Clay remove a tiny pill bottle from his trouser's pocket. He shook it idly. It sounded like it had only one pill inside. I knew he didn't take medication for his heart, like Dr. Strothers wanted.

I asked, "What's that, sir?"

"I can't be taken alive."

It took me a moment. Then I was aghast. "General Clay, you've been carrying around a cyanide pill? You can't—"

"Don't worry, Jack. I'm not going to eat it until the last moment."

"But, damn it—"

He waved away my objection. "That's why I don't take those goddamn blood pressure pills Strothers is always lecturing me about. I don't want to get my pills mixed up."

Looking back, it seems childish that I next asked him, "Why wasn't I issued a cyanide pill? I know as much about deployment of our forces as you do."

Clay thought for a moment. "I tell you what, until I can get another, I'll cut this one in half and give you a half. That way, neither of us will die, but we'll both get real sick."

I think he was joking. He continued to rattle the pill bottle. I was forgotten.

A flare ignited outside. Brilliant light streaked into the room through the bullet punctures in the blackout curtain. The wall above signal carrels was spot-lighted. The hammer of a machine gun came from the garden.

"General Clay?" Captain Swain called out.

"Over here."

Swain appeared above us. "General, we need to get you out of here."

"What's going on out there?"

"Enemy paratroopers. We don't know how many."

Clay said gruffly, "Clear them the hell out and let me get back to work. That's was the U.S. Army is paying you for, Captain."

"I intend to, sir." Swain used an obstinate tone the general rarely heard from subordinates. "The army also pays me to insist you evacuate when I deem it imperative."

Hargrave, on the floor nearby, said loudly, "Get going, General. Gene and I will follow you."

Clay climbed to his feet, shaking off Captain Swain's hand at his elbow. "We're retreating before we've fired a shot. Is that it, Alex? I'll be goddamned if—"

Captain Swain cut in, "Let's go, General."

Even in the darkness, I could see the glower on Clay's face. I thought he was going to bust Swain and send him home. Instead, the general slapped dust off his shirt sleeves and began toward the door. He barked, "Come on, Jack."

The gunfire faded. A phalanx of Captain Swain's soldiers met us in the courtyard. They surrounded us, a human shield, and walked us to an M20 armored utility car. Clay and I climbed through the hatch. It was dark and cramped and smelled of oil, exhaust, and the general's *wurst*.

The driver said, "Hang on, sirs. We'll get you out of here." He had a southern accent. He engaged the gears and accelerated.

We bounced around, banging ourselves against the steel walls, which were over three-quarters of an inch thick.

Clay said bitterly, "This is it, Jack, the absolute nadir of my command, and you can write that down."

He was silent for a moment. Then he said, "Do you realize what I'm doing here? I'm fleeing my command."

"Sir, I don't view it that way. I think—"

"Darius, pursued by Alexander, abandoned his family and his traveling palace and his war chariot and his soldiers, so anxious was he to escape, and we remember his infamy twenty-two hundred years later."

"Well, sir, that's not really analogous—"

"During the Battle of Camden in 1780, General Horatio Gates was forever disgraced when he fled the field, outrunning his men in his haste to escape."

"I don't think—"

"French infantry commander Clerambauld deserted his troops at Blenheim, to his eternal dishonor."

"Sir—"

"At Gettysburg, General Schimmefennig spent most of the battle hiding in a cellar in town."

"Sir—"

"At Austerlitz, General Buxhouden escaped, leaving most of his men behind, to his lasting shame."

From the driver's seat, the corporal spoke up, "And didn't old Jeff Davis turn tail and skedaddle from Richmond at the first sight of U. S. Grant's army?"

Clay looked bleakly at the driver.

"Well, hell," the driver said, "we don't hold that against him, much."

"Thank you, Corporal." Clay looked back at me and stabbed his head with a finger. "Every one of them memorized, Jack. Every one."

When we arrived at the air strip, we pushed and levered ourselves out of the armored car. More guards ushered us toward Terry Norman's plane. The engine was already turning, and even though morning was breaking, I could see flames from the exhaust pipes. I scrambled into my seat behind the pilot.

"Morning, General," Captain Norman said cheerily. "Where to?"

I expected Clay to order us to I Corps HQ, our reserve headquarters. And I hope my jaw did not drop when he said, "I promised Winnie I'd tell him where the goddamn German is landing, and I intend to do just that. Toward the channel, Captain. Let's go take a look-see."

"Righto," Norman said, grinning.

Clay believed for a while that German commandos had been assigned to assassinate him, either in retaliation for his Flanders raid with the Rangers "or just on general principle," as he put it.

We later discovered that a plane of Wehrmacht paratroopers lost its engines, and the commandoes bailed out short of their target. They landed at Eastwell only by accident. Captain Swain's troops killed twenty-three of them, shooting many before they landed in the gardens. Another nine were taken prisoner. A few escaped into the night. Headquarters company lost two soldiers.

I report here also that the next time General Clay fell asleep, which was many hours in the future, I dug into his pocket, found that small bottle, ground the pill into powder, and cast it to the wind. He never mentioned it to me.

I gripped the seat back as the Cub began down the pasture. The engine soon pulled us into the sky. We were in for a rough and frightening flight.

Our men, a wall of them, squared themselves to the danger. Backs to the land, they braced themselves. The Germans appeared with the tide, washing in on the island shore. Crashing and pounding and grinding, the enemy host came. All along the coast, lives were joined. The sound of battle soon soared above the waves.

Today, tide and wind have almost healed those shore battlefields, burying the debris of war, filling craters and dugouts, washing away blood, and covering bones under sand and saltgrass. These days visitors to the beaches pick through the dross of battle, discarding some, carrying some away. Even the most permanent reminders of that day, the concrete battlements, will not last, as moss has begun its work on them.

Memories are more persistent than the waste of war. Bodo Moelders, an infantrymen with a motorized infantry regiment attached to the Wehrmacht's 7th Division, had never before been in a boat. Even his training had been from a shiplike structure built on dry land. And—he would have laughed at this that morning had he the strength—he had been trained against seasickness on a mechanism resembling a rope bridge, bouncing and rolling as his comrades shook the ends of it. It had not worked. In his youth, Moelders had suffered pneumonia and cholera. He had never been this sick.

He had started vomiting before the ship left Boulogne, and continued to shudder and heave the entire journey. When the whistle sounded to disembark, his legs were too weak to carry his weight. He was left behind on the ship. He told me after the war that he "will carry that shame to my grave" and would brook no argument from me that seasickness was as disabling as any wound and could not be helped.

Oberschutze (private first class) Rudolf Richter made it a little farther, but not much. Richter was a signalman in a *Jaeger* (light infantry) battalion with the 28th Division. With his pack radio on his back, he climbed down the net of rope from his ship. The *Marinefahrprahme* bounced against the ship's hull below him. Richter kept stepping on the soldier's hands below him as he descended.

Finally, three feet above the bobbing landing craft, Richter jumped. One leg landed on the craft, the other slipped between the ship and the craft just as the vessels rolled together. Richter's leg was crushed. A moment later, silently weeping from the pain, he was raised to the ship deck in a sling.

Manufacture of specialized craft for opposed landings was new in warfare, "and we Germans didn't really get it right," Max Staubwasser said during an interview after the war. Other than those on the new *Marinefärprähme* and a number of *Sturmboots*, most of the invaders were transported on canal barges, which had no means of self-propulsion and could accurately be called lighters. The barges were towed by tugs and other vessels, usually in pairs, an unwieldy maneuver fraught with risk, particularly when the vessels reached the range of shore fire, when the tug released the tow line and motored to the aft of the barges and pushed them toward land. This arrangement was clearly inferior to landing crafts, the LCIs and LCMs developed by Americans for use in the Pacific later in the war. But then, as General Clay said, Germans are landsmen.

Staubwasser was with the 17th *Panzerjaegerabteilung* (antitank battalion) posted to the 17th Division. Slung over his shoulder were a 2cm Solothurn antitank rifle and his carbine. Half his battalion was being ferried to shore on a barge pushed by a canal tug. The barge had undergone few modifications other than a forward sheet of steel passing as armor. "Even to my farmer's eyes, I could tell that barge wasn't seaworthy," he said. "But the channel's calm water that morning was our great stroke of luck."

Morning was breaking, revealing the hills behind the English shore, which drew ever nearer. Staubwasser heard the steady pinging of bullets bouncing off the steel plate. The luck ended when the lieutenant colonel ordered the battalion into the surf.

"Six fellow soldiers were ahead of me in line on the barge," Staubwasser recalled. "They jumped in, one after another, and drowned, one after another. We were too deep. Finally the colonel called a stop to it, and let the barge be pushed further inland. I was the first one off the barge who didn't drown. Even so, the water came to my chest before my feet found the bottom. I thought my weapons would pull me under, but slowly I made my way up the shore, for all the good it did me. My right foot was blown off by a mine a few minutes later, so my war ended on the beach."

Not all injuries came from enemy explosives. *Matrosen-Gefreiter* (Able Seaman) Rolf Deecke was a loader deep inside a battleship turret below a battery of fifteen-inch guns. He was naked to the waist, except for his cap, across which was the name of his ship, *Tirpitz*. Sweat rolling off his arms and back had soaked his trousers. Deecke's team handled the block and tackle and sleds necessary to cart the two-thousand-pound shells from the ammunition room into the turret, then into the breech. Some of this maneuver was hydraulically assisted, but much of it depended on back-breaking labor.

"The noise in the turret was paralyzing," he told me after the war. "The geared turbines, the high pressure water-tube boilers, the turret engines and the gun engines, and of course the blasts of the guns. And everybody yelling. And then there was the suffocating smell of cordite and oil and grease and sweat. And no place could I stand completely upright. I had no idea what was going on topside or anywhere else in the world, only that somebody was being badly punished with our shells. Add to that the certain knowledge among us turretmen that we are never told when our ship is sinking, and the first we'll learn of it is when the sea water gets to our ankles, because what a Kriegsmarine captain wants to see just before he puts his pistol to his temple is his big guns still firing as the ocean water reaches them and the barrels begin to sizzle steam. That turret was hell on earth."

Deecke was injured by what Americans call a come-along, a chain-tightener. After an hour of steady firing, a link on a come-along around a shell popped, and the handle snapped up and broke Deecke's jaw and cheekbone. He collapsed to the deck, was pushed by his fellow sailors to a bulkhead, and remained there, ignored, for three hours until a spare hand could help him to the surgery.

Explosives were blameless in other injuries, such as those suffered by Aloysius Meyer. The rifleman with the 2nd Company, Hindenburg Regiment, 34th Division, waded toward shore, the surf bucking him left and right, bullets splitting the air above him. Courtesy of the German navy, a walking barrage plowed up mountains of sand ahead of him, moving inland at a speed equivalent to seventy paces a minute. He had been told he could safely get to within twenty-five yards of the barrage. He didn't believe it. He planned to follow it at a hundred yards, close enough.

Meyer heard a warning shout above the bedlam of surf and explosives. He glanced over his shoulder just as one of the newly designed landing boats, a *Marinefahrprahme*, hit him in the back, thrusting him into the surf, scraping him along the rocky bottom, then sledding over him.

"I rolled and rolled under the hull of the craft, taking in huge mouthfuls of water. My pack was torn off, and I lost my helmet and rifle. I was going to be crushed or drowned, I was sure of it. Then the propeller whirled into me, digging out gouges. Later I saw the wounds in a mirror. My back resembled a plowed field."

Meyer was spat out the aft end of the landing craft, bleeding but floating. Waves sent him to shore near the landing craft. He crawled onto dry sand and lay there until a medic found him.

Chief Petty Officer Helmuth Goerlitz was at the wheel of a tug, guiding two barges in front of him as the waves nudged the crafts to shore. "I had endlessly trained for this, how to guide the barges to land, how to keep them from jackknifing on me, and I was doing a fair job of it, but I just did not see the dragon's tooth."

Hidden from *Ober-maat* Goerlitz's view by the barges' armored gunwales and by the Wehrmacht soldiers readying themselves to leap into the surf, a sharpened iron post the size of a man's leg ripped into the belly of the port barge, cleaving open its underside like a can opener.

"Water shot up from the tear like a geyser, and the barge immediately began to sink. My men, my charges . . ." Goerlitz turned away as he recalled that day, and could continue only after a moment, "began leaping out of the barge. We were still too deep for walking. Many drowned. I can still hear them cry out as they were pulled down by their jackboots and packs and ammunition belts."

Crewmen on Goerlitz's other barge cut the disabled vessel free, and the chief petty officer was able to push it to shore, leaving the damaged craft tossing in the surf, "a hulk, doing nothing but clogging up those who came after."

Unterfeldwebel (Staff Sergeant) Waldemar Rasch had jumped into the surf from a *Sturmboot*, a powered eight-man raft launched by cradle skids from an auxiliary minesweeper. Rasch's most vivid memory of that morning was of his exultation when he reached dry sand with his entire squad of ten soldiers.

"Our boots sank with every step, as if the sea was trying to reclaim us, but I was overjoyed we made it out of the water," the sergeant told me after the war. "And then it seemed some

246

terrible, silent, swift disease, a plague, hit my squad. One after another they pitched forward onto the sand and lay still. All ten of my men. Not one of them made a sound that I could hear, all down within the course of fifty yards of beach, hit by enemy rifle fire."

Suddenly a leader without followers, Rasch waited a few minutes behind a concrete cone until the remnants of another Wehrmacht squad passed by on its way inland, and he joined it.

Corporal Lonnie Linder may have caused the demise of Rasch's squad. The corporal was with the 138th Regiment, 35th Infantry Division, overlooking St. Mary's Bay. He was from Kansas, "born with a deer rifle in my hand," he said. "By age four, I was already a better shooter than anybody in my company would ever be, which ain't saying a whole hell of a lot."

Linder went on, "The service-issue M1 was a pretty good weapon, I have to admit, but I brought with me my Winchester Model 70, a 30-06 bolt action repeater, outfitted with a five-power sight, the same rifle I'd been hunting and plinking with for years. I'd worn the wood shiny. Our lieutenant, a goddamn ninety-day wonder, didn't like me bringing my own rifle much, but he shut his trap soon enough."

Linder began loosing off bullets when the Germans were still three hundred yards away, far out of effective range for other riflemen in his company. The invaders began to fall, one per shot. "I started out with five shells in the rifle, and a cardboard box of fifty more on the sandbag next to me. I emptied the cardboard box before we were taken. And I think I missed four shots."

Astonished, I asked this latter-day Sergeant York, "You mean you brought down fifty-one Germans?"

"Those krauts didn't have the sense God gave a goose, because the more of them I killed, the closer the rest of them got. Easier than the target shoot at the county fair. And a lot easier than recovering from the fourteen assorted bullet and shrapnel wounds that put me out of action a few minutes later. So the krauts, they kind of evened things out, don't you see?"

Rushing up the beach, Dieter Wolff felt betrayed when he saw the coils of barbed wire ahead of him. "Miles of it, rows of it, intact and waiting for us."

Captain Wolff felt he had been double-crossed by the Kriegs-marine, which had promised it would cut apart the wire before his company reached it. "We were told that so much antiwire explosive would be thrown at the British beach that no piece of wire would be larger than a forearm, and we'd be able to run right over it."

Wolff was trapped. With machine gun and rifle fire pouring down at him, he pushed ahead, right into the coils. "It seems stupid now, looking back," he told me. "But I surely was not going to retreat, and I had nowhere else to go."

The captain continued, "That wire must have been alive, like an octopus. It reached for me and pulled me in, suspending me above the sand. And there I stayed for two hours, helpless. I did not have anything else to do with S-Day, other than to blunt those wire barbs with my skin—I had over two hundred punctures and cuts—and stop two bullets, one with a thigh and one with my shoulder."

The captain also felt betrayed by Goethe, who had witnessed the famed barrage at Valmy during the French Revolutionary Wars. "Goethe described the cannonade as 'the humming of tops, the gurgling of water, and the whistling of birds.' Nothing of the sort. Artillery sounds like men screaming."

Corporal Alfred Junger's Bergepanther may have been the first Wehrmacht vehicle to reach the beach. Junger was a driver, and the Bergepanther was a refitted Panther ausf D, with the turret replaced by a two-foot-high steel box across the width of the hull and along its length. Most Bergepanthers were tank recovery vehicles, outfitted with winches or earth spades, but Junger's tank chassis was equipped with a mine flail.

"I was first in line," he remembered. "And when the barge hit the sand, the plank was lowered, and I rolled my Berge-panther right onto English soil. I engaged the accessory gear, and the drum out front began to whip the chains around, beating the sand, throwing a cloud of it into the air."

A Wehrmacht lieutenant crouching behind a dragon's tooth fifty feet inland motioned to Junger. "I could see some of his soldiers lying on the beach, horribly injured by mines. I pressed the clutch and turned my Bergepanther toward him. I passed him—trying to dodge the wounded, but I've never been sure how well I did—and immediately the flails detonated mines, one after another, blast after blast under the drum. I drove toward the enemy redoubt at the top of the beach. Behind me the lieutenant set out green smoke canisters to signal a pathway through the mines."

A bullet entered the Bergepanther's viewing portal, missing Junger by the width of a hair. "The bullet bounced around inside the driver's box. I still remember it pinging and whistling, and then it punched into my neck hard enough to bruise my spinal cord."

Junger instantly collapsed, his feet slipping forward on the dual clutches, bringing the flail to a stop. The Wehrmacht lieutenant ran forward, climbed into the driver's compartment, and pushed Junger aside. "The officer, I'd never seen him before, was bleeding along his left arm, but he got the Bergepanther going again, and we didn't stop until we got to a grassy hill behind the beach, where an antiarmor mine blew the tread off the flail."

The lieutenant was killed as he tried to climb out of the Bergepanther. Junger remained inside, slowly regaining sensation in his arms and legs as the lieutenant's blood cascaded down onto him. His disabled flail was ignored for the rest of the battle.

Gefreiter (Lance Corporal) Hans Langangke remembers the charge as an eerie dream. Langangke carried his submachine gun across his chest as he sprinted up the sand. "I looked down at my boots as I ran," he told me when I interviewed him, "and one lace was undone, was flapping against my ankles. It was the oddest thing—I was oblivious to everything else for a while except the unfairness that my boot lace had to be undone now of all times. Then I noticed as I ran that I could hear nothing but my own breath, loud inhales and exhales that oddly drowned out the shouts and the explosives. I saw my sergeant yell right at me, and I simply could not hear him." It was like a dream, Langangke recalled, with some sensations muted and others amplified, much of it nonsensical.

The soldier in front of Langangke fell, so Langangke took a few side steps to run with a friend of his, who immediately was shot. "Right through the neck, and down he went. This was the worst place in the world to be alone, so I moved a little further left to run with my sergeant. And just then he took a bullet in the chest and collapsed. I knew then that I had the power of life or death over my comrades. Anyone I neared would die. God alone should have this authority."

He went on, "All the way up the beach to the American dugouts, any Wehrmacht soldier I neared was killed. And then I got to the Americans, and they started to die, but this time I had something directly to do with it, my Schmeisser and I."

God was with the Wehrmacht soldiers that day, many of them agreed. Wolfgang Kleber felt a presence beside him, guiding him, as he struggled up the beach. He looked left and right. No one was there, other than his fellow infantrymen. But when Kleber stumbled over a wounded soldier, he felt the presence again, lifting him by the arm and helping him on.

Berndt Klein also claims to have been visited by God. Klein's head was grazed by shrapnel, knocking him to the sand. He felt a spirit next to him, nothing but a soft light, lifting him to his feet. "I saw nothing, but knew it was there anyway." The spirit put a hand on Klein's back, moving him up the shore safely through the still life of the dead and dying.

Franz Eberbach tripped when a bullet tore into the leather heel of his boot. He lay face down on pebbles and seaweed for a moment, unable to rise, uninjured but terrified. Fellow soldiers passed him, dashing up the beach. He tried to rise to his knees, but fear had frozen him. Then a warm gust of air brushed him and lifted him to his feet.

"I know it will not make sense to you," he said, "but I was escorted across the minefield and through the streams of machine gun bullets. The spirit held my arm, guiding me."

I asked Eberbach if he was talking about intuition.

He fiercely shook his head. "A force, something as tangible as my helmet or rifle. I'm telling you, it was the embodiment of a merciful God."

As part of their feint, the Wehrmacht had landed at low tide. It may be presumed OKW knew the price that would be paid, and Private Douglas Stubbs extracted that price. Crouching behind sandbags and his Browning machine gun, he fired until his barrel jacket was glowing, until Rupert Mitchum's hands were bleeding from ammo belts coursing through them.

An area receiving machine gun fire is called the beaten zone. "When they first got off the boats, they must have been three or four hundred yards away. I fired at a steep elevation, so my bullets fell over a wide area, pretty much randomly on the beaten zone. Then when the enemy got closer, I fired at fixed points, compact cones of fire, coordinating with other Third Platoon gunners. But, son of a bitch, there were still some left, marching up the beach as if they didn't give a damn what I did to them, so I switched to short-range tactics, traversing bullets in an arc across the line of attacking troops."

"And they still came?" I asked.

He pointed out an angry crease behind his ear and another along his leg. "A stick grenade got us first. Knocked me cold, then I think some kraut, likely mad as hell, stood over me and fired into me three times."

Stubbs and I were sitting in a restaurant in St. Louis, but that didn't prevent him from standing and pulling up his shirt to show me three scars from puncture wounds. "I have no idea how I lived through it, none whatsoever. My next memory is of lying on a narrow litter in a German hospital ship. Rupert never made it, though. He was seventeen years old, and he'll remain seventeen forever."

Arnie Fowler, the Cincinatti pitcher, waited for the Germans with two dozen grenades. "I was so accurate with the grenades, I thought the Germans would never get within fifty yards of me. I was ready and able to put those babies right down their shirt fronts."

Fowler saw his first German, raised his arm to launch the grenade, and felt a searing heat in his hand. Shrapnel from a Wehrmacht mortar round had severed tendons in his throwing hand. He was taken prisoner moments later. "I never threw a grenade, and I never pitched in the bigs again, either."

Corporal Allen Wilkes, of the 38th Field Artillery Battalion, to whom General Clay had lectured about German radio propaganda, remembers his arm tiring from pulling the howitzer's lanyard. "We loaded grapeshot canisters, one after another, and I'd yank the cord, time and again. Hardly bothered to aim

251

the gun. I just don't know how the enemy made it up that beach. General Clay was right, the Germans were sitting ducks. It's just that there were a lot of ducks."

Wilkes' pillbox was wild with smoke and thunder, with too many soldiers crowding each other and a weapon that bucked dangerously with each round. Orders were given by panto-mime, as all had lost their hearing. "Open, eject, load, slam, yank, open, eject, load, slam, yank, endlessly."

Then a grenade came through the gun aperture and landed near the howitzer's spokes. A loader calmly scooped it up and punched it back through the portal. Outside the pillbox, the grenade's blast did no damage.

Wilkes told me, "I had this insane idea, kneeling next to the howitzer with the cord in my hand, that that potato-masher must be the best the goddamn Third Reich could do, and we were home free. That was the Germans' one shot at us, and they failed."

But next came the nozzle of a *Flammenwerfer* 41, and the pillbox filled with an evil hiss and rushing fire. The stream shot over Wilkes, with only drops of flame splashing onto his back and arms. "My throat burned, as if I'd inhaled the flame. The loaders were covered in fire. They ran around, human torches, until a couple of the poor bastards found their way out the back of the pillbox, where they were shot down. The others just toppled over, scratching blindly at the ground, and died."

Among his howitzer team, only Wilkes survived. He spent much of the next two years in and out of hospitals, fighting pneumonia and infection in his scalded lungs.

Ray Chase won his race to the parapet. The instant the bar-rage ended, he scrambled to the top of the trench. There, arrayed before him, was the German infantry scurrying his way. "The enemy was pouring through gaps in the barbed wire. Somehow the Germans had even gotten tanks to the beach. Behind all this, the channel was so filled with German ships it looked like a city skyline."

The barrage had ended, but the strafing had not. Just as Chase swung his M2's barrel toward the invaders, a tracer lashed into a nearby sandbag, spraying dirt and wood splinters into Chase's eyes, instantly blinding him. Screaming in pain, both hands to his eyes, he slid back down the trench, where he sat until captured. "I didn't fire a shot." He regained the sight of one eye several weeks later, but one eye remains blind.

Private Karl-Heinze Brennecke was a machine gunner aboard a *Leichter Panzerspahwagen*, a four-wheeled light armored car. The car resembled a beetle, riding high on its chassis, with its steel body at seemingly disjointed angles to deflect antiarmor shells. The 2cm KwK gun had been replaced by a machine gun. The armored car followed a flail up the beach, with Brennecke not bothering to answer the small-arms fire that smacked into the car, sounding like a spoon beating a pan.

Brennecke braced himself behind his machine gun, an MG 42, waiting, feeling almost safe as they rolled up the beach. The true danger to armored cars comes from rolling over at high speeds. And Brennecke's driver, Padewski, was a madman, straight from *Wolkenkuckucksheim* (cuckoo cloud-land), who liked to accelerate the Horch engine until it sang soprano. Here on the beach, what could Padewski do, tucked behind the Bergepanther flail and in low gear?

At the top of the beach, with so many bullets glancing off the car's armor Brennecke was reminded of a ringing telephone, Padewski turned the *Panzerspahwagen* parallel to the first trench. Brennecke raised his grip and fired the weapon into the trench.

"Padewski zigged and zagged, following the trench, and every time he turned, another bunch of Americans who hadn't seen us coming were surprised into fits. I'd fire and fire. I wore a reinforced glove, because after five belts of fifty rounds each, I'd have to change barrels. I'd release the catch, toss aside the hot barrel, put a new one on. I could do it in five seconds. I don't think I missed any of the Amies. I was good with a machine gun, I assure you."

What had finally stopped his car?

"Padewski was a goddamn Pole from Danzig, although he liked to pretend he was a German. He zigged when he should have zagged, and the *Panzerspahwagen's* right wheels fell over the side of a trench. The car toppled into the ditch. I wasn't hurt, but fuel began pouring on me, and I feared my barrel would ignite it. So I scrambled out of the car, which was standing on its nose."

An American charged from the rear, and a bayonet blade popped out the front of Brennecke's uniform blouse. He lay in his own blood at the bottom of the trench until Wehrmacht corpsmen reached him. He does not know what happened to Padewski.

Brennecke laughed. "Can you imagine? I was probably the only soldier in the entire battle to be undone by a bayonet, something out of the Franco-Prussian War."

Father Rafael Rodriquez knew better. "I gave final offices to hundreds of soldiers. On a number of bodies, broken bayonet blades were still protruding from chests or stomachs, the result of savage hand-to-hand fighting. I spent the entire day saying last rites, hardly had time to catch my breath between them."

Captain Ross Walton knew that his command, Baker Company, 1st Battalion, 38th Infantry Regiment, was slipping away from him. He ran forward from his post along a communication trench to the first dugout, then along the trench, stepping over some bodies, slipping on others, feeling like a tightrope walker.

Under a machine gun post that was still operating, he yelled into the ear of one of his lieutenants, "You making it?"

The lieutenant flinched as a grenade detonated nearby. "Half my men are down, sir. Same with Brown down the line."

"Let's get out of here. Tell the machine guns to give you three minutes, and we'll cover their retreat from the rear."

"Sir?"

"You heard me. We're pulling out."

Overhead, the gunner groaned and slipped sideways on his platform. He clung to the weapon's grip, and the barrel swung across the sky, firing in a useless arc. Blood splattered onto Walton, dripping off his helmet onto his shoulders. Then the gunner fell, bouncing at the captain's feet.

"Get going, Lieutenant."

Captain Walton told me after the war, "I should have accounted for all my men. I should have carried away our equipment or destroyed it. I should have waited for orders to pull back. A dozen other things I should have done. But only ten minutes elapsed between when we saw the first Wehrmacht infantryman and when we were overwhelmed. No time for any of it. Sometime during those few minutes a bullet passed through my right biceps, and I didn't know it. I didn't have time to notice it."

Nor was there time anywhere else along the English Channel. Thousands of little dramas, explosive and bloody, fearful and appalling, were being played out. And it was quick work, taking only the few minutes before dawn. The sun had not even risen on S-Day, and our Allied beach defenses had already been overrun.

14

Winston Churchill later called the general's flight "Clay's caprice."

That snappy phrase was all he allowed to leak to the press. To Clay's face, the prime minister termed the flight "brazen, asinine, senseless, eccentric Yankee clownishness, a crack-brained, muddle-headed, clottish, dizzyingly stupid act of puerile glory-hoarding." (General Clay replied, "Let's not mince words here, Prime Minister.")

Churchill was correct, in a way. Clay risked himself—the commander in chief of the American Expeditionary Force and all the experience, judgment, and knowledge incumbent in that position—for a glimpse of the action.

Justifying his flight, Clay later claimed that even as late as daybreak, AACCS did not know the location of the invasion. History has supported his argument. It is difficult to believe now, with time's precise hindsight, that the Germans could by sun-up have occupied for an hour a sixty-mile strip of English soil without the Allies knowing with certitude the locations of their landings and without the Allies fully abandoning their notion that the invasion would take place—indeed, was taking place—across the North Sea. General Clay's report was the first irrefutable evidence provided to the Defense Committee and AACCS that the German horde was coming from France.

The English Channel at Folkestone was only sixteen miles from headquarters at Eastwell, and we arrived moments after take-off. The low cloud cover was spotty, and Captain Norman piloted the Cub from cloud bank to cloud bank, plunging us into white blindness, then abruptly emerging to view the coast below, each time with more clarity as we neared the coast, as if we were increasing the powers of a laboratory microscope.

We turned southwest at Folkestone to follow the channel, and there below us was the vast panorama of the invasion. The silver water was strewn with German vessels. Countless ships. I could not imagine where the Kriegsmarine would have fitted in more ships, had they the ships. Barrage balloons floated above many of them. As far as the eye could see to the west, the channel bristled with the vessels, a staggering display of Teutonic will and strength.

General Clay said over the hum of the Cub's engine, "Any more ships, we'd have to sandbag the coast just to keep the seawater from overflowing."

Terry Norman jinked the plane into another cloud. He had scarcely bothered to look at the channel. There were as many Luftwaffe planes over the coast as there were ships below. To this day I have no adequate explanation why our tiny, slow, defenseless Cub was not spotted and shot down. Certainly Norman's evasive piloting helped. With typical modesty, he claimed later the Luftwaffe was consumed by ground support and was rightfully anticipating weak resistance from the RAF. They weren't looking for us, so they didn't see us. Or perhaps the German pilots mistakenly identified us as a German spotter. So many Luftwaffe planes buzzed around us we could have been part of a Luftwaffe formation. I was terrified.

"Take notes and photos, Jack."

"Yes, sir."

Clay dictated, "The vanguard of the invasion fleet, the mine-sweepers and buoy-layers and motor launches and cutters, have already turned around. Approaching the shore west of Folkestone are four, no, five lanes of ships. A battle ship, the

Tirpitz, and three cruisers, one is the *Scharnhorst*, stand off shore, and are now shelling," he paused to look through binoculars "three or four hundred yards inland."

I could see the flash and smoke of their targeted fire, a rim of explosives that had walked inland from the beaches.

"Barges, hundreds of them, ranging out five miles to sea. Also, there's a pocket battleship further along the line. The *Lutzow*, I think. Yes, the *Lutzow*."

I hadn't thought the general knew ships from Shinola, but he continued his dictation as we ducked in and out of the clouds. "The transport fleet is an amalgam. In the first waves are minesweepers and the others. In the second are the barges and smaller craft, a number of them already ashore. In the third are freighters and coastal steamers, some look like rust-buckets. Also numerous tankers. I'll be damned, I also see an ocean liner."

We found out later it was the *Europa*. I removed the Leica from its leather case, then leaned over Norman's shoulder to take several photographs.

Clay went on, "Surrounding the convoy at its edges are antisub patrol boats, S-boats, and destroyers. Further out look to be depot ships and tenders, two hospital ships. And oilers."

We learned later this convoy was ferrying the soldiers of the XIII Corps. They had set sail from Rotterdam, Antwerp, Ostend, Dunkirk, heading west in four lanes, converging in an assembly area in the channel German sailors promptly dubbed *Unter den Linden*.

Our plane bobbed and weaved over Dungeness to Rye Harbor. Here the Wehrmacht's VII Corps (we determined later) was landing, having sailed from Antwerp and Calais. The soldiers swarmed ashore along the coast from Rye to Hastings. General Clay described as much as he could, including sighting the passenger ship *Bremen* and the heavy cruiser *Admiral Hipper*.

"A fantastic array," General Clay said. "Every goddamn stick of wood that can float in the Third Reich is down there. Look at them." His binoculars were jammed to his eyes. "River patrol boats, Mediterranean pleasure yachts, and, by God, they've enlisted the *Horst Wessel*, their cadet training sailing ship." He pointed across Norman's nose. "It's under power."

We flew low over the hills behind Hastings, emerging at the coast again at Bexhill, where the XXXVIII Corps was landing, between St. Leonard's and Beachy Head. They had sailed from Boulogne and Etaples, in the Artois region of France. From our height, the battle seemed frighteningly one-sided. The mighty procession of war ships was pressing against the coast, and the only visible resistance was the swinging sprays of AA tracers. Most death in battle occurs in narrow killing zones. Here it was the beach, where the war was being waged with ferocity we could not see.

Clay pointed to a transport ship listing offshore, then to another. We could see the soldiers climbing down lines into the sea as the ships rolled. "Looks like we've gotten a few licks in."

We found out in subsequent days that in fact the Allies had given very few licks. The ships in trouble had foundered on the treacherous spits and rocks along the coast, another price the Germans willingly paid for the surprise of a low-tide landing. Rocky ledges emerged at low tide off some of the coast, such as at Bexhill. At other places, such as Dungeness, sand bars allowed only two feet of clearance. Some of the obstacles were notorious in maritime history, such as the Royal Sovereign Shoals, lying from four to eight miles east of the lighthouse at Beachy Head toward Dungeness.

Nowhere along the invasion coast were there adequate port facilities for the taking. Brighton's famous promenade piers stood in shallow water, and in any event had been rendered unusable by RN engineers. Rye Harbor was inaccessible. The pier at Eastbourne Bay allowed only ships with drafts of less than two feet at low tide. The entrance to Shoreham harbor, west of Brighton, was made dangerous by rocks at depths of two to nine feet. Those few ports with sea-going capacity, such as Folkestone and Newhaven, were heavily defended. So the Germans had to hit the beaches.

General Clay's comment on the loss of German shipping during the assault was, "You throw enough cow pies at the side of a barn, some of them will stick."

And they were sticking. Despite the perils of the channel and of our defenses, the Kriegsmarine's movements seemed precisely synchronized and perfectly executed. From three thousand feet, we could see little of the chaos German soldiers and sailors would tell me about after the war: bungled rendezvous, vessel collisions under smokescreens, detonations of overlooked mines, barges sinking under the weight of armored cargo, blasts from remaining Allied coastal artillery, vessels splitting open on unseen rockshelves, the dogged harassment from the surviving Royal Navy ships, the drownings and fires.

In the Cub, our horizon was distant and hazy, and the scene below was plodding, even peaceful. For German servicemen at the waterline, the short horizon was filled with the bizarre and the violent and the dead.

We flew behind Beachy Head toward the River Cukmere. Along this shore, from the Head to Rottingdean east of Brighton, VIII and X Corps were landing. They had crossed from Le Havre.

The western edge of their front ended before Brighton. Clay said, "They didn't hit the towns. Folkestone, Eastbourne, Brighton, all are being ignored. Know why that is, Jack?"

"Of course. Against—"

"Against stiff resistance it can take twelve hours to clear one city block. So the German just skips the towns. He'll come back and clean them up at his leisure. Or raze them."

Clay spoke dispassionately, as if he were working an adding machine in some office. Bofors shells exploded near our left wing, rattling the Cub. Norman seemed not to notice.

I repeat here that I was cold with fright. I later leafed through the notes I took during that flight, and my handwriting is crabbed and scratchy, and not from Norman's tight maneuvers with the Cub. I was grateful for the engine noise, because my voice was wavering even during the few syllables allowed me by the general.

Clay said, "That looks like all of them. Sixty miles of coast, from Folkestone to Brighton. Let's head north."

That was not all of them. A hundred ten miles to the west of Brighton, thirty thousand soldiers of the German II Corps were landing. They had departed from Cherbourg and sailed northwest to assault the beaches at Lyme Bay. There the British V Corps reeled under a massive assault. We learned later that the Germans employed over four thousand vessels on S-Day.

260

I was vastly relieved to be away from the coast. General Clay said only one sentence the entire way to London. "Winnie is going to crap himself."

We landed in Hyde Park forty minutes later. The streets were eerily empty. Londoners were inside at their radios, listening for word from the BBC. We quickly arrived at the war rooms and were escorted inside. It was just after 7:30 in the morning.

Clay paused at the door to the cabinet room a moment, with me at his shoulder. The intelligence chief, General Cadogan, was at his map. Near him, talking with animation, were Generals Stedman and Alexander. Winston Churchill stood over his place at the felt-covered table, staring down at a report. Other Defense Committee members were in front of maps or at telephones along a wall. Tension was thick, apparent in the rigid stances, in the few inches separating the noses of arguing generals, in uncharacteristically large gestures, in the wadded fists and narrowed mouths. I actually saw the prime minister close his eyes and pinch the bridge of his nose. But only briefly.

General Cadogan's map was spotted with colored flags, reports of engagements with the enemy. Many were on the channel coast, and many were along the North Sea coast, some as far north as Edinburgh. The map reflected the confusion. The enemy had been on English soil for over two hours and still arguments raged as to whether they had come from the east or south.

The room abruptly quieted when General Clay appeared. He was supposed to be at Eastwell. Only the sound of several swivel fans could be heard as he walked toward Cadogan's map. His chest was out and his jaw set. This was now his show.

"The German has landed from here"—he punched a finger at Folkestone and in a historic sweep brought it east to Brighton—"to here."

Cadogan brushed back a wave of hair. "Yes, well, we do have increasingly reliable reports to that effect, but also, we've heard from—" He moved to point to the shore north of London.

"General," Clay interrupted forcefully. "Here to here." He slapped the map twice, Folkestone and Brighton.

Winston Churchill said, "We cannot be absolutely sure yet, General Clay."

"But we can." Clay's sense of timing was exquisite. He waited one long breath. "For I have seen the invasion with my own eyes."

General Clay's flight has become one of the fabled adventures of the war, and the story has already gained a high gloss. Soaring over the crescent of battle, impervious to shot and shell, one man, one lonely soldier, risked his life to bring word of the battle. A Paul Revere or Pheidippides. Another braid on the Wilson Clay legend. The tellers of tales and singers of songs will likely forget—have already forgotten—that Captain Norman and I were also in the plane.

The German subterfuge, called *Herbstreise* (autumn journey) "was sheer goddamn military genius, I guarantee you that," Clay concluded when the operation's breadth became clearer.

He asked, "Jack, do you know who said, 'Deception is the sharpest weapon'?"

I wrinkled my brow. "Thomas Edison?"

"Jesus H. Christ, Jack. You're going to make me burst an artery one of these days. It was the Chinese philosopher of war Sun Tsu, and he was right."

OKW reaped immense rewards for its risky deceit. In the Allies' rationing of battered and scarce military resources, hard decisions had been made, and they were made wrongly, thanks to *Herbstreise*. The finest Allied soldiers—veteran British troops—had been assigned to defend the east coast, while the green Americans were given the beaches less likely to be hit. The more complete RAF squadrons were assigned to Group 12, guarding the east coast from Digby, Wittering, Duxford, and other stations. The devastated Royal Navy posted a preponderance of its remaining ships to the North Sea. Just before the invasion, the Defense Committee released the British XI Corps, which had been held in reserve north of London, to the east coast.

In the weeks before the invasion, the committee had been painfully aware it might be taking the bait of an elaborate trap.

But General Clay and most other committee members firmly believed the Germans would come to the eastern shore. He later said, "We had to act on our best information. And we did, to our sorrow."

How were we fooled?

Parts of *Herbstreise* were revealed to the stunned Allies the morning of S-Day. Other fragments of the deception were disclosed only when Wehrmacht commanders began bragging about them—publicly tweaking our noses—later in the war. Intelligence contacts tripped over some of the plan. And in interviews for this narrative, I dug up a few segments of the puzzle myself.

Here too I tried to talk to the first person to know, the first person to discover some portion of the German plan that so grandly duped us.

Peter Vanderhoff was a bulb grower near Schiedam, just west of Rotterdam. Two months before S-Day, an official from the *Reicharbeitsdienst* (National Labor Service) drove up to Vanderhoff's small home, rolled down the window of the black sedan, and announced that Vanderhoff and his family were to be off the property within twenty-four hours. The RAD officer drove away without further explanation or any apology.

It was the Dutch experience that their German occupiers meant what they said. Vanderhoff, his wife, and three children moved into his brother's tiny cottage in Schiedam the next morning, bringing in their cart every stick of furniture and their dog. Two days later Vanderhoff tried to visit his farm, but was turned back at a road block. On his toes, Vanderhoff could see construction in the distance. The Wehrmacht sentry grabbed his shoulders, spun him around, and shoved him away. Every four or five days, the bulb farmer had returned to see if the Wehrmacht would give back his property.

That morning, which Vanderhoff would later learn was S-Day, the roadblock and the sentry were gone, unexpectedly and mysteriously. He walked along the dirt road toward his farm, his black and white Border collie spinning and yipping at his heels, ecstatic to recognize old smells and sights. The dog was worthless, except for its frantic carrying on at Vanderhoff's feet, which the farmer had learned to enjoy, except for the dust cloud the collie always kicked up with its happy whirling. Vanderhoff walked in a low cloud most of his days.

Vanderhoff approached his home cautiously. He was within a hundred yards when he saw the tanks of a Panzer regiment in his tulip field. Dozens of tanks, aligned in rows. He groaned at what they must have done to his crop.

Yet where were the tank crews and mechanics and support vehicles and the commotion that always accompanied an armored regiment? The Panzers sat there in his field, unattended and ignored. Vanderhoff stepped along his walkway. The Germans had taken his front door and his planter boxes that had hung under the leaded windows. Why would a Panzer unit need planter boxes? The bastards.

He rounded the corners of the cottage. The nearest tank was parked in back of his toolshed. When he opened the shed, the dog rushed in. It was empty. The Germans had taken the lot of it. Bastards. In a rage, the farmer slammed the shed door. He ran toward the nearest tank, intent on spitting on it.

This Panzer was peculiarly disheveled, its armor plating a bit awry—and could it be that the cannon barrel was bent out of true? Vanderhoff slowed and squinted. He was astounded. The barrel had a crook in it. He would have expected the Germans, of all people, to be able to mill a straight tank barrel. It was part of their genetic inheritance.

As he drew near, the tank began losing definition and menace. And by the time he reached it, he knew it was made of wood, coarse planks nailed together haphazardly, then painted gray, with cupolas and tank wheels drawn in black. The barrel was a wood pole. A mock tank. His dog lifted a leg to it. The farmer walked around the vehicle. Fake tread marks had been dug into the ground behind the tank, maybe with the shovels and hoes they had stolen from him.

Vanderhoff turned a circle. The other tanks in his field, dozens of them, were also wood facsimiles. Vanderhoff bit his lower lip, not making sense of it at first. Then he understood, and he prayed the British across the North Sea had discovered the ruse before he did.

The bulb farmer returned to his shed hoping the Germans

had overlooked his crowbar. He wondered how long it would take him to disassemble the tanks. His brother would help. There would be a strong market for wood planks in Rotterdam, he suspected.

Johann Lubbers was twelve years old and preferred fishing to schooling. The boy had been born in Amsterdam, but when the war started, he and his mother were sent to a farm near Vlaardingen, on the river below Rotterdam. He fished on the Nieuwe Maas, the right branch of the Merwede, which enters into the North Sea at the Hook of Holland. He did not care what he caught. His mother could cook anything, even eels, and was grateful for anything be brought home. There was usually little else on their table.

A month before, barbed wire barricades had appeared overnight on the riverside road, blocking him from reaching his favorite fishing bank on the lower river. Gruff sentries in field-gray uniforms turned him away at a road barricade. They were soldiers of the Kriegsmarine infantry. While he watched, the sentries waved through a caravan of trucks, most of them Johann recognized as Opel Blitz three-tonners, a standard Wehrmacht transport. He regularly dumped handfuls of dirt into fuel tanks of unguarded Opel Blitzes, a risky little business he had told his mother nothing about. Had the sentries looked closer, they might have seen that Johann's rod was notched forty-two times above the handle, just like the gunfighters in America that Johann read about in his Karl May westerns. But Johann's notches were for tires he had slashed on Wehrmacht vehicles. Anderson the barber had once told him during a haircut that if he truly despised the Germans, he should come and talk to him on his thirteenth birthday. Johann could be useful some way, he had promised. The barber had said nothing more, and Johann knew not to ask. But the boy wanted a record of success to tell Anderson the barber when they talked in two months.

Johann had walked home that day with an empty net. Over the weeks he had returned frequently, checking to see if the Germans had abandoned his fishing grounds, and looking for unprotected Opel-Blitzes or *Kübelwagens* or Borgwards. On the morning he would later learn was S-Day, the saw-horse barricades across his road were untended. The guardhouse was vacant.

He passed by the barricades carefully, looking over his shoulder, wondering why the Germans would suddenly abandon what they had so painstakingly guarded for weeks. He nervously walked along the dirt road, feeling the onus of his one-boy underground war.

He had fished many times from a rickety pier on the river. As he approached it, he saw that buoys now surrounded the structure, set in a pattern that ran perpendicular to the pier. At each float was a strange shallow-bottomed craft.

Johann walked down the gravel approach to the river, then stepped onto the pier. He could recognize the fishing boats that used these waters, and the Kriegsmarine's patrol launches and minesweepers and S-boats. These vessels were nothing he could identify. They were square and flat. He realized they were unfinished, not much more than floating boxes.

The vessels were tied to each other, bow to stern, and anchored to the buoys. Johann lowered his small tackle box to the pier, then braced himself on a pylon, leaned toward the water, and pulled a line. The boat drifted nearer. He was perplexed. It was nothing but a box, with a beam of about five meters and a length of fifteen meters, and crudely constructed. What he had thought at a distance to be the boat's equipment —bits and capstans and cleats and lines—was painted on the flat surfaces of the vessels. An AA gun had been drawn in black paint on the nearest craft.

Johann knew instantly what this counterfeit navy portended for the British. With his pole in one hand and his tackle box in the other, he sprinted from the pier and turned toward town. Anderson the barber would know what to do with this news.

Captain Siegfried Neuss prided himself on his position as leader of the only signal company with the XXX Corps, stationed at Bremerhaven, at the mouth of the Weser River in north Germany. He told me he may have been the lowest-ranking Wehrmacht officer to know of the magnificent illusion.

Neuss' invasion duty ended the day before S-Day, when

radio silence had been imposed. By his figuring, he had slept less than four hours a day over the past week. The 120 signalmen in his scattered unit—some in the hut, others in Wilhelmshaven and other posts in Lower Saxony, and still others in Groningen in Holland—had worked just as hard. They had joked about their hoarse voices and cramped sending hands, their bleary eyes and jaws strained from yawning.

On that day, utterly exhausted, he watched the second hand on the wall clock, and when it reached twelve, he called out, "That's all, men. Congratulations."

His soldiers applauded and hooted, then rose from their chairs, rubbing their shoulders and working out the kinks in their legs and backs from sitting so long. They left their stations, the banks of radio equipment lining the communications hut's walls. Neuss rose from his desk at the back of a hut to shake their hands one by one as they filed by. They headed to their bunks in the nearby barracks.

The signalmen in his unit had transmitted, again by Neuss' figuring, over 210,000 messages in the past week. Every one of them bogus. Luftwaffe and Kriegsmarine and Wehrmacht messages. All fraudulent.

Not just random broadcasts. The messages had been drafted one by one to form an intricate pattern showing that an entire Wehrmacht army had formed and was readying for transport by the navy, a growing wave of broadcasts, a crescendo of military communication.

There were times these past few weeks when Captain Neuss almost started to believe his own messages. With this much planning, with this many signals, there had to be Germans units acting on them. There were none, of course. His messages, all 210,000 of them, were ignored by the invasion forces. But not by the British.

Neuss walked to his quarters. He laughed aloud around a yawn. No, certainly not by the British and their partners, the Amies, poor fools.

Luftwaffe Lieutenant Friedreich Rollman was also exhausted. His duties were ending the morning of the invasion, and he had flown all the previous night. He tipped his plane at the runway, jockeying the stick. One more landing, and he could sleep in a cot, a real cot. He blinked away sleep. His eyelids seemed to have weights on them. The runway dipped and rolled in front of him. The plane closed on it.

His plane, a Messerschmitt Bf 109B, was a veteran of the Condor Legion in Spain. It was outdated, with a top speed of less than three hundred miles an hour, but adequate for its duties from the airbase at Aalborg in northern Denmark. Two MG 17 machine guns had been removed, leaving only the gun in the propeller boss. Two supplementary fuel tanks had been added.

Rollman's assignment had been to stay in the air as long as humanly possible, or for as long as his plane would hold out. He had spent weeks dodging in and out of British radar and being spotted by Royal Navy patrol boats. Sightings of his plane filled the British Observer Corps' logbooks at their CH stations at Crone Hill, Danby, and West Beckham, and the CHL stations at Easington and Shotten and Cresswell, all in the English eastern counties.

His crew had performed maintenance on the Messerschmitt while the lieutenant slept in the cockpit. He had been rationed caffeine pills. He had flown himself groggy. And, finally, as he approached the runway early S-Day morning, he knew his mission was over.

He touched down on all points, then bounced along the runway as the Messerschmitt slowed. He turned it to the hangar. His crew was jubilantly waving handkerchiefs at him. He flipped off the fuel lines, then pulled to a stop in front of them. He threw the engine switch and unhooked the cockpit latches. He climbed out. The leg bag caught on a clasp, rupturing, spilling urine down the inside of his flight suit. Nothing new there.

The shouting mechanics pulled him off the wing and carried him on their shoulders toward the barracks, patting his back and yelling congratulations. The lieutenant was asleep before they lowered him to his cot. His was the sound sleep of victory, despite the urine. For a week, Rollman had successfully imitated an entire flight of Luftwaffe airplanes.

After the war I spoke with Inspector Charles Bradley of Scotland Yard's counterespionage department. MI5 insisted on a representative at the questioning of selected prisoners of war, and *Oberleutnant zur See* (Senior Lieutenant) Gerd Haas was deemed eminently worth the inspector's time. Haas was the commander of the Kriegsmarine midget submarine caught by the Royal Navy off Benacre Broad. Bradley spoke German.

The interrogation of Haas was conducted in an empty munitions warehouse in Lowestoft, on the North Sea shore in Suffolk. Lieutenant Haas had endured hours of questioning, during which he gave his name and rank and nothing else. His confidence increased when he began to understand the British limited their tools of interrogation to psychological ploys rather than truncheons. Inspector Bradley recalled with some irritation that toward the end of the questioning, Haas appeared rather relaxed.

At the end of the last session with Haas, Bradley said to the German, "Do you know that your countrymen have landed in Kent and Sussex and Dorset?"

The submariner had no visible reaction. The RN interrogator ordered the guards to remove Haas and bring in the next German sailor, one of Haas' crewmen.

Charles Bradley told me, "Of course, we suspected by then the German pathfinder submarine had been part of the deception. Despite his obstinate refusal to say anything, Haas confirmed it to us. He couldn't help it, I presume. Just a surge of joy."

"How did he confirm it?" I asked the inspector.

"On his way out of the room, Haas passed Petty Officer Manfred Detmers, one of Haas' crewmen, who we were bringing in for another go at questioning. Haas grabbed Detmers and gave him a huge hug. Right there in front of us all. It quite startled Detmers."

"A hug?"

Bradley nodded. "The submarine's mission had been to misdirect. They succeeded. That hug was all we needed to confirm that Haas had deliberately allowed his sub to be captured by the RN."

Jean Lechavalier was the owner of Café Anglais on Rue Victor Hugo in Le Havre. He was also a sector chief for the French underground, responsible for six resistance cells in the city. The cells were insulated from each other, and Lechavalier knew many more of his *maquis* than knew him.

The café had been short-handed since the war started. One evening shortly after S-Day, he was waiting tables. In one corner a German officer and a French woman ordered a Pernod and *à pression*. The very idea of a French woman consorting with the despised occupiers sickened Lechavalier, and he vowed to make a few inquiries to determine her identity. After the war, he promised himself, she would regret this indiscretion.

But when he bent low over their table to deliver the beer and aperitif, he recognized by the candlelight one of his soldiers, a woman who had never seen his face, Clara Gaudet, the prominent physician.

"That terrible instant will be pressed into my memory forever. Here she was in my café, toasting the progress of the war with a Wehrmacht colonel. And she was one of my own."

By the time Lechavalier told me the story, he had lived with the revelation for years, yet he stilled purpled when he told it. "Three of my fighters died stealing the radio she used. And, my God, how many English and Americans fell because of her treachery?" He spat, "The infamy, the perfidy, the outrage."

I asked him why she would be so careless as to be seen with a German officer in a café.

"Her assignment was complete," Lechavalier reasoned. "She was no longer useful to the Germans, because once the true location of the invasion was known, the Allies could readily deduce she had fed them lies and that she was an Abwehr double agent. She must have hated her countrymen so, to rub our faces in her treachery by publicly celebrating with a Bosch officer."

"Would she not be in danger from your underground?"

Lechavalier looked at me as he might at a simpleton. "Good God, I would have strung her intestines over my brasserie had I been able to find her without her Wehrmacht colonel. But mission accomplished, she disappeared."

Mme. Gaudet's lies were that the Wehrmacht 8th and 28th Divisions were moving from Normandy toward Belgium. She had provided another part of the false puzzle for the Allies.

I interviewed her daughter, Anna, at length. I also spoke

with several of her Le Havre friends and even an Abwehr controller. No one knew what turned Clara Gaudet, of the tragedy or avarice or confusion that led her to betray her country to the Germans. She took the secret to the grave after the war. She was placed in her coffin with her neatly guillotined head under her arm.

The British have not released the name of the originator of the second false radio signal received just before S-Day, this one from Merksem about the claimed movements of the Wehrmacht's 30th Division. They will undoubtedly deal with the double agent when he or she is found.

The citizens of Norwich were more successful than Jean Lechavalier in seeking revenge. Many townfolk are ashamed of it now, though some swear they never will be. Their ancient town lay in ruins from the Luftwaffe fire-bombing. I walked through Norwich after the war. It reminded me of old photographs of San Francisco after the earthquake and fire of 1906. Some buildings had one wall remaining. Others had nothing left above ground but plumbing standing stiffly into the air. A dusty pall hung over the town. Even years after the bombing, my footsteps blew up puffs of ash.

Townspeople had quickly concluded that the devastation of Norwich had been part of the ruse. The Luftwaffe turned their village into an inferno, forcing citizens to flee into eastern county roads, clogging them, further convincing the Allies that the invasion would come from across the North Sea.

Two weeks after S-Day, a Luftwaffe pilot—the only survivor of the only bomber shot down over Norwich—was being transferred from Norwich Castle, which had escaped destruction, to a POW camp in Scotland. The castle had been used as a prison from the reign of Henry III to 1884 and was so used after the fire bombing. The airman was still wearing his tan, summer flying suit over his service tunic, and his breeches were tucked into his tall leather and suede boots. His steps were reduced by shackles, and his hands were bound behind his back. He was easily recognizable for what he was.

As he was marched toward a truck, an elderly man stepped from his tent, pushed his spectacles back on his nose, then yelled, "That's one of them. Right here, one of them."

The old man was a resident of a tent city erected since the fires burned themselves out. He continued to shout, and other residents of the canvas shelters emerged to stare at the German.

Someone yelled, "Look at him. Bloody cocksure and proud."

Another followed with "We've got nothing but ashes, and he goes to a camp to eat our food."

"He killed hundreds of us."

A crowd gathered. The army guards hurried the German along the street toward the truck.

"My boy is dead, and he's to blame."

"He shouldn't live when our town died."

"Rotter."

At first the assembly stepped hesitantly toward the airman, but anger urged them on. They spilled into the street after the prisoner. The homeless throng quickly grew to a hundred. The guards might have outrun them, but the German was hindered by the leg irons. He tripped, stumbling into a guard, who tried to right him. The crowd gained on them.

The cries were of outrage and sorrow. Motion added to the rage. The pack roughly pushed aside the guards and clutched at any part of the German the villagers could reach. He was lifted above their heads, carried on a dozen pairs of hands toward an elm tree, denuded of leaves by the fire's heat, "but with enough spring left for our purposes," one Norwich resident who wished to remain anonymous told me.

A rope was produced from somewhere. A boy was hoisted to the first branches. While the crowd cheered, he climbed as high as he could before tying a rope end to the trunk. He dropped the rope to the mob.

Many hands pulled on it, bending the tree top almost to the ground. Another Norwich citizen opined, "You Americans are better at nooses than we are. This wasn't art, but it did its duty." The noose was fitted around the terrified German's neck.

With cries of "Stand back, stand back," the rope was released. The elm straightened like a bow, dragging the hapless airman after it.

A witness said, "He kicked for five minutes, would have been longer but for the leg irons weighing him down. Then he hung there for a full day before anybody had the courage to cut him down."

Omar Hacheim had been on the German payroll for ten months and on the British payroll for nine. Hacheim was a man of principle, but he cared not a whit for either side in the war that had engulfed his homeland, so his principle was to collect as much salary as possible from both and thereby guarantee that at least one of his currencies would be worth something after the war.

Hacheim was a water vendor, a trade inherited from his father. Omar had sold his father's camels, and by dint of hard work now owned four tanker trucks, supplying water to whichever line he found himself behind. He also sold information.

Two days after S-Day, Omar and his drivers were in the German-held town of Derna on the north coast of Libya, a hundred miles east of the British line at El Gazala. Hacheim kept his notes in a tin under the dashboard of his lead truck. Lately few pages had been filled.

He was encamped near the north end of the sand airstrip at Derna. The sun was high, and Hacheim and his workers were idling. They heard the soft drone of a small plane. When it drew nearer, Hacheim recognized it as a Fieseler Storch, a scout plane. It landed lightly. Heat waves rising from the oiled runway seemed to twist the wings and fuselage. When a Mammut command car drove to the edge of the runway, the water vendor lifted his binoculars from the truck seat. Few Germans rated a Mammut.

The plane taxied to the command car. Hacheim squinted into the glasses. Out of the plane climbed a stout, thick-necked officer who moved quickly from under the wing toward the car.

Rommel, Hacheim knew at once. It must be. But Rommel had left Libya and was commanding an army in northern Europe, or so Hacheim had heard. The heat waves cleared momentarily, blown back by prop wash. Hacheim could see clearly as the German officer withdrew a pair of Perspex goggles from his bag. Rommel's trademark. The general had returned to the desert, back to the red sand and shrieking *ghibi*.

Hacheim reached into the cab for his notebook, changed his

mind and left it hidden. He would remember Rommel without notes. The British in Alexandria had given him a wireless he kept under the truck seat. They would pay well for this intelligence.

After the war Omar Hacheim complained bitterly to me that he had been cheated out of his reward for information about Rommel reappearing in Africa. By the time he sent it, Rommel's return to Africa was old news and worthless to the British.

The disastrous sum of these and a hundred other parts was that the German Army Group C, that battle-hardened Wehrmacht and Waffen SS army ready to pounce on England from across the North Sea, was a *Schatten* army, a shadow army.

The deception had been built nail by nail and plank by plank. The XXX and XXIV Corps and the XII Waffen SS Corps were decoys, intricately crafted chimeras. The supporting Luftwaffe squadrons were paper formations. Unknown to the Allies, the German navy had virtually abandoned the North Sea by S-Day.

The shadow army existed only in our minds. There it waited, in ominous detail and with fearsome purpose, until the dreadful revelations of S-Day.

15

Biographers of brilliant men suffer for their subjects' brilliance. Genius is mysterious to those of us without it. Twists and turns of a facile mind may be invisible to the writer. Nuances are lost. So I fear it is with my record of General Clay. Put bluntly, he was smarter than I was. I missed a lot.

My chronicle has been of Clay's travels, his close calls, and his histrionics. The mechanics of his command were more complex than I have so far been able to relay.

Only five percent of a commander's responsibility involves devising and issuing orders. The remainder is spent insuring those orders are carried out. But that five percent wins or loses the battle. One hour of Clay's command, examined closely, gives an idea of the general at work.

At ten o'clock of S-Day morning we walked into Bilswell Manor near Storrington, where Clay had met his commanders the night before. On Clay's orders AEFHQ had been moved there while we were in London. The planes with HQ personnel and equipment were still landing. Bilswell was also I Corps headquarters. The location was ten miles inland from the channel town of Worthing.

Here is the one hour. At 10:05, Clay conferred with Lieutenant General Alex Hargrave, who reported that the enemy units that had landed between Brighton and Beachy Head (we learned later it was the Wehrmacht's VIII Corps) were off the beach and were pressing across the South Downs toward Lewes. Initial reports indicated they were wheeling west behind Brighton. Toward us, I might add.

At 10:09, Clay put a call through to General Franks of the 1st Armored, which was between Portsmouth and Worthing. Franks told him that his beach units were not engaged, and nothing was on the channel horizon. While Franks waited on the telephone, Clay consulted with Hargrave, then said into the phone, "Roger, we think the German has staked out his beaches and that his second wave will hit exactly behind the first. Any beach not hit by now won't be."

Franks must have agreed, since Clay then said, "We'll need support along a line from Horsham to Worthing. Tell me what you can do."

After a moment and a nod from Hargrave, Clay said, "Do it immediately."

Clay turned to a stenographer. "I have approved the movement of the 13th Armored Regiment east toward Horsham and the 1st Armored Regiment east along the South Downs in the direction of Brighton. They are directed to form a perimeter roughly between Worthing and Horsham."

He waited until the stenographer looked up again, then ordered, "Read it back to me."

The stenographer complied.

Clay said, "I want you to have Franks' steno repeat it when you're done, Corporal."

"Yes, sir." The stenographer hurried to the signal station.

Headquarters personnel from Eastwell filtered into the room. Clay moved toward the fireplace and turned his back to it as if to warm himself. He rose on his toes several times, his arms behind his back. There was no fire. I joined him.

He said, "You know why I always have them repeat it?"

"Yes, sir, I do," I replied.

"History is replete with appalling tragedies due to misinterpreted orders. During the Crimean War, Lord Raglan's order to Lord Lucan, bungled somewhere in the transmittal, resulted in the disastrous Charge of the Light Brigade, and 'All that was left of them, left of six hundred.'"

"Yes, sir." I add here that Clay maintained a running dialogue with me throughout S-Day and the days that followed. He gave his own play by play, just like a radio broadcast of a baseball game. Most of the time he cared not at all whether I heard or understood him. He needed to fill the brief silences with the sound of his own voice.

"At Colenso during the Boer War, General Buller upped the time of attack by forty-eight hours, but forgot to send the order to General White, which resulted in a debacle."

"Yes, sir."

I thought I was in for a long siege, but at 10:14 General Clay was called over to the dining room table where David Lorenzo had spread out his ever-present maps. Alex Hargrave followed us. Signalmen were working swiftly, pulling lines through a window and unpacking more communications equipment. A TWX was already clicking.

Lorenzo never fully trusted technology and was always accompanied by cages of London messenger pigeons, but wire was the first significant technological advance in military communication in the millenia, and the G2 took full advantage of it. He already had a telephone at each ear. His dark brows were knitted together, and he dictated positions to subordinates, who marked them with colored stickers on a map of Kent and Sussex.

Lorenzo handed the phones to a signalman. He pointed at a map and said to Clay, "Those sporadic reports of German commandoes from Selindge and Stanford, behind Hythe, now indicate a full-scale airborne operation there."

His finger traced an eight-mile arc behind Hythe, a town on the channel. "They've landed on this stretch, three, four, and five miles inland from the town. We think as many as two or three brigades, maybe as much as a division, have dropped."

We learned later these were the troops of the Wehrmacht's 7th Parachute Division.

"This has taken a while to confirm, General," Lorenzo went on. "But instead of punching inland, the German paratroopers are almost doubling back, moving east, paralleling the channel inland, toward Dover and Deal. The 134th has been hit hard."

"Behind our beach lines," Clay commented, his finger following Lorenzo's. "They're trying to roll us up."

"Yes, sir."

"Any reports yet of landings on the Thames estuary?"

"Nothing."

Clay spoke with General Hargrave for a moment, then turned to Captain Branch. "Get me Carsen."

At 10:18 Clay was connected to Roderick Carsen, commander of the 5th Infantry, at his headquarters near Canterbury. Clay plugged an ear against the increasing noise. He spoke with Hargrave again. Clay's deputy, Lieutenant General Patrick Neil, joined them and added a few sentences. I couldn't hear much of what was said. Then Clay spoke again into the phone to Carsen.

He waved over another stenographer and said, "I have approved advances of the 5th Antitank and the 19th Field Artillery battalions and the 10th Infantry Regiment to the south on a line corresponding to the Canterbury-Dover Road, the mechanism left to Carsen's discretion. Read it back."

The steno did so, then left for Branch's desks. Yet another stenographer replaced him. They had been trained to run in relays.

At 10:23 one of Clay's secretaries announced, "General Stedman is calling."

Clay pointed to one of Lorenzo's telephones, and a few seconds later it buzzed. He put on his spectacles, lifted the phone, bent over Lorenzo's map, and said, "I'm putting my G2 on the line, Arthur."

Lorenzo lifted a telephone. He pulled over another map and began tacking colorful markers on it.

Clay said, "A diversion, you think, Arthur? . . . Too heavy? . . . Where'd they come from? . . . Do you need anything from my end?"

Clay was learning of another prong of the German attack, the landings at Lyme Bay.

The general continued, "I'm going to order the same thing, Arthur, as much as it eats at me. What does Alexander say?"

Alexander was commander in chief of Joint Army Operations, Clay and Stedman's superior.

"I'll hear from you soon, Arthur. We'll make it." Clay lowered the receiver onto its brackets.

While Lorenzo took more reports, Clay walked out of the dining room. He lit a Pall Mall, then said to nobody, "Stedman will be my Eugene, my Jackson."

Clay was immodestly referring to the most successful military partnerships in history: Marlborough with Prince Eugene of Savoy, and Robert E. Lee with Stonewall Jackson.

At 10:28, General Hargrave approached Clay again. Hargrave had left his pipe somewhere. I was startled. I did not think he had an existence apart from his pipe. His mouth was a thin line. He said quietly and precisely, "We have lost contact with 9th Infantry Regiment and the 15th Field Artillery Battalion near Hastings. I presume they have been overrun."

Hargrave was interrupted by a signalman who handed him a report. He glanced at it, then said, "Colonel Williams of the 38th Infantry has requested pullout of his regiment to positions inland. Burt Jones has approved. Williams estimates the 38th has a seventy percent casualty rate. Two battalion commanders, Lieutenant Colonels Halperson and Lawton, have been killed."

"We'll go with Jones' decision," Clay said with a curled mouth, as if from an acrid taste.

At 10:33 David Lorenzo waved for Clay. His cluster of red tags had moved inland on his map. He said, "Generals Girard and Hammond on the line."

Clay took the telephone. He listened for a moment to the commanders of II Corps and the 35th Infantry, then said, "Did any battalions get out? . . . Any companies? . . . All right, move right now to save remaining shore regiments. Pull them back. Don't reinforce defeat by throwing in your reserves. I will get back to you within ten minutes."

He put down the phone, pointed at the map, and said, "The enemy punched through and enveloped the 137th Infantry and two regiments of the 60th Artillery. The Wehrmacht arrived just in back of 60th's positions, destroying supply and signal. Those units are lost."

By 10:36 David Lorenzo had his team in place and his large map pinned on the east wall of the dining room. G2 clerks stood in front of it much like Wrens before a RAF filter room map table. Messages flooded Bilswell Manor. Lorenzo's staff, now numbering about fifteen in the manor house, sorted and routed them. Divisional level communications were immediately given to the G2. Others were studied by Lorenzo's subordinates, who would order a change on the maps if necessary. Other clerks logged the messages.

Bulletins from the line were unremittingly bleak. Breaking through, flanking, encircling, pursuing, the AEF was on the wrong end of it all. Red flags, moving progressively inland, showed the tenacity of the assault. Our coastal wall was proving to be porous. Each tiny shift of a red flag represented a mad melee, a cosmos of terror and death.

Without looking away from G2's new map, Clay ordered, "Captain Branch, put me through to the War Ministry. And tell Lieutenant Gupka to keep his seat. We don't have time for the niceties."

Clay and Hargrave and Lorenzo discussed the evolving map for a few minutes. At 10:52, Branch yelled from the dining room, "The prime minister and Generals Barclay and Alexander are on the line, sir."

Clay again lifted the telephone. He briefly summarized reports. Then he said, "I advise we establish a new defensive line from Worthing inland to Horsham, then east to Uckfield, Tenterden, Ashford to Canterbury, then south to the channel again at Dover."

With those words, the general admitted he could not hold much of the southern counties. The new perimeter would be ten to fifteen miles inland from the channel.

Clay said, "Yes, Prime Minister, I fully realize that I propose to cede a third of the English soil between the channel and the city. It is an exchange of land for time."

He paused for a moment and said to Hargrave and Lorenzo, "Winnie and the others are arguing among themselves."

The general lowered his chin to the telephone again. "Yes, Prime Minister, I understand England does not have a thousand miles of steppes to cast before the enemy, as the Russians did before Napoleon."

He paused, then argued, "U. S. Grant gave ground at Shiloh."

Clay waited again, then said, "Yes, sir, I'll henceforth keep my American history to myself. . . . No. We will hold Ramsgate and the peninsula because I can turn my 5th Infantry around slicker than hell, and I don't think the German can cut through to the Thames estuary there. The line will run from Canterbury to the channel."

Another moment elapsed, then he said, "Good. I'll issue the orders immediately. I also request that the Canadians be released to my command."

The Canadian I Corps was in reserve just east and south of the London.

Clay listened for a moment, then argued, "I don't give a good goddamn if Henry will have a fit. I don't want to quibble with that quarrelsome Canuck about committing them when the time comes."

The general grimaced, then said, "I hope you'll get back to me on that quickly, General Barclay. And XI Corps?"

The British XI Corps had been held inland until the day before, when it was ordered to reinforce the North Sea coast. It had done an about-face that morning and was now returning south in a daylight march. It was suffering murderous losses to the Luftwaffe.

Clay listened, staring at a point above the entry to the dining room. "General Barclay, I've got to have those soldiers under my command. Our area of exposure is now known to us and all the rest of God's people. It's my area. Troops of my 35th Division are as green as an Englishman's teeth, and I'm going to need your people right now."

The general was quiet for a few seconds, then continued, "All right. Let me know within an hour, General Barclay. . . . Yes, Prime Minister? . . . All right, I'll listen to the BBC at nine o'clock tonight if I have time."

Clay pursed his lips. "It won't go to my head. . . . Yes, I understand that the flattering things you'll be saying about me to the British people tonight are only part of your morale-lifting campaign and are not to be taken seriously by me. . . . We'll speak again shortly, Prime Minister."

Clay tossed the phone to his G2. "Jesus, I wonder what got under Winnie's skin."

I offered, "Perhaps it was having the Germans invade his homeland and having his people's teeth called green, all in the same morning."

Generals don't listen to ADCs at times like this, fortunately for me.

He called out, "Pat, will you come here?"

AEF's deputy commander trotted in from the living room signal station. The building had filled and was bustling.

It took Clay less than sixty seconds to outline his plan. He finished with "We are going to retreat in an orderly and fighting fashion, in short stages just in front of the enemy. We will inflict casualties as we pull back, and we will avoid any hint of a rout."

He brought his gaze up from the map. "Pat, you are to relay this to Gene Girard at II Corps."

"Yes, General."

"You tell him in no uncertain terms that the 5th has got to come about."

"Yes, sir."

This was not the winking, chuckling commander who had reviewed his troops on the beaches the day before. General Clay always showed a harder face to his staff and intimates, except to me, because I was a proxy for him when he was talking to himself.

Hargrave and Neil went to their business. Clay grasped his hands behind his back and walked back into the manor's main room. I walked with him. He said, "Short and sweet."

"Pardon, sir?"

"Keep orders short and sweet. Never more than a page. Do you know why?"

Why bother replying?

He explained, "In the Great War, Haig's chief of staff, General Kiggel, issued an order for attack consisting of fifty-seven goddamn pages, excluding appendices. Never issue an order that takes longer to read than it does to execute."

282

"Yes, sir."

He stepped around to face me directly. He locked me up with his gaze. This time he was not talking to himself. "Nothing is ever as bad as is reported to headquarters, Jack. Remember that."

I believed him, despite all the evidence.

It was eleven o'clock in the morning of S-Day. The evidence was bad, and it would get worse.

I can recall General Clay and the prime minister's argument about courage as if I had taken notes. It occurred in Churchill's study at Chartwell a week before S-Day. The topic was whether a drunk can be courageous. An hour and a half I listened, contributing nothing but an occasional cough.

I sat near the Tudor doorway, in front of a table on which were several unidentifiable busts and a cigar box. Above me were rafters and beams dating from before the Renaissance. A bronze cast of Jennie Churchill's hand was on the windowsill. Bookshelves lined several walls. Two desks were opposite each other across a worn Persian rug. The taller desk was for working while standing, with a slanting top in the Victorian fashion. Churchill was wearing his work outfit, a scarlet, green, and gold dressing gown. We were drinking three-ounce scotches, Churchill's brand, Johnny Walker Red.

Churchill said, "But we do not praise a drunken man for his fearlessness. Valor must be sought. Shakespeare termed it 'The pursuit of the bubble of reputation even at the cannon's mouth.' "

"Shakespeare?" the general replied mildly. "The English writer?"

The prime minister's glare could have burned through metal.

Clay ignored it and said, "Forethought is not a requirement of courage. It can be impulsive."

"You are saying then, General, that an animal may be courageous?"

"Of course."

"Rubbish. A dog in its ignorance is fearless, which is far less than courageous."

The general countered, "Lincoln said, 'Courage can be found in the suddenness of the moment.'"

"Which Lincoln?"

They went on and on, and believe me when I say history will forgive me for not recording it all here. General Clay always wanted the last word, and he invariably had to wait until he and I were alone again to get it. This time, as we entered the jeep, Clay said, "Palmerston, Pitt, Baldwin, they all liked the sauce. Now Churchill. Something about leading the English people turns a man to drink."

I set out a portion of their debate on courage because on this argument the events of S-Day made me side with General Clay.

Five Congressional Medals of Honor were granted for exploits of the invasion, and two Victoria Crosses. I have read these citations and similar ones for German servicemen and have talked to some of the soldiers and sailors. These gallant acts may not have occurred had there been time to think of them. At least, that is the servicemen's testimony. Let me mention a few.

A sure way to win our nation's highest decoration for bravery is to fall on a grenade. Private Murray Cooperman did just that and lived to tell about it. Cooperman was a rifleman with Company B, 2nd Battalion, 38th Infantry Regiment at Pevensey Bay, the precise landing place of William the Conqueror 876 years earlier.

Cooperman said, "But unlike the Anglo-Saxon defenders, we had automatic weapons and bazookas, which can be helpful in those situations."

His squad was defending a fortified house two hundred yards behind the beach. The survivors of the beach bulwarks were streaming past in stunned and wounded disarray.

"I remember that lull, between the last staggering American to clear our field of fire and the first Germans. Seemed like two hours, but it was five minutes. Then an enemy squadron appeared from behind some bushes, and they ran full bore toward the house, no cover, nothing. I opened up with my M1, but I was a piss-poor shot and don't think I hit a one of them.

We had a light machine gun at another window, and that made them dive for cover."

Cooperman went on, "But I give the bastards credit. They kept coming, using high grass, hugging the ground, as there wasn't anything else to hide behind. I'd see an enemy's helmet here, a quick movement there, a muzzle flash somewhere else, always closer, but never much of a target, like prairie dogs. They were providing cover for a grenadier."

A spray of bullets hit the sill below Cooperman, some bursting through wood and plaster into the sandbags. The rifleman ducked, and more bullets coursed through the window, stitching the wall behind him. Cooperman's sergeant went down with a pierced thigh. A grenade came through the window.

"The potato-masher can be thrown farther than an American grenade, but that German was right under the window. I don't know how he got there. So I left my rifle and leaped across the room to fall on it."

"What were you thinking?" I asked Cooperman after the war.

"I didn't think."

I was determined to get to the bottom of such a crazed act. "Surely something entered your head. I mean, a body just doesn't fall on a grenade."

"Yes, it does, and mine did. And nothing entered my mind, or I probably wouldn't have done it."

The stick grenade was silent.

"After about twenty seconds our medic crawled over. With my nose dug into the floor, I said to him, 'These things got about a five-second fuse, don't they?' The medic said they did, and I said, 'Well, I'm no chicken and this's no egg, and my time is up warming this goddamn thing.' "

That's what Cooperman claims he said anyway.

The rifleman was shaking so violently the medic had to help him up. "I felt somewhat foolish. I picked up the grenade gingerly, like it was a tea cup, my little finger sticking out, and I crawled back to the window and dropped it out. That's when it exploded, killing the fellow beneath the window. A faulty fuse saved my life. But I got the medal anyway. My captain, who was in the room and saw it all, saw to that."

General Clay once told me that the receipt of wounds, rather than the infliction of them, is historically how the British demonstrated courage. He said, "Witness the 27th Regiment, the Inniskillings, who at Waterloo stood in their square, motionless for four hours, while being cannonaded by Napoleon's artillery." If Clay was correct, then Edgar Sisler won the Victoria Cross in the time-honored manner.

Sisler and I had a few beers after the war. Between carefully measured sips, Sisler told me, "I look much the worse for my Victoria Cross, I must say."

Indeed, Sisler had more scars than I have seen on any other person, and in my travels for this narrative I have seen plenty. His scars ran like road maps from place to place, with perforations at some locations, rolled and pleated scar tissue at others, a mess. He was proud of them.

Sisler was a machine gunner at Lyme Bay. His weapon was a .303 Vickers. He said, "A machine gun is used to freeze the front. And we wanted it frozen right there on the beach. But the Germans kept coming, and our captain ordered a retreat. I volunteered to cover it. He kindly left his service pistol for me."

Sisler twisted the Vickers left and right, spraying the beach as his mates pulled back. "On defense, the machine gun must be kept firing at any price, so I had to stay the course, don't you see."

Alone, Sisler tried to keep the invaders at bay, firing at anything that moved in front of his dugout. A bullet passed through the meat of his right arm.

"I don't remember any pain from that one," he told me. He put down his beer to roll up his right sleeve. Just above his elbow was a crater the size of a quarter in his biceps and another rougher one caused when the bullet exited the triceps.

He continued to fire. A few seconds later another bullet took off half of his right ear.

At the pub, he pulled back his hair to show me the remainder of his ear. It was clipped neatly. "The upper half, fortunately," he said. "I can almost hide it under my hair."

Then the Germans employed an antitank grenade launcher against him. "It hit the front of the sandbag and the blast took off quite a bit of my scalp," he said, which explained the purple and blue welts covering his forehead.

"A machine gun gets all the attention, and that was my problem at that point," Sisler told me, signaling for another beer.

While he was reloading, a bullet creased his neck.

He lowered his shirt collar to show me the ridges of skin.

When he took the Vickers' grip again, a bullet dug into his wrist and wormed its way up the length of his left arm to pop out at his elbow.

He again lowered his beer to the table. He rolled up his other sleeve to display the line of damaged tissue extending from his wrist to elbow.

He kept firing. "I was a madman, I tell you. There was nothing left on this earth but that Vickers and me. A grenade blast threw shrapnel into my left leg."

Sisler rolled up his pants. By now everyone in the pub was watching him, including the publican behind the counter, a woman whose figure resembled a barrage balloon and whose mouth was turned down in disapproval. Sisler's leg was serrated horizontally with scars, looking like evenly spaced railroad ties.

Another grenade blast knocked him over, and he rose to find his left arm was limp.

"So I used my right hand," he explained as he unbottoned his shirt far enough to show me the streaks of scar tissue on his shoulder, looking as if someone had applied the scar with a putty knife.

He kept firing. Another explosion, and steel needles entered his chest and cheeks.

Over the beer he pointed them out, pleats of purple skin that looked drawn with blue ink.

That detonation bent the Vicker's barrel out of true. Sisler lifted his Enfield rifle and began rhythmically pulling the trigger. "Blood was coming down my face in sheets. I had to wipe my face with my sleeve."

Another bullet hit him in stomach.

"That's the wound that told me my time was nigh." He stood over the beer, lifted his shirt, and pointed to the abdomen scar.

It reminded me of an egg fried over easy.

He does not remember how many rounds he fired from the Lee Enfield. "There was a two-minute period there when I didn't receive any new wounds. I was quite encouraged. Then I ran out of shells for the rifle. I reached for the captain's pistol, a Webley. Didn't take me long to empty that, either. I fired blindly, blood blocking my vision, until the hammer was falling on empty chambers."

He continued, "The Germans must have thought I'd gone for a burton. So they rushed the dugout. I swung my rifle by the barrel, like a cricket bat. I killed two of the buggers that way. Then I fainted dead away. A man only has so much blood."

"What accounts for you sitting across from me today?" I asked.

"My captain, bless him and his children, returned after he had taken the others back. Now you might be wondering why I sit on this bench at an incline."

I hadn't noticed.

He said, "The captain threw me over his shoulder and ran back along a communication trench. My rump was exposed, and it took more shrapnel, which tore out some padding. I'd take down my trousers to show you, if the proprietor weren't a lady, at least from outward appearances."

Obergefreiter Franz Stahl and the others in his rifle platoon were trotting behind two panzers across a narrow pasture, between rows of trees. He preferred open areas because then the tanks led. In woods or thickets, the infantry led the tanks. It was safer at the rear, far, far safer.

A mine detonated under the lead tank, throwing the panzer's tread. Stahl remembers it as being an insignificant explosion rather than a hint of what was to come, a muffled puff that sent a few treads off their rail. Abruptly propelled by only one tread, the tank spun left. Then the treadless wheels dug into the soft pasture. The panzer stalled. The second tank almost rammed into the disabled panzer. The vehicle turned left just as an AT barrage opened up.

Fifty yards behind the panzers, Corporal Stahl heard the metal clang and smothered roar of an AT hit on the second tank. The fire came from a 37mm gun hidden in the woods. The weapon was being directly layed, fired over open sights, because barrages did not work against armor. The second tank's cupola flew open, and Stahl saw a hand try for a grip, then a torch of flame blew out, and the hand disappeared within it. The crew was cooked alive.

A machine gun sounded from the woods, ringing the first tank like a bell. Small arms fire scattered clods of dirt in front of Stahl, who dove to the ground. He heard a scream to his left. It sounded like his sergeant.

The lead panzer's cupola opened and out came the commander. He was instantly hit, and he slid off the turret into the camouflage foliage strapped to the aft deck. His black uniform was designed to disguise grease and oil stains common among armored crews, but it also masked blood. Even so, Stahl saw the red blotch spread along the commander's thigh.

Undoubtedly knowing the AT gun would soon find their disabled tank, the gunner, loader, and driver came next, one at a time, each to be cut down before they could find cover. The tank commander remained alive, and perhaps the driver. The commander began crawling away from his vehicle, but was waved back by Stahl's lieutenant, who yelled, *"Minen, minen!"*

"Well, perhaps I was inspired by Hansel and Gretel," Stahl told me after the war. "But actually I can't recall making any sort of decision."

Stahl rose and began pumping for the tank. As he ran, he dropped parts of his kit, first his canteen, then his spade, then his respirator case, then his haversack, marking his path through the minefield.

"I ran in a straight line, and I knew that any step might be my last," he recalled. "Bullets flew all around, making this funny fizzing sound."

Hours later, when the corporal had a moment to take inventory, he found two holes on the left side of his tunic, where a bullet had passed between his arm and his chest.

Breathing heavily more from fear than exertion, Stahl rounded the burning tank to reach the crew of the lead tank. He sank to the ground among the panzer's dead and wounded crewmen. The tank commander's eyes were closed, but his mouth was moving. He was alive. The driver moaned, alive also. Stahl lifted the commander onto his own back, then crawled toward the nearest marker, his haversack, which loomed like a harbor beacon in front of him. By then his platoon had set up their two machine guns and were returning fire, covering him.

Stahl made his way steadily, arm over arm, his face just above ground. He felt the tank commander's blood on his pants. They passed the haversack, then the respirator case. He heard a shell scream into the lead tank. When he glanced behind, the turret had been blown off the chassis and was upside down on the ground, looking like a turtle on its back.

He carried the tank commander to the platoon, which was now dug in and giving more than they were getting. The American machine gun may have been knocked out by this time, Stahl was not sure. He immediately turned on his belly and retraced his route, wondering when his luck would end, spitting out grass and bits of thistle that caught in his mouth.

The driver was still alive when the corporal returned. Stahl yanked him onto his back, and began again toward his platoon. The driver's mouth dropped onto Stahl's ear, and every time Stahl pushed himself forward, the driver clamped his jaw painfully onto his rescuer's ear. The corporal's legs were cramping. His back felt like flame was searing along it. His throat was so dry it felt like canvas.

Except for his gnawed ear, Stahl made it back to his platoon unscathed. Gunfire from the woods redoubled. A squadron had encircled the American unit. Wehrmacht soldiers had been told the Yanks were underequipped, undernourished, and undertrained. They would not last long.

Stahl received a firm handshake from his lieutenant. The Reich was more generous, awarding him the Knight's Cross.

General Clay once said, "Canadians are odd ducks, and the French are crazed, so when you add the two, the combination can scarcely be imagined." Sergeant René LaPoint, a French-Canadian, may have proven the general correct.

LaPoint, from the town of Laval near Montreal, had joined the British Army the day after the German invasion of Poland. His avocation was training dogs for search and rescue in the north country, and he was a member of the Quebec Rescue League. LaPoint shipped four dogs with him to England. I have seen the memorandum written by Commander in Chief, Home Forces, Arthur Stedman, reluctantly approving LaPoint's plan. The memo stressed the dire shortage of antitank weapons.

LaPoint taught his German shepherds that food would be found under a tank. For weeks, he fed them only under a panzer mock-up, and in the days before S-Day, he kept them a bit hungry. He endured the taunts of his fellow soldiers, who called him Canine René. He vowed he would show them.

On S-Day, the 4th Panzer Grenadiers, an armored infantry regiment, pierced the line and gulped up half a dozen miles of southern England. The sergeant, his dogs, and two other French Canadian canine trainers had been detached from their unit and rushed south to meet the German armor. The Germans who had landed east of Brighton were pivoting west. The sergeant and his dogs found the 4th Panzer just inland from Worthing.

LaPoint and his team hid in a farmhouse north of Worthing. He was gratified when the panzers stormed by, then paused to regroup a hundred yards behind him. The armor had outrun their infantry support.

He left the house with the other two trainers and his four dogs. The animals were on tight leather leashes. Robespierre —whom LaPoint had nicknamed the Incorruptible, the same nickname given to the revolutionary—led the way. On each dog was a pack containing three sticks of dynamite and a detonator. The sergeant carried rolls of wire, an electric switch, and a battery. The tanks had churned up a cloud of dust, which helped hide the French Canadians as they ran tree to tree, closing in on the German armor. Danton, the second dog, barked. LaPoint flicked the German shepherd's nose to silence him.

The AT team stopped behind a hedgerow fifty yards from the nearest panzer. The tanks were painted in what was called an ambush scheme: patches of red-brown over a yellow base coat with spots of yellow on top of it all, to simulate sunlight filtering through trees. The tanks were almost invisible, even at LaPoint's short distance. Through the dust and tree

291

branches he thought he could see a tank commander standing in the cupola of his machine, using his radio.

Messerschmitts soared overhead. The sergeant connected the wire to Robespierre. He quietly thanked the dog, wished him God speed, then ordered, "Robespierre, go."

The dog trotted around the end of a hedgerow. The wire peeled off the spool in LaPoint's hand as Robespierre traveled toward the nearest tank, an Ausf E.

Feverish with his imminent redemption from all the jokes that had been told about him and his dogs, the sergeant readied his hand on the switch. At his feet, Danton and Marat and Abbé Sieyès patiently waited their doom.

Twenty yards from his target tank, Robespierre paused to lift his leg on a beech tree. Then the German shepherd looked over its shoulder at LaPoint and apparently decided it was not hungry enough to crawl under a tank. Robespierre lay down, resting his muzzle on a foreleg, duty forgotten.

LaPoint heard the other two French Canadian soldiers laugh derisively from the safety of the hedgerow.

Rage enveloped LaPoint. His failure would be reported to all his scoffing friends. He was still angry when I interviewed him at his home in Quebec after the war. "That mangy cur, that ingrate, that mutt."

Flushed with anger, the sergeant jumped over the hedgerow and ran through the woods to his dog. "I was so mad it didn't cross my mind that I could be spotted by the tanks."

Robespierre leaped up to greet him, panting, happy for the sudden reunion. LaPoint yelled, "You do as I tell you, god-damn it."

He reattached the leash to Robespierre's collar and started toward the tank. Just then the panzer's driver wound up his engine, and the dog balked. This was no wood mock-up. Cursing, the sergeant dragged the dog between trees toward the panzers. LaPoint bellowed at Robespierre, "I will not be disgraced by a bastard mutt."

But twenty yards from the nearest tank, Robespierre dug in his heels and refused to take another step. "The Germans must have expected nothing to approach from their rear. They simply didn't look back."

Blind with fury and humiliation, LaPoint yanked the dynamite sticks out of Robespierre's backpack. "This is what I've trained you to do, you son of a bitch mongrel. You watch this."

Carrying the explosives, the sergeant dashed to the rear tank. He threw the packet under the chassis and retreated, trailing the wire behind him. Robespierre followed.

LaPoint threw the switch. The explosion ruptured the tank's belly and was quickly followed by the blast of its ammunition, which blew the vehicle onto its back and knocked down three nearby trees. The ground under LaPoint's feet shuddered with the tank's weight.

"The Incorruptible, my ass," LaPoint said as he attached another wire to Robespierre. LaPoint's fellow soldiers looked on in awe from the hedgerow. The sergeant signaled one of them to bring another package of dynamite.

The lead panzer's commander had dropped back into his turret, and the three other tanks slowly moved ahead and fanned out, looking for the American AT team. They rolled over elm saplings, which bent to the ground under the panzers' weight.

LaPoint dropped the dynamite into the satchel and made the connection. "Now, Robespierre, go."

The dog took off again, aimed at another tank. The wire played out from the spool. The German shepherd ran, then walked, then dawdled, then sat and yawned, looking without interest at the burning, overturned tank.

"Bastard," LaPoint screamed over the guffaws of his friends.

In a white fury, he raced again to Robespierre. "You flea-infested pile of fur. I'll teach you if I die trying."

Again he withdrew the dynamite from the pack and bolted after the German armor. The aft tank's turret spun his way, but stopped before it drew a bead and then swiveled back. The sergent gained on the tank, hurdling over fallen elms. "That goddamn kraut dog."

The tank abruptly stopped. LaPoint ran up the tank's exhaust plume and hurled the sticks under it. He retraced his steps, playing out the wire. The panzer turned in its own length. LaPoint felt the cold wash of fear and sensed the periscope finding him.

The ball-mounted MG 34 spewed bullets, felling a tree near LaPoint and Robespierre. The sergeant flipped the switch.

According to the two French Canadian onlookers, who testified on behalf of LaPoint's decoration, the panzer lifted five feet off the ground, all fifty tons of it, then dropped to the earth in a landing that must have shaken the entire county.

LaPoint made it back to the hedgerow and was reaching for another charge when the other French Canadians wrestled him to the ground. They shouted that he would never make it again, that his berserk luck would surely end.

Frothing, LaPoint yelled back, "I'm going to strangle that goddamn Robespierre."

They held him on the ground, LaPoint shaking with rage and screaming he was going to kill the dog the first chance he got. Then panzer machine gun bullets piped overhead, sobering the sergeant. Without another word the three rose and scampered along the hedgerow, a full retreat, the dogs in tow.

"I've never felt I deserved the Victoria Cross that I received," LaPoint told me. "But my friends testified that I ran up to the two panzers and destroyed them single-handedly. They never mentioned that mutt Robespierre or my demented rage."

At the end of our interview, I asked him what had happened to Robespierre. LaPoint shrugged, "He's in the kennel out back with the others. I'm trying to teach him to find lost hikers, but as you've gathered, he's a slow learner."

A silver star is not a Congressional Medal of Honor or a Victoria Cross. But I'm proud of mine, and let me report here how I earned it.

Five days before S-Day, General Clay and I were on one of his endless inspection tours, this one in Kent. We had just finished meeting with Colonel Richard Barnes of the 46th Field Artillery Battalion, assigned to the 5th Infantry Division, and were driving by a supply depot on our way to the 5th's headquarters near Canterbury. The depot was hidden among trees, with camouflage tents strung from trunk to trunk. An air raid siren sounded—the constant refrain of my stay in England—so I pulled the jeep under a roadside glade of trees to wait for the all-clear.

AA guns near the depot rumbled. The general and I stepped

out from under the branches to watch the shells explode high overhead. German airplanes—I couldn't tell which kind, or even if they were fighters or bombers—flitted in and out of the clouds.

Its stertorous sound indicated the AA gun was a three-inch M3, which fired shells to an altitude of over three miles. At the beginning of the war, the Americans guessed that one German airplane would be shot down for every fifty AA shells fired from the ground. "We had hoped for the Kipling equation," Clay said, " 'Ten thousand pounds of education drops to a ten rupee.' " Events had proven the ratio to be one plane for every twelve thousand shells. The AA units' long and pounding productions usually produced very little. "All pop and no punch," Clay summarized.

But this time, as he shielded his eyes against the luminous clouds, the general said, "I'll be go to hell. They got one."

The AA gunners were on a ridge two miles to the east. Their victim left a blazing trail as it fell from the sky. The pilot desperately tried to right the plane, and he almost accomplished the manuever, but the craft dipped and rolled. As it rushed across the sky toward us, I recognized the plane as a Heinkel Griffon, a fighter bomber that appeared to have only two nacelles and propellers, but I knew to have four engines in pairs on each wing. Prone to engine fires, it was an experimental plane that had somehow made it into general Luftwaffe service. German pilots called it the Flying Coffin.

"Jack, with that plane gliding right in at us, I'll bet you're tempted to run or duck," Clay said.

It came on steadily, billowing black smoke.

I replied, "Not at all, sir." A whopper. The damned thing seemed headed straight for the bridge of my nose.

Losing altitude quickly, the Griffon streaked across the pasture east of us, then ripped into the trees fifty yards up the road. An explosion shook the trees, and a yellow mushroom of flame lifted skyward.

The general and I arrived at the crash sight a moment later. The plane had landed in the depot, tearing away camouflage nets and branches before it skidded into a quonset hut to explode, shooting balls of flame in all directions. The remains of the Griffon were lost in the roaring conflagration. A dozen fires dappled the depot grounds. Three flatbed trucks were blazing, as was a hill of gunny sacks, perhaps flour. Fire was eating at one end of a stack of crates. Stripped away by a tree, one flaming wing had spun into the quartermaster's tent. Pillars of flame rose from the canvas, lapping at the tree branches above.

Clay climbed out of the jeep, intent on directing fire control. I heard a cry from the tent, then a muffled whimper. I dislike reporting here that my first thought was, "I shouldn't be expected to check this out."

There was no one else near, so I ran toward the tent. I slowed several times, praying someone would overtake me. No one did. The wing had sliced off half the immense tent. Flame crawled along the remaining portion. The fire made a frightening hiss. I circled the tent until I found the entrance. The flap was on fire. I stepped toward it, close enough to feel the heat on my face. I heard the cry again.

"Goddamn it, I don't want to go in there," I said to myself bravely.

Inexplicably, I did, bowing my head and raising my arm, a fullback's charge through the flap. Heat engulfed me. I took a breath and the air seemed to scour my throat and lungs. Mad waves of fire danced all around.

Two soldiers were on the ground at the back of the tent, trapped in the canvas that had been pulled down on them by the wing. One had a bloody slash on his forehead and was burbling, but may have been unconscious. The other, tightly swaddled in the canvas, was wailing in terror. Fire was crawling along the rumpled and twisted canvas toward them.

Unable to breath, I stumbled forward. The conscious soldier's arms were pinned behind him, so I grabbed him by his armpits and yanked. I was losing strength to the heat. I pulled again and again, tugging him bit by bit from the cloth. He finally slipped out, kicking and yelling. He stood, but locked his legs against moving toward the burning flap. I took him by an arm and towed him through.

God, it was wonderfully cool outside that tent. I breathed an enormous draft of air. I felt parboiled. A stave snapped, cruelly reminding me there was another soldier inside and inviting me in for another go.

I later told General Clay, "I was scared to death, and I honestly don't know why I ran back into the tent."

He replied, "You knew that if I saw you standing there picking your nose while one of my soldiers burned to death, I'd shitcan your ass back to San goddamn Diego before the last embers died."

"That must have been it, all right."

I lunged back through the flaming flap. The tent roof sagged. Fire was all around, shimmering walls of it. I was terrified. I dug into the canvas folds, trying to pry the other soldier free. A piece of flaming canvas dropped onto my back. I frantically brushed at it. The place was filled with bitter smoke, making me cough and gag. I lifted rolls of the canvas, burning my hand, then tugged as hard as my ebbing strength would allow. I kicked at the canvas and shoved it back, grabbed him, then slid him out. Walking backwards, I dragged him through the tent. The burning flap raking my back.

When Wilson Clay later pinned the silver star on my chest, he said, "Don't let this go to your head. I give these away like candy at Mardi Gras."

I knew better. And as he said it, his voice caught in his throat.

16

Lady Anne Percival stalked General Clay like a coyote after a rabbit. She traced him across the sky like a gunsight on a Browning .50 caliber. She set a snare for him, carefully laying the wire across his path. I'm tempted to add half a dozen more bad similes.

But after the war, when General Hargrave and I were sharing memories, he offered his own, "You know, Wilson Clay lit out after that English woman like a hound on a scent."

I was astonished. General Clay chasing Lady Anne? What sort of heretical revisionism was this?

I was a civilian by then, so I could risk impertinence. "You've got it backwards, don't you, General?"

Alex Hargrave laughed. "You were devoted to the man, Jack, and like a government mule, you were wearing blinders."

Devoted, to be sure. That's part of an ADC's duty. But blinders? I doubt it. General Clay and Lady Anne's relationship was a patchwork of meetings. I witnessed most of them, thinking at first they were happenstance, then suspecting otherwise.

Much of General Clay's job was to show the flag and cement the alliance. After a long day at his desk or on inspection, he would fly to a social engagement to fraternize with Britain's powerful. He loathed this assignment, or so he said.

Shortly after the general and Lady Anne's first meeting, she began appearing regularly at these dinners, escorted by an earl or a viscount—she had an inexhaustible supply of nobility—whom she would discard at the first opportunity. Then she would materialize alongside the general.

She appeared at Admiral Fairfax's home in Portsmouth wearing widow's black and diamonds, a breathtaking vision. She was on Viscount Vanderman's arm, until she left him at the bar in the library. She spent the rest of the evening in General Clay's circle, which, predictably, became Lady Anne's circle. She showed up at General Stedman's dinner at his London flat, escorted by Sir William Tally, who mysteriously disappeared after cocktails. She sidled up to General Clay near the globe in the library, and they were scarcely apart the remainder of the evening.

She appeared once at Chartwell for a dinner, the hottest ticket in the kingdom. She came in with General Sutton of Fighter Command, a notorious bachelor, who grinned slyly as he handed her over to Clay as if by some prearrangement. At an opportune moment, I asked Churchill's valet as tactfully as possible how Lady Anne's invitation to this dinner came to pass. With the innate confidence one underling has in another, he replied out of the corner of his mouth, "I'll be deuced if I know."

Lady Anne sent the general a series of gifts, always delivered by a liveried servant in a Bentley. So peculiar were the presents that I took them for a code. She sent him a canary in a cage, then came a French horn with a dent in its neck. Next came a crocheted shawl, white with a red fleur-de-lis in the center. Then came a boa constrictor wrapped in a deathgrip around a mongoose, one of those taxidermal horrors common in taverns in the States.

General Clay accepted these gifts without saying anything, until the boa and mongoose. As he inspected the thing, holding it away from him as he might a soiled diaper, he muttered, "This woman's crankcase may have frozen long ago, Jack. What do you think?"

I wanted to shout, "Good Christ, yes, General. Abandon ship and save yourself." I knew better, so I clucked noncommittally.

Among the soldiers of the 1st Armored, General Clay was venerated not so much for his command abilities or his bravery, but for the thirty minutes he spent in one of their tanks.

We were inspecting one of their units, the 13th Armored Regiment south of Guildford, midway between London and Portsmouth. The 13th had made a fine show of it, with a parade roll-by and an intricate maneuver replete with crewmen on the turrets waving red flags to indicate when the tanks fired. Ammunition was too scarce to waste on maneuvers. Clay congratulated Colonel Joe Dane on the 13th's performance.

Just as we were about to return to the plane, Lady Anne's maroon Bentley rolled up. This was an outrageous breach of decorum—breaching decorum being among her singular traits —and I expected her to receive a curt dismissal from the general. Instead, he grinned widely, helped her from the automobile with a flourish, and introduced her to Colonel Dane.

Dane nodded uncomfortably, and his eyes widened with distress when Clay said, "I'd like to take Lady Anne for a ride in one of your new Shermans, Joe."

"Of course, General," he answered briskly, but with a strychnine expression. "You want a driver, or will you steer the English lady around yourself?"

"Calm yourself, Joe, and I'll thank you for a driver."

Lady Anne was wearing a sable coat over a black silk blouse and four strings of pearls in a choker. We walked toward one of the Shermans. Her two-inch heels sank in the churned ground, and when she climbed to the deck of the tank, her coat scraped along a patch of grease, picking up a black stain. She seemed indifferent to the spoilage.

The congregation of soldiers around the general was increasing quickly, curious about the limousine. Anxious for a glimpse, tank crewmen were popping up from their cupolas and drivers were leaving their fuel trucks. Major General Franks drove up in his command jeep and without getting out asked me, "Now what?"

The general and Lady Anne disappeared through the turret. Her coat trailed after her like a squirrel's tail. The driver followed, to the catcalls of some of his mates.

The Sherman blew exhaust and trundled forward. It traveled less than a hundred yards across the pasture, away from the armored formations, then stopped. The Continental engine was turned off. After half a moment, the driver climbed out through the hatch and jumped to the ground. Grinning, he walked toward us.

When he arrived he announced loudly, "The general wanted to give the lady a tour of the inside of my tank, but didn't need my help."

This was greeted with hoots and whistles. The crowd was growing, but maintained its distance from Clay's tank. The minutes passed. Speculation among the gathering soldiers as to events transpiring in the tank was rampant and lewd. Several wagers were made.

Out of loyalty to my commander, I felt it necessary to leave the ribald talk, so I walked toward the tank, across the pasture, following its track, avoiding flattened cow pies when possible. I arrived at the tank and leaned against a forward fender, trying to appear inconspicuous, which was difficult when two hundred tankmen were pointing at me and calling out vulgar suggestions.

I spent the next thirty minutes glancing at my watch, cracking my knuckles, scratching my nose, and doing other small gestures to look occupied. The gathering of onlookers increased all the while, becoming an irreverent mob. The tank was silent.

Finally, the cupola slid open and General Clay's head appeared. The throng let loose with a roar. Clay smiled and climbed out. He bent over the cupola to assist Lady Anne. She emerged and the ovation grew. He helped her from the turret to the deck, and I took an arm to assist her to the ground.

Then, by God, in the next instant before the general descended from the tank, she gold-plated forever the general's reputation among the soldiers of the 1st Armored. I was blocking the tankmen's view of her. She quickly reached to her neck and yanked on her blouse, tearing it from the collar to the second button, exposing a glimpse of her brassiere. She ran the same hand along her lips, smudging the lipstick. And then she ruffled her black hair. By the time the general landed at her side, she was in a state of unmistakable sexual disarray.

The general did not notice, or seemed not to. The three of us marched back across the pasture, leaving the tank. We reached the soldiers, who parted for us. She smiled demurely, something I did not think her capable of. For a moment the soldiers were quiet, stunned, I think. But as they surveyed Lady Anne (she had deliberately slowed her pace), the commotion grew, and grew.

Now, I saw two games of the 1940 World Series, and not once did the New York fans cheer as wildly as those troops of the 13th Armored Regiment at that moment. Their general was a stallion, and he had proved it in one of their Shermans.

I'm sure General Clay was puzzled, but he was not one to let that expression cross his face. He grinned, even bowed slightly, and escorted Lady Anne to her Bentley.

The inspection of the 13th Armored took another hour, and as he passed them in review, the soldiers grinned and leered, gave the thumbs up and flashed V-for-victory signs, an unprecedented, regiment-wide display of impertinence.

The tank was later rechristened Clay's Lay.

What do I think happened inside that Sherman? Less than Lady Anne would have us think, but, otherwise, how would I know? I was separated from General Clay and Lady Anne by two inches of protective steel and am glad of it.

Then there is the Mystery Flight, as my memory has named it. Only three people in the universe know the answer to the impenetrable riddle presented by the Mystery Flight, and I am not one of them. Captain Norman is, but he would not talk, at least with a straight face.

The flight occurred several weeks before S-Day. We had been inspecting the 68th Field Artillery Regiment, 1st Armored, near Chichester, and were scheduled to depart from the RAF sector airfield at Tangmere. The jeep drove along the airfield to Terry Norman's plane, and just as I thought we were to board, the general said, "Let's wait a moment, Jack."

Twenty minutes elapsed. Clay did paperwork on a clipboard. I made entries in my journal. In the Cub's cockpit, Captain Norman made his endless checks and adjustments.

At noon the dreaded Bentley appeared, rolling silently up to the plane. Lady Anne emerged, beaming at Clay. She was wearing black pearl earrings and a white and red print dress. He climbed out of the jeep and shook her proffered hand.

The general said, "Jack, I'll be back shortly. Wait here for me."

To my consternation, he helped her into the Cub and closed the hatch, leaving me on the runway. Norman gave me a desultory salute and revved the engine. The Cub pulled away. I got behind the jeep's steering wheel and followed the Bentley to the edge of the runway. The chauffeur found a protected area under several trees, and I parked the jeep next to the limousine.

I waited. The sun set, and the English chill settled on the airfield. I waited. Midnight. Her chauffeur invited me to sleep in the backseat. He and I spent the night in the Bentley. He rolled up the window separating the driver from the passenger seat to block out my snoring. Morning came, and I was still waiting. An RAF cook thoughtfully brought us breakfast, then lunch.

I was beginning to feel like the famous Labrador retriever in Portland, Oregon. The dog's name was Angel. One day its master ordered him to wait outside a downtown store. A few minutes later, the master died from a heart attack on the second floor of the store. His body was removed from a rear door. A night watchman fed the dog that night, and every night for the next seven years until Angel died, still at the department store's entrance, obedient to his master to the end.

The Cub reappeared at two in the afternoon. They had been gone twenty-six hours. The chauffeur and I drove our vehicles out to meet them. General Clay and Lady Anne stepped down from the Cub, and he bid her a businesslike goodbye. She was wearing the same clothes and earrings.

General Clay lifted his clipboard from the jeep's seat and said, "Have Signal tell Burt Jones to meet me at 0200 at the 2nd's HQ."

I followed him back into the Cub. Thus began a stream of orders that continued until we touched down in London.

Later that day, I asked Terry Norman, "Where the hell did you take them?"

"Well, two minutes after we took off, the Cub's engine started coughing. So I put down at Portsmouth, ten miles west of here. The general did his generaling from there until the plane was repaired this morning. Then he and the lady came back to get you."

"You must think Norma and Ed Royce of San Diego, California, raised a complete dunce for a son, Terry."

He smiled. "Well, that story is good enough for you and me, I'm told."

I heard later that Lady Anne was sighted in Dublin that day. So perhaps the Mystery Flight was to Ireland. I won't speculate further as to their destination. And I won't speculate at all as to their purpose.

I hasten to add that the Mystery Flight was the only holiday General Clay took during his long stay in England. And with Lady Anne along, he probably wasn't relaxing.

Had you asked General Clay how well I served him, he probably would have replied that I carried out my duties diligently, conscientiously, and loyally, which would have sounded like a Legion of Merit citation. But in his heart of hearts, he knew I served him best in my affair with the *Brighton Times*.

One morning while we were meeting at the 5th Infantry's headquarters near Canterbury, the general abruptly turned to me and said, "Jack, the *Brighton Times* plans to run a photograph in tomorrow's edition that shows me standing with Lady Anne at the Duke of Norfolk's home. I understand the newspaper may run some idle gossip along with the photo."

He paused a moment. I prompted him with, "Sir?"

"I want you to stop them."

"Sir?"

"I'm releasing the Cub and Captain Norman to you. You get down there and fix it."

"Yes, sir."

He turned back to General Carsen. I left Canterbury without a plan, shaken by the responsibility. I landed near Brighton, and first visited the 4th Engineer Battalion, 4th Motorized. Then I arrived at the *Brighton Times* building, a three-story stone edifice on St. James Street, and was shown into the corner office of the newspaper's publisher, Taylor Hayworth.

"Mr. Hayworth, I am General Wilson Clay's aide, Colonel Jack Royce."

"A pleasure to meet you, sir," he said without conviction. He spoke loudly, above the sudden sound of heavy trucks on the street below. His face was drawn, with sunken cheeks and a pencil mustache. Strands of gray hair were swept across his baldness, making his head look wet.

"Mr. Hayworth, the American Expeditionary Force has a problem, and I'm afraid only you can help us with it."

He smiled uncharitably. "I know your problem, and it is going to appear in tomorrow's *Times*, right on the first page. And you're here to talk some sense into me, as you Americans say." He rose from behind his desk. "It won't work, Colonel. You can save your breath."

I worked my face into a puzzled expression. "Pardon me, Mr. Hayworth? I'm having difficulty following you."

"Don't toy with me, Colonel."

I shrugged. "Let me begin again, Mr. Hayworth. As you know, the AEF has been charged with the defense of Brighton. We have decided to redouble the city's fortifications. Our engineers have determined that only the heaviest street blockades will deter panzers. So we are requisitioning your printing presses in your basement."

Perplexed, he chewed on his mustache a moment. Then he began to color, first a pink, then a gratifying red. "You—you have the gall to come in here and bluff me like some Chicago gangster?"

"If you will step to your window and look below, Mr. Hayworth."

Stiff with anger, he rose from his chair and marched to the window. He leaned out to see the street.

The 4th Engineers were staging quite a production. Filling St. James Street were bulldozers and a crane and two backhoes, generator and compressor trailers, and several 6×6 heavy trucks. Engineers were removing jackhammers from the trucks.

I said over the roar from the street, "We intend to remove your printing presses by their roots, and place them across King's Road at the foot of West Street. Those presses, plugging up the street, will give the panzer commanders something to worry about after the invasion."

Hayworth's voice sounded as if his collar had been suddenly cinched from behind. "This is an outrage. For you—you foreigner to dare come into this office—"

"I only request any architectural plans you may have, so the engineers can best avoid structural damage to your fine building here."

An engineer started an air compressor. A jackhammer fired, echoing along the street.

Hayworth gasped for breath. "This is filthy blackmail."

"I also recommend that your people leave the building for the rest of the day, for their own safety."

He held up his hands. His breathing was ragged. "All right, Colonel. I surrender. I will cancel the photo and story."

"Sir?"

"I won't print it. Call off your dogs."

"Once again, Mr. Hayworth, I'm not following you. But perhaps in the interest of cooperation among allies, I can postpone this operation, if that's your request. And several days from now I'll review whether we need your printing presses."

I nodded good-bye and left him standing at the window. Half an hour later, when the last of the 4th's machines pulled out of St. James Street, he was still at the third-floor window and still red.

The photograph was never published. The gossip was never printed.

Next day, General Clay threw that morning's *Brighton Times* on my desk and said only, "How is a baseball fan supposed to follow the Dodgers when all he's got are these goddamn English newspapers?"

General Clay met with Lady Anne's father, Earl Selden, half a dozen times before S-Day. General Stedman usually went with us. The three would pore over their charts and move their tank models over a table. I would watch Lady Anne as she sat in a leather wingback chair, her legs crossed, her red mouth slightly puckered, her sable hair framing sublime features. She seemed to be simmering.

She was a skilled pianist. Frequently, as her father and the two generals discussed tactics, she would walk to the Bosendorfer piano and play Chopin or Debussey from memory. She played liltingly, hauntingly, in sharp contrast to her character, I thought. At these times she appeared contemplative, staring at the wall or the dried flowers. General Clay was so immersed in the earl's lessons and the tactics they were hammering out, I'm not sure he ever heard her.

But this ethereal piano-playing may have been a ploy, another part of her carefully constructed self. On one occasion, Generals Clay and Stedman and the earl left the study for a walk, the earl first dipping into a humidor to remove three Cuban cigars. The moment they were out of earshot, Lady Anne broke into boogie woogie. It was an American beerhall tune, "Over the Bars," by James P. Johnson. Her head bent low, she beat the keys while her leg jumped in time. I would not have been more surprised had she broken wind.

When the boogie was finished, she moved immediately into a stride tune I didn't know, another St. Louis number, her left hand fanning left and right as she pounded out the bass. She shook the piano. A line of sweat appeared on the nape of her neck, glistening in the low light. After she had flattened the keys with the last chord and the echo had fled the room, she said to herself, "Well, let's be proper, shall we?" And it was back to Chopin well before her father and the generals returned. I never mentioned her boogie to the general, because I didn't think he would have believed me.

In all the time I was with General Clay and Lady Anne, the only time she recognized my existence, other than by handing me her wrap on occasion, was during the last meeting at the earl's home. She was sitting under a lamp gazing at a prewar copy of *Country Life* without turning the pages. She wore the inward, focused expression of one scheming.

Abruptly she looked up from her magazine. Her gaze swept the room to find me. She caught my eyes for a full five seconds. Then she winked. A full-blooded, daring, omniscient wink. Something an American steelworker would do. She stapled me to the chair with it. She smiled quickly and returned to her magazine.

I confess it worked. Layers of intrigue fell away from her.

Light in the room seemed to shift, making shadows on her face less wicked. The breezes of conspiracy that always brushed her hair and carried her scent were stilled.

With the wink Lady Anne told me she was in this life for a frolic. I believed her, and I worried less about General Clay from then on.

But I'm not done with my examination of her, or of their relationship.

Why mankind is afflicted with war is an enigma that may never be solved. The question has perplexed our greatest thinkers for centuries, and I will leave the puzzle to them.

But each war, each battle, produces a host of small riddles, miniature mysteries made trifling by the vast sweep of appalling events. I list several here because they were as much an ingredient of the invasion as were the combatants' lofty military tactics, and because, unlike the grand questions of the ages, these puzzles are more my size.

Six days before S-Day, a Stuka swept across a field on the Isle of Sheppey in the Thames estuary. Its Jumo engine had stalled for lack of fuel, probably due to a leak in the tank, Coastal Command later concluded. Ten feet above the ground at the edge of a field of winter wheat, the dive bomber's starboard wing clipped a power pole. The plane flipped. The Stuka landed on its back, crushing the pilot and copilot. The plane did not burn.

Coastal Command removed the bodies, the machine guns, and ammunition belts. Curiously, the plane was not carrying its standard complement of three bombs. Rather, under each wing, where a 110-pound bomb usually was, was a wood crate.

"Rather fragile wood boxes," Harold Dartmore told me. "They were designed to crash open when dropped from the dive bomber."

Dartmore was with the Civilian Repair Organization during the war. A day after the Coastal Command stripped the Stuka of everything lethal, Dartmore and his crew arrived with their blow torches and trucks. Anything of use would be wired onto

308

RAF planes or melted down. Sixty percent of all damaged RAF fighters were returned to the air by the CRO, an amazing record.

"We stopped the lorries on the road, intent on first inspecting the plane," he told me. "The power pole was still down, so we gave the wires a wide berth. The Stuka was about fifty yards in from the road. I walked across the field, the green wheat not much above my boot tops, and I tripped over a clump of dirt. Almost fell to my knees. Only it wasn't a clump of dirt. It was a rat, dead as you please."

Dartmore and his crew continued toward the German plane. "Then my boot hit another rat, lying still in the furrow, and nothing is more dead than a dead rat. Its little eyes were bugging out, and there was a patch of dried spit at the corner of its mouth, and the flies were working on it. I would have felt sorry for the rat, had it not been so ugly."

Dartmore and his crew became more careful, watching their steps. "We circled the plane and found a dozen more rats, all dead. The closer we got to the Stuka, the more there were. And some dead birds also."

The CRO team then found the wood boxes, shattered, their contents spread over the furrows. "And there was meat inside the boxes, or what was left of the boxes. Some of the meat had been strewn about by the impact. There seemed to be oatmeal mixed with it. It appeared the Germans were bombing us with Scottish haggis."

The meat had poisoned the rats and birds. Laboratory tests later showed the meat to be horse, which along with the oatmeal had been spiked with cyanide.

"Now why would the Germans want to bomb us with poisoned meat and porridge?" Dartmore asked me. "It's a mystery, and I've never figured it out."

I told Dartmore that the Stuka's mission had puzzled General Barclay, AACCS commander in chief, and others of the Defense Committee when Barclay presented details. General Clay had shaken his head, without a clue. Then Winston Churchill had rumbled forth: "That dive bomber's mission is obvious."

"The prime minister knew of our Stuka?" Dartmore asked me, gratified.

"Certainly."

That day in the war cabinet rooms, Churchill said, "They were after the ravens."

All heads nodded with immediate understanding and agreement. Only General Clay and Admiral Stanton, commander of the U.S. Atlantic Fleet East, were still stumped.

As I relayed this to Dartmore, he said, "And I'm still stumped."

I replied, "The Tower ravens."

Dartmore's eyes widened. "Of course." He slapped a palm on the pub's table. "How could I have not known? That's just what the jerries would do."

The six ravens in the Tower of London loiter on the Tower Green, squawking and preening their clipped wings. When one dies, it is replaced by another. The birds are cared for by a raven-master. And they are well cared for, because legend has it that if all the ravens die, the British Empire will fall.

The Stuka's mission had been to murder the ravens. Hitler, a mystic, may himself have believed in the legend. Or perhaps it was an attempt to cripple British morale. But it was a puzzle for many, until the prime minister, with his fabled lucidity, had quickly solved the riddle.

Not all answers were revealed. Private Philip Hardin was a rifleman with Charley Company, 1st Battalion, 137th Infantry Regiment near Dymchurch on the channel. He told me, "The Wehrmacht's 17th Division hit us so hard on the beach we just collapsed. I was blown down by a blast, and when I raised my head, I was looking into four German rifles. I may have the humiliating distinction of being the first American captured on S-Day."

Hardin and ten other stunned and bleeding 1st Battalion survivors were huddled together on the beach, guarded by two Wehrmacht soldiers. German soldiers raced up the beach. Shells crackled through the air overhead.

Hardin recalled, "I had fallen on my rifle stock and knocked out my front teeth, top and bottom. My clearest memory of those two hours on the beach is of the blood in my mouth and the beach master's whistle. I can't imagine where he found the wind, blowing and blowing. All the while German troops and traffic roared up the beach from their landing vessels."

A Wehrmacht lieutenant appeared above the group of POWs. "He was carrying a notebook, and he glanced at it. Then he said in accented English, 'You prisoners come with me.' He held a Luger on us, and marched us up the beach."

The guards lowered their rifles. The German lieutenant followed the POWs closely, keeping them in line.

"He walked us toward the hill rising behind the beach, then up and over the hill. Fighting had pushed inland, and we marched toward the line, past a barn and several houses. Wounded were lying all about, German and American. Machine gun fire was steady. We walked, but I can't remember how far. My head was still foggy. I started to wobble, but one of the other prisoners put my arm over his shoulder and helped me along."

Hardin and the other prisoners were ushered into a cottage, half of which had been destroyed by artillery fire. Bewildered and frightened, the prisoners lowered themselves to the floor. Hardin told me, "And then our captor put the pistol into his holster and said, 'You men are now behind American lines. You'll want to get further inland as fast as possible.' One of the other POWs tried to ask him a question, but the German cut him off by saying in English, 'Get going. You don't have much time.' And that was the last I ever saw of the lieutenant."

The POWs limped north, their hands over their heads. They were soon hailed by American troops, who turned them over to the medics.

"Then a day or two later, it suddenly hit me that the words the German lieutenant said to us in the cottage were completely free of an accent."

I asked, "You've admitted being groggy. Maybe your memory of his accent, or anything else, isn't accurate."

"No question about him being a German, at least his uniform was. He was wearing an olive green tunic and a cap called an M1938 officers' side cap. He wore a decoration, the German Cross in gold, below his right shirt pocket. I know all this because I studied Wehrmacht uniforms after the war, looking for an answer."

Then Hardin smiled as he handed me a sheet of paper. "I knew you wouldn't believe me. Here are the names and addresses of three other prisoners who were with me on that beach. You give them a call, and they'll confirm my story."

I did, and they told me identical versions of their mysterious liberation.

Whether the officer was an American in a dead Wehrmacht lieutenant's uniform or a sympathetic German officer with a mastery of English may never be known. Nor, probably, will his fate.

Another small mystery. Never was I more impressed with Wilson Clay's composure under fire than that day in the cabinet war rooms when the Execution Order, as it came to be called, was produced. The Defense Committee was in the middle of an interminable discussion of convoy problems when Winston Churchill said, "I must interrupt this discussion to ask our American friend General Clay a brief question."

I, and the other Flying Buttresses, detected a change in the prime minister's tone, a strange tinniness. We lowered the front legs of our chairs to the floor, expecting a show.

Churchill raised a sheet of paper from the green table and rattled it. He brought it closer to his eyes, then moved it away in a display of distaste. He intoned, "I regret even having to ask this of you, General Clay."

All eyes turned to Clay.

"I have in my hand an order over President Roosevelt's signature. I cannot tell you at this time how I came to possess this document."

Churchill looked over the edge of the paper at Clay. He said, "It directs you, General Clay, in the event of an imminent surrender of Great Britain, to carry out the assassination of the British royal family to prevent their possible collaboration with the Third Reich."

I could hear my heartbeat in my chest. The men around the table were as still as a photograph.

Churchill asked, "Do you have a comment on this order from the president?"

Clay slowly moved his hand up from the table. He pointed at the sheet of paper and perhaps at the prime minister. He said in an iron voice, "I state this categorically. That document is a forgery. It was planted by England's enemies, by those who want to destroy the Anglo-American alliance."

The prime minister said calmly, "I never thought otherwise, of course. You might want to investigate it, General." He passed the document along the table to Clay.

The meeting continued, but Generals Alexander and Douglas could not take their eyes off Clay. They may have been horrified by the audacity of the forgery. Or perhaps deep inside their minds, made fertile and distrustful by their island history, they suspected us Americans of diabolical treachery.

General Clay made no further comment during that conference. But the minute he and I were alone, he slammed the document into my hand and ordered, "You get to the bottom of this, Jack. Jesus H. Christ, I want someone hung by the balls."

I never found anybody to hang by the balls, try as I did. But proof of the forgery came easily. I forwarded the document to the FBI in Washington. They readily proved that although the typewriter, the ribbon ink, and the paper had been manufactured in the United States, the ink on the printed White House logo at the top of the document had been made in Dresden by the Fascht Company, renowned in Germany before the war for the manufacture of printed wedding invitations. The FBI also found that the chemical breakdown of the ink indicated it had been made since 1940.

I gave this information to General Clay, who immediately forwarded it to the prime minister.

The next time they were together, Clay said, "Prime Minister, I hope you reviewed our FBI's report on that forged document."

Churchill waved his cigar "I am offended you think I need proof it was a forgery."

Clay said, "But you read the report?"

The prime minister put the cigar in his mouth, pushed it to one side, and said, "Closely, General." He smiled at me. "Very closely indeed."

A forgery, proven beyond a doubt. But the precise origin of the document, the implausible scheming by an unknown team in Berlin, may be cloaked in mystery forever.

Then there were the tiny household puzzles reported by English citizens. Randolph Deacon, an air raid warden in Ashford, fled inland on S-Day, leaving behind everything he could not carry on his back.

He told me after the war, "It broke my heart to leave my belongings. But I was an essential worker and couldn't evacuate until the last minute. So I buried a few things under the floorboards, including the beautiful Black Forest cuckoo clock my father brought back from the Great War. It kept time well, but the cuckoo had never worked. My father said he broke it showing it off on the way back across the channel in 1918. And the only times I ever saw the little cuckoo bird was when I pried open the door to look inside."

After Ashford was overrun, Wehrmacht troops used his home as a bivouac.

Deacon said, "I returned to my home after the Germans had pulled out. The place was in chaos. My furniture had been reduced to ashes in the stove. The plates and saucers were gone. Many of the windows were broken, with glass lying all about."

Deacon was distraught, until he saw the clock on the wall. "I'll never forget that moment. It was one minute to noon. Amid all the debris of my shattered possessions, there was my clock, in perfect running order, its Black Forest oak polished, its pendulum swinging. Someone had found it under the floor and placed in on the wall. Then, for the first time in almost a quarter of a century, the cuckoo shot out to call the hour. It chirped twelve times."

I asked Deacon how this could possibly be.

"Some German clockmaker, drafted into the Wehrmacht, fixed my clock. How else?"

"Why would he have done that?" I asked.

Deacon shrugged. "That's the puzzler, isn't it? But I'm thankful to him, whoever he was. The cuckoo has worked ever since."

Another small event, perfectly explained by the evidence of its own existence, is the painting John Bridgman found on his return home. Bridgman was an amateur landscape artist. After the war he said, "I had a better eye than I had a hand. I knew just enough about painting to know I'd never be much of a painter. Not for lack of trying, though."

Bridgman lived in Horsham. His row house was given over to his passion for painting. Canvases, empty frames, easels, and tubes of paint and thinner filled it, often covering his bed and desk, cluttering his tiny kitchen. Bridgman escaped the town a few hours ahead of the Wehrmacht.

"My flat was filled with half-completed landscapes. I usually put my brush down intending to finish a canvas, but seldom did, once I looked critically at it."

One of the unfinished paintings in Bridgman's sitting room was of the Silent Pool near Guildford. Legend said that King John had watched a local girl bathing at the pool. When she discovered him, she drowned herself in a fit of shame.

"I had tried to capture her spirit in the green pond and in the trees circling the water. But I had failed and gave up on the project. I left the half-finished painting behind when I hastily departed Horsham and thought nothing further of it."

Until he returned. Bridgman told me, "My building was the only one standing in the block. All the others had been reduced to rubble. I climbed the stairs, hoping against hope that the Wehrmacht soldiers had not destroyed my flat. The door lock had been kicked in, but other than that, there was no damage to my place. And standing in the middle of my sitting room was my painting of the Silent Pool."

Bridgman showed me the piece. The canvas was now filled with paint. I asked, "So you finished the painting?"

He stared at me for a moment, then asked, "You know nothing about art?"

"Sorry."

"This landscape was finished by another hand. You don't need to know anything about art to see that."

"I guess I know even less than that."

Bridgman nodded. "Have you ever heard of Wilhelm Udet?"

"Sorry."

The painter rubbed his forehead with frustration. His story was losing momentum due to my ignorance. He continued, "Udet is a seminal German painter. He joined the Dada movement right after the first war and then became a founder of surrealism. He is famous for his precise execution of fantastic visions."

"That does ring a bell," I granted, lying.

"Wilhelm Udet was in my flat right after S-Day, and he finished this painting. See for yourself." Bridgman held the painting closer to me.

He explained. "I paint upper left toward lower right. The lower right half of this work is fully his. Notice the bold, decisive brush strokes, the immeasurably better use of the blues and greens."

"Now that you mention it, I do notice it."

"And look here, under the waters of the Silent Pool is a fish with Satan's head. Nice touch, but nothing I would ever do."

True enough, the fish, barely observable below the shimmering surface, had horns and was carrying a red trident in a fin.

He said, "Then he signs it in black. His signature reads, 'One-slash-two Udet.' Half Udet."

Bridgman beamed. "That's as close to a great painting as I'll ever do. Half Bridgman, half Udet. But why he thought to finish my painting remains a mystery."

Another mystery, this one grotesque, began with the bombing of Madam Tussaud's waxworks in London. The morning after the blast, many of the costumes were missing. The police were baffled, and Londoners were outraged at this petty crime committed during the horror of the London bombing.

As General Clay put it diplomatically to the prime minister, "You English have a penchant for bizarre crime, but you aren't looters, normally."

Pedro Esteban was with the U.S. Army Graves Registration Service. His duty was to locate and attempt to identify the bodies of soldiers killed during the invasion, then move them to approved cemeteries.

Esteban complained to me after the war, "I signed up hoping to be a Ranger, and I ended up using a number two idiot stick my entire enlistment."

Several citizens of Coldred, a tiny village just inland from

Dover, suspected a common grave was to be found in a pasture east of the town. Pedro Esteban and his crew arrived to find freshly turned earth and the faint scent of rot.

"We began digging, knowing what we'd find. In those two years, I dug up more bodies than Carter's got pills."

After several shovels of dirt were tossed aside, the blade hit a metal belt.

"A gold belt," Esteban said in his Spanish accent. "I brushed aside more soil to find gold and jewels on a breastplate. I thought I'd dug up an old English king. Damn, we were excited. We dropped to our knees and began brushing aside dirt with our hands, figuring we'd hit it rich, just like Forty-Niners."

Esteban learned later the jewels were cut glass and the gold was paint. "The body was real, though. A German with a hole through his neck. Then one of my team shouted, "That's Henry VIII.""

So it was. The Wehrmacht soldier was wearing one of Madam Tussaud's costumes.

"We lay the king aside and pulled up another body. This one had on a dress and a white wig. I didn't know it then, but it was Marie Antoinette's costume. That German's lower legs were missing, probably from a mine. Then we pulled out Lord Nelson, then Ben Franklin, and Dick Turpin, the highwayman. All were Wehrmacht soldiers who looked like they'd been killed in action."

Esteban and I were sipping tequila, which, frankly, I wasn't familiar with. I will relay his final words of the interview as accurately as I remember them. He said, "You know, we in the Registration Service began to think after only a week on the job that we'd seen everything. How many goddamn ways can a guy be killed, and how awful can they look when they're dug up? I thought I'd seen it all. But I never saw anything like this, before or since, and it spooked me. I never figured it out." '

Neither did the U.S. Army or Scotland Yard. The costumes were returned to the rebuilt waxworks after the war, where they appear today, little the worse for wear. I suspect their appearance in a Kent pasture will always remain a mystery.

I have had a bit of fun setting out these insignificant puzzles for you. But I'm done with it and must return to the battle for England. There was nothing mysterious and nothing fun about the largest armored battle of the invasion. We move to that next.

17

"I have visited hell," Fritz Stumpff told me, "and now I'm afraid of dying because I might return there."

Stumpff's hell was in the turret of a *Panzerkampfwagen* III during the Battle of Haywards Heath, which lasted most of the second day of the invasion. Corporal Stumpff was a gunner with the 4th Panzer Regiment, 8th Division, in the first landing wave.

The engagement is known by the name of the village where opposing armored forces first came fully to grips.* But Haywards Heath was only the easterly edge of the fray, which was fought on a fifteen-mile long, fifteen-mile deep battleground. There are early indications that Haywards Heath may surpass Custer's Last Stand (342 books with doubtless more to come) as the most analyzed battle of all time. But I find that sacrifice is necessary for this narrative, lest I bewilder myself and you by trying to write down all I learned about Haywards Heath. Rather, I take a magnifying glass to the battle map and focus on several small skirmishes, negligible of their own right, but accurate miniatures of the vast and bloody contest.

German military historians call the engagement the Battle of London Road, after the road between Brighton and London.

"Our *Schwerpunkt* broke through the American line," Stumpff said. "But then, just when my company pivoted left to hit their flank, we came to a fierce pocket. It mauled us."

The panzer regiment was caught in what Earl Selden called a web defense. No one in the history of blitz warfare had divined how to stop panzers massed on a narrow front. The old British armor theoretician came close.

"The inside of the turret was about the size of two coffins placed side by side. So you see my problem, don't you?"

I conceded that I did not. We were sitting in the rebuilt Hoffbrau Haus in Munich, the site of the beer hall *putsch* in 1923. He pushed the bench back and stood. He was over six feet tall.

He explained, "I'm too big. Panzer units usually recruited people a head shorter, or else they'd get bumped around too much. At the physical exam, I slouched low, compressed myself, so I was allowed to join an armored regiment. Shows how smart I was."

He pulled at his beer and said, "So there were three of us in the turret: the commander, the loader, and me. We sat almost shoulder to shoulder. And below us were the driver and radioman, who was also the hull gunner. We had destroyed two American tanks and were looking for our third."

The tank commander, a lieutenant, sat directly below the cupola. Stumpff was to his left, bent forward, an eye on the sighting telescope and his forehead against a rubber bumper. His left hand was on the elevation handwheel. On his left was the traverse indicator, and on his right was the 50mm gun breech, which had a shellcase deflecting shield to prevent spent shells from ejecting into the commander's face. The gun was muzzle-heavy, so a lead ingot was mounted on the deflecting shield as a counterbalance.

To the right of Stumpff's head were two voice tubes. Behind him was a gas mask canister. Also in the turret were a co-axial machine gun in front of the loader, water canteens, machine gun belt bags, a signal flare bag, a rack of spare vision blocks, and a Schmeisser submachine gun and a service pistol on racks.

Five rounds for the cannon were under the gunner's seat

and another twenty-two were in a locker behind Stumpff. Seventy-six more rounds, each the size of an arm, were stored elsewhere. Surrounding the crew was rolled homogenous steel plate.

"It was close, very close, inside that turret, you understand," Stumpff said. "Every time the tank hit a bump or a hole, which was constantly, I banged my head or my chin or my shins or an elbow. But even so, we felt invulnerable. Tank crewmen feel indestructible. That's the big lie that makes any young man want to be a panzer crewman. Why be a *Landser*, carrying a puny rifle with only your trousers for armor, when you can be a tank crewman, surrounded by all that steel, unconquerable." Stumpff laughed harshly, lest I miss the irony.

The driver yelled through the tube, "*Panzerspähwagen, links fünfzig.*" Armored car, fifty degrees left.

Stumpff adjusted the sight and found an American M8, a six-wheeled vehicle carrying a 37mm gun and a crew of four. The car was three hundred yards in front and to the left of Stumpff's panzer, and was traveling at less than ten miles an hour.

"They didn't see us," Stumpff concluded, waving at a waitress.

The commander ordered, "Kill it. Fire when ready."

Stumpff cranked the handwheel. Stumpff and the commander's seats were attached to the turret, and swiveled as the turret spun, but the loader had to walk after the gun breech, scooting left and right, trying to avoid being hit by the swinging breach and deflector. "Loaders were as dumb as they came, so it gave them something to think about."

Stumpff switched to the fine-laying gear and traversed the gun into line with the moving armored car, leading it like a bird. He turned the range wheel until the required marking was opposite a pointer at the top of the sight. By manipulating the traverse and elevation controls, Stumpff lay the sighting mark onto the target.

"Got it," he cried above the panzer's Maybach engine.

Stumpff pulled the trigger. The gun fired, filling the turret with a roar. A hydropneumatic buffer containing filling liquid, known as a Braun, absorbed the recoil.

Smoke hid the target from Stumpff, but the driver called out, "A hit."

Wind moved the smoke. The corporal then could see what remained of the armored car, little more than three wheels and a twisted chassis. Its rear-mounted engine compartment had disappeared. Shards of metal lay about. Fire boiled from the remnants.

"You learn quickly not to gaze into the wreckage of a kill, or else you see black and twisted things you'll never forget."

The panzer's loader opened the sliding door behind him and removed a round. He was wearing a glove to protect his hands against hot shell cases. He slid it into the breech and slammed it shut. The temperature in the turret rose as it filled with propellant gases from the breech and engine exhaust leaking into the fighting compartment. The panzer was buttoned up, and there was little ventilation.

"Sweat began rolling down my forehead," Stumpff said. "Every few seconds I would have to wipe the headrest with an empty ammunition bag to prevent the eyepiece from fogging."

The panzer rumbled forward. The commander yelled into his radio, coordinating movement with the other armored vehicles in the platoon. With every gear change, the turret sounded as if it had been hit with a hammer. Only by bellowing could the crew be heard above the tank's engine. From below came the sound of the machine gun, an ear-rending racket. The tank's steel plate acted as a sounding board, capturing and amplifying the sound and turning it inward. The radioman had seen something. He swore loudly.

"Smoke," the commander yelled. His face was pressed against a green-tinted glass block on the cupola. He moved the shutter latch from its intermediary to the open position. "Shit, I can't see anything."

He spoke loudly into the tube to the driver, then said, "Werner's blind, too."

The commander twisted to another vision block in the cupola. "Goddamn it, I'm blind in all directions." He turned to the loader. "You get yourself on your machine gun and cover me. I'm going up for a look."

The commander reached for his binoculars hanging from a

stud on the turret. He raised himself on his seat, unlatched the hatch, pushed it up, and swung it to one side. Smoke poured into the turret from above. He slowly stood.

Stumpff said, "His legs immediately buckled, and he collapsed back through the hatch onto the turret floor. His jaw had been shot off. Nothing below his nose but ooze and blood. A ragged hole opened to his throat. He screamed and screamed, clutching his head. Blood spread along the turret deck and seeped down onto the driver.

Stumpff was second in command. He roughly pushed the lieutenant to one side and climbed into his seat. He would now act as commander and loader. The loader crawled over the wounded man to the gunsight. Every soldier could do every one else's job in the panzer.

Stumpff stuck the voice tube onto his mouth, "Werner, full ahead. Get us out of here."

Over the intercom, the radioman said he had lost contact with number two tank, probably knocked out. The engine howled. The lieutenant wailed and burbled, his legs flailing at the gun breach.

The panzer jolted ahead and soon approached twenty miles an hour, then abruptly twisted right in a wild spin.

"We had thrown a tread," Stumpff told me, spreading his arms. "Blown off by a mine, probably."

More feared by tankmen than being cooked alive by an armor piercing shell is dismounting the tank in a firefight. When the tank is disabled, there is no choice, because antitank squads will quickly home in on it, wanting the crew as prize as well as the tank.

The corporal shouted at the loader, "Get out of here. Make for the tree line, and I'll lay fire for you."

The loader launched himself at the hatch, threw the hasps, stepped on the deflecting shield for support, and scrambled out, almost. He tumbled back, bounced off the breech, and slid onto the commander, who shrieked with renewed agony.

Stumpff recalled, "The loader's head had disappeared, just blown off. A geyser of blood from his severed artery sprayed the inside of the tank, splashing across me and painting the turret walls."

Stumpff thought the enemy might have crawled onto the turret, ready to drop a grenade. He yelled into the mouthpiece to abandon the tank, then grabbed the submachine gun. He fired it up through the open hatch.

"The engine blare, the Schmeisser racket, the commander sobbing and moaning and kicking. The fumes, the splashing blood, the heat, the sweat, my tears. The ejected submachine gun shells bouncing around, smoke funneling down the hatch into the turret. God, what a mess."

"I see what you mean," I said. "Hell on earth."

He looked at me scornfully. "It had been a picnic so far."

Stumpff hesitated, then looked away from me, his eyes glistening. "I couldn't leave the lieutenant there, and he was suffering a horrible, slow death. So I ended it for him with his service pistol."

Just as the corporal gathered his feet under him to make his dash out the turret, a tracer shell, perhaps from a strafing Luftwaffe fighter trying to clear the turret for the panzer crew's escape, skipped down through the hatch and ricocheted inside the turret.

"It was like a bell ringing, clang, clang, clang. And between each clang a piece of me was ripped off. Chunks of my thigh, my forearm, a crease across my stomach. Finally the bullet, still glowing, lodged itself in an ammunition bag. And, damn my luck, if it wasn't the flare bag."

A signal flare instantly ignited, filling the turret with blinding light and ferocious heat. Stumpff fell back against the commander's seat, then slipped on the bloody turret deck. He pitched forward into the gun breach, breaking his jaw and his nose. The flare filled the turret, setting Stumpff's uniform and his hair on fire and blasting his eyebrows from his face.

"I felt like I was inside a burning coal, nothing but red-white light, no escaping, no retreating from it. With every breath I seared my thoat."

Stumpff lashed out with his legs, fighting upward like a drowning man. His head bounced against the extractor fan housing, then against the cupola ring. He pushed off against the commander's chair.

"I squirted through the hatch. I must have looked like a flare myself, all on fire. I slid off the turret to the engine deck, then fell to the pasture. I rolled and rolled to smother the fire, then I crawled away from my panzer, thinking it might blow. It didn't, but I never found out what happened to the driver and radioman."

I tried again. "Hell on earth."

"I'm not done," he said testily. "So there I am in that pasture. Burned to a blackened stump. Wounded and bleeding in four or five places from the tracer. My jaw and nose broken. But the worst was to come, because I lay in that field for two days before the medics could get to me. Of all my terror and pain, the worst was my thirst during those days. I almost died for lack of water and a kind word."

During the Battle of Haywards Heath, while we quickly dismantled HQ at Bilswell Manor because the panzer thrust was closing in from the east, General Clay explained to me the Wehrmacht's moves. Or he might have been talking to himself. "A panzer regiment acts as the spearhead, rushing ahead on a narrow front, sometimes only three thousand yards wide. The tanks' guns are concentrated in a wedge, called a *keil*. Each wave has been assigned destruction of some defense. The panzers punch through by their sheer weight. Then come the motorized rifle regiments to take out bypassed points of resistance and hold captured ground. Next come the antitank units to defend against counterattack. Then come the mechanized artillery batteries to support the tanks with fire against heavily defended points slowing the advance. It's all according to the book. I read the book."

The most decorated American unit in the war was the 82nd Armored Reconnaissance Battalion, universally called the Slant Eyes. The battalion's 640 soldiers were all Japanese Americans, largely from California.

General Clay said, "We were short on antitank weapons, but

I knew if I sent the Japs against the panzers, they'd fight like demons. They are a warrior race, and they'd try to make up for their treacherous cousins at Pearl Harbor."

Wilson Clay made a better general than he would have an ambassador.

David Yamashita told me after the war, "They called us a reconnaissance battalion, but that was a lie so that we wouldn't be scared. We were a tank destroyer unit without antitank weapons."

Private Yamashita had been told that panzers without infantry leading them to point out targets were largely blind and could be snuck up on.

"Can you imagine?" he asked me. "We were trained to single-handedly stalk and disable tanks. We had been told that because tanks are so noisy, they can't surprise you and so killing them would be fun and easy. In theory, it should have been, I suppose."

"Was it?" I asked.

Yamashita laughed lightly. "The maxim was that tanks were no longer a technical surprise, but only a tactical surprise. To hell with that. One of a panzer's chief effects is on morale. They just scare the crap out of you."

"I can imagine."

"You were an aide at headquarters, so you probably can't imagine."

This was a theme I heard again and again during my interviews. I didn't like it much.

Yamashita snorted, "We didn't have bazookas, so they gave us mines and smoke bombs and called us 'assault engineers.' All you need to be an antitank assault engineer are Jesse Owens' legs and a frontal lobotomy."

An assault on a panzer was made by a two-man team, the smoke-layer and the mine-layer. "My teammate, Francis Noguchi, and I flipped a coin. I won, so I was the mine-layer, which was lucky for me because the smoke-layer usually gets killed."

At the Battle of Haywards Heath, Yamashita and Noguchi had run ahead of a lead panzer that was engaged in a short-lived firefight with a Sherman. They used a glade for cover. A hundred yards ahead of the German armor, they sprinted into the pasture and threw themselves onto their stomachs. Yamashita and Noguchi were forty yards apart, waiting as the growl of the tanks' engines grew closer.

"The grass wasn't very high, and my nose was right down in the dirt. And on they came. The ground trembled under me. It was my first crack at this duty, and I was so afraid I started chewing the dirt under my mouth. I've no idea why I did that, but it calmed me some."

The panzers were in a loose deuce formation, two of them side by side. Both rolled east of the American antitank team. Noguchi waited until the nearest panzer drew abreast before he jumped to his knees, twisted the fuse on a smoke bomb, and hurled it in front of the nearest tank. He pulled another grenade from his belt and threw it mightily. Then he sprinted toward the panzer and threw yet another.

Smoke billowed from the grenades and began drifting across the field in trailing gray clouds. The nearest panzer's turret immediately swung toward Noguchi, who was still lobbing one grenade after another. The smokelayer dropped to the grass, but the turret machine gun roared. Bullets bit into the field in swaths that after two short swings found Noguchi, lifting him into the air above the grass, then blowing him back, rolling him over and over.

He had accomplished his mission. The panzers' vision was obscured by thick haze, and they could not cover each other.

Yamashita leaped to his feet and charged the nearest tank, a *Tauchpanzer*, a diving tank, made for amphibious landings and river crossings. Rubber sheets had covered the commander's cupola, the hull machine gun hatch, and the mantlet, but had been blown off by small charges detonated from inside the turret once the tank had gained dry land. The *Tauchpanzer*'s crew had not had time to cut away the air hose, held on the surface by a buoy when the tank was under water, and the tube followed the tank like a tail.

The panzer's turret began its terrifying swing toward Yamashita, searching for him. But it took the gunner forty-four cranks on the traverse handwheel to bring the turret half a circle, a slow operation. The tank began pivoting on its tracks. The panzer crew would know he was coming.

"It was a matter of geometry, really," Yamashita told me. "I had to stay in the blind zone until I got to the undefended angle."

The blind zone was on either side of the tank when the turret was pointing ahead or to the rear. The undefended zone was below the turret and hull machine guns' ranges, in the dirt insanely close to the grinding monster. The co-axial machine guns' vertical movements were severely limited.

"I sprinted as fast as my legs and the AT mine and Thompson I was carrying would let me. I truly believe I was crazed with fear, simply out of control. I was yelling at myself, 'You're running the wrong way, fool. You're running the wrong way.' But, by God, I beat it. I dove and rolled toward the treads. The turret swung above my head, its machine gun blasting. The bullets soared harmlessly over me."

Yamashita grinned at me. "I have never felt better before or since. I was the king of England, standing alongside this fifty-ton killing machine, knowing it was utterly helpless."

The *Tauchpanzer* whirled on its treads, spinning to find its tormenter, but Yamashita ran easily alongside it until he came to a U-bracket on the aft deck. He tossed the mine onto the engine deck and climbed after it, keeping his submachine gun aimed at the commander's cupola.

He crawled forward. Heat rose through the engine screens. The turret swung. He gained his feet and walked around the deck to keep pace with the undefended back of the turret. He glanced over his shoulder. The smoke screen was still holding. He bent to attach the mine where the turret met the ceiling armor. He threw the switch, then jumped from the deck.

To protect the mine-layer, the mine had only a two-second delay. "Just as I hit the ground, the panzer's turret blew a dozen feet into the sky, rotating twice in a full circle, looking like a maple seed pinwheel, before it landed on the ground."

Yamashita lifted a grenade from his belt, pulled the pin, and lobbed it over the roadwheel fender and into the exposed turret ring. The fiery blast soared skyward.

"I used the dead tank as cover as I ran back into the trees. I was laughing all the way. A fool's laugh, I suppose. But I felt good."

General Clay explained Earl Seldon's invention. "He called it 'islands of resistance,' and its innovation was its depth. There was something repelling about deliberately letting Wehrmacht armor through the line, but he convinced us it was the only way to stop them."

The islands of resistance were pockets of antitank guns, mortars, machine gun nests, and medium artillery. Depending on terrain, the islands were five hundred to a thousand yards apart. The weapons could fire to the flank or rear as well as to the front.

Clay said, "Each island could defend itself with fire. But also, two, three, or four islands could cross fire into open spaces between them. And each island could protect one or more of its neighbors with fire."

Earl Seldon's islands were designed to absorb the shock of the *Schwerpunkt*, the hard point. General Clay had held back units of the 1st Armored and 4th Motorized divisions from the beach front to form the AT pockets.

Clay said, "The islands acted like sponges, sucking the tanks in, absorbing them. Instead of breaking through a strongly defended line and then finding everything behind it easy traveling, the Wehrmacht was caught in withering crossfire wherever they turned."

Corporal Jamie Shaw was harnessed into the driver's seat of his Sherman, Cock of the Walk. His hands were wrapped around the track steering levers. His waxed paper bag was tucked into the top of his uniform blouse like a napkin to keep it at hand. It was half full. He was leaning forward, his eyes squinting at the direct vision visor, around which were stowed gas capes tied against the turret with lengths of leather cords.

"I was in fourth gear," he told me after the war, "traveling about twenty miles an hour. My commander saw something and ordered me hard left, so I shoved in the left clutch pedal and pulled on the left track lever."

At that instant, the entire tank chimed like a barrel hit with a hammer. A German AT shell coming in at too great an angle had wormed under the hull above the tread. The glancing blow fouled the left brake and gear box. Another would surely follow. The commander ordered Shaw left into a glade of wild rhododendrons.

"I yelled that I couldn't turn that way. I had a runaway power train to the left side. So he ordered us right, anything to get out of the line of fire. I spun us around, and through the visor I could see a *Panzerfaust* crew lifting another pipe to the gunner's shoulder. Three of them, the gunner and two mules."

The *Panzerfaust*, a one-shot disposable unit resembling a plumber's helper, was the best hand-held antitank weapon of the war, far outshining the American bazooka.

"We opened up with the turret and hull Brownings. Wiped them out just as they loosed the shot. Their round soared over us."

Shaw's Sherman was crossing an oat field, chased from the protection of a nearby thicket by Wehrmacht AT teams. The Sherman rolled into the middle of an enemy tank charge.

"We were all alone, boxed by three panzers. I was so afraid. I knew the Sherman was prone to catching fire. Tank crews called it the Ronson. I had nightmares about being brewed up."

And Shaw was regurgitating. "Swaying, swerving, weaving, rolling, lurching up and down. God, I was sick. I threw up breakfast, dinner from the night before, an entire enlistment of mess hall food. At least, with our left side out, I had a free hand to hold the waxed bag to my mouth."

I spoke with four Wehrmacht soldiers who witnessed Cock of the Walk during the next ten minutes, a panzer driver, two members of an AT team, and an ME109 pilot, all of whom were trying their best to perform the coup de grâce on the lame Sherman. They described a berserk tank that raced, twisted, and crashed through anything and everything.

"Well," Jamie Shaw said, "that about sums it up. I do remember busting through a nice picket fence, then through a tool shed, then turning right and going sideways through a barn. I was locked into fourth gear, and it was twenty miles an hour or nothing. And we went through a dog run, then smashed through the front porch of a house. All the while, I was vomiting up my lungs."

Shaw's memory is selective, and perhaps with his Sherman in and out of the enemy crosshairs every few seconds, it deserves to be. I have pieced together those runaway ten minutes during which Shaw's Sherman dodged the increasingly impatient Wehrmacht and Luftwaffe. In addition to the collisions remembered by Shaw, Cock of the Walk ran over six telephone poles, destroyed a dozen apple trees, blew through a power substation, demolished five farm implements (a disk, binder, harrow, and two hay-balers, all of which belonged to farmer Felix Armstrong, who opined after the war that perhaps a German occupation would not have been so bad by comparison), crushed a goat shed, dug up a three-hundred-year-old cemetery, crumpled a Bedford truck, ripped out the newly constructed annex on the St. Bernard parish church, and burst through Edward Petrie's shed, in which was stored a Panhard automobile, manufactured by the Daimler Company in 1895 and lovingly preserved by three generations of Petries.

Edward Petrie said later, "There was nothing left of my beloved Panhard larger than my fist, and knowing as I do how ungrateful colonials often feel about their mother country, I suspect that Sherman traveled back and forth over my Panhard three or four times."

"I didn't do any of that on purpose," Jamie Shaw defended himself. "First, we were running for our lives, and second, I'd filled up my waxed bags, and my periscope and direct vision visor were covered with puke, and I couldn't see too much. Plus, hot drops of oil from the breech were dropping down the back of my neck."

Shaw went on, "Our gunner, Dinkie Welch, was a prodigy. I once saw him spit a horsefly out of the air. He was just as good at the gunsight."

While Cock of the Walk crushed under tread much of southern England, Dinkie Welch repeatedly fired the Sherman's 75mm gun. Shaw said, "Every time I straightened the tank out, he'd let loose another round. And one kill I'll never forget.

Our shell blew the panzer's turret and the hull hatches straight into the air. When the turret came down, its gun barrel slammed into the open driver's hatch. So the turret was stuck in the air far above the hull at the end of the long barrel. It reminded me of a child's lollipop, sticking up there."

The list of the Cock's kills reads like a child's math primer: five armored cars (four Mercedes Benzes and a Krupp command car), four panzers, three half-tracks (one Demag and two of unknown manufacture), two Marder self-propelled guns, and one *Radschlepper* (artillery tractor).

"If Dinkie could see it, he could bust it," Shaw said.

Low on fuel and ammunition, Cock of the Walk then fled west. When Shaw needed to turn left, he had to spin the vehicle almost a full circle.

"From a hill, my squadron leader was able to watch the last half mile of our retreat, and when we climbed out of the tank, he demanded to know what I'd been drinking. And I was covered with vomit, which confirmed for him I'd been tipping the bottle inside the hull. It took me a while to convince him otherwise."

But convince him Shaw did. Mechanics worked on Cock of the Walk for three hours, and away Shaw and his crew went again. "I had time to eat lunch, a Spam sandwich. It tasted better going down than it did coming up, which it did as soon as we were underway again."

The stories I have told of the Battle of Haywards Heath are random samples. Similar incidents ranged over Sussex as far north as Crawley and as far south as the channel. Estimates are that over seven hundred German armored vehicles were engaged in the battle and almost five hundred Allied vehicles. The battle entered military history as one of the most ferocious armored engagements ever fought.

"Earl Seldon's invention worked," General Clay summarized. "We bloodied the panzers. I'm sure OKW was stunned by our resistance island tactic and by the extent of their losses."

But by then, the German second wave was rolling into battle.

Clay said, "They just kept coming, more and more of them. And they finally broke our back."

Truly decisive battles are rare events. But by nightfall of the invasion's second day, Allied defenders in Sussex had been overwhelmed. "To German commanders, it must have appeared that little now lay between them and London," General Clay said. "And it sure as hell looked that way to me."

PART THREE

War, "the feast of vultures."
                    —Byron

18

At midmorning the next day we crested the hill to see black smoke churning from a shattered farmhouse. Our driver accelerated the jeep through the gate and along a stand of oak trees toward the remnants of the house. He slowed near what was once the front door. This was the 1st Armored's headquarters, and we arrived five minutes after the Luftwaffe had departed. Cordite was still in the breeze.

We climbed out of the jeep. I hurried after General Clay as he ran toward the house, stepping around masonry fragments, patches of roof thatch, splintered furniture, glass shards, a bed frame, and the twisted wreckage of a command scout car.

Half of the house was gone, blown out over the grounds. The stone shell of the other portion remained upright. Smoke rolled in and out of the remaining windows. A corner of thatch was on fire, but two soldiers on the roof were dousing it with an extinguisher. The section of house still standing was ragged with broken window frames and exposed beams. HQ company soldiers were removing casualties from the house, placing the dead alongside a rose trellis. We walked to the bodies.

General Clay said, "Goddamn it, the first body here is the 1st's commander, Roger Franks. Not a mark on him."

Franks' wig had been carelessly tucked into his shirt pocket by one of the soldiers. Part of it hung out like a handkerchief. I was stupidly embarrassed for him.

Clay moved along the line, his cap in his hand. "And next is J. P. Thurow, his deputy. Jesus."

Major General Thurow's head had been vertically halved, ear to ear. His face looked up at us, but there was no head behind it. Blood stained the ground under the body.

Clay breathed rapidly. His face was the color of paper, which made his freckles stand out like tattoos. He said in a low voice, "Next is Bernie Holt."

Colonel Holt was the 1st Armored's G3, in charge of plans, training, and operations. His uniform was smeared with blood from cuffs to collar.

We walked quickly down the line of nineteen bodies, almost all of the 1st Armored's command staff. General Clay had begun to limp. Two tents were being righted, where litter bearers were bringing the wounded for treatment by HQ medics.

Clay said quietly, "They hadn't been here long enough for the Germans to pinpoint them. War is the province of chance."

He did not say this to me particularly, although I was the only one within earshot. One of General Clay's command peculiarities was that when the action heated up, he incessantly talked to himself. He caught me staring at him during one of his one-person talks, and he snapped, "Henry VI sang tunelessly throughout all his battles, so there's historical precedent for you."

We quickly crossed the grounds. The door was blocked by a fallen beam, so we entered through a piano-sized hole in a stone wall. Dust and smoke were still swirling in the air. Charred maps lay on the floor, and communications equipment was strewn about. In the turmoil of the ruined headquarters, several soldiers were trying to put the place back in order. They moved as if in a daze. One was sweeping with a broom, carefully avoiding the wounded. The other was methodically dusting a card table with a cloth.

Another soldier was leaning against a wall, blood running from a forearm. Coughing against the smoke, a corpsman knelt over him, applying a tourniquet to his biceps. A wounded officer was sitting in an overstuffed chair near the hearth. A bandage was wrapped under his jaw and secured above his head with an oversized knot that looked as if he tied it himself. He gazed out a window with unblinking eyes.

Clay high-stepped over fireplace tongs to him. "What's your name, Lieutenant?"

The officer gathered himself. He rose unsteadily, and said through clenched teeth. "Lieutenant Gregory Sessions, signal officer, 1st Armored HQ, sir."

"What's your problem?"

"My jaw's broken, sir." He winced as he said it. Three lower front teeth had been broken off at the stumps. His flat nose was off-center and may also have been broken. "Got hit by some debris, a kitchen cabinet, I think."

"Christ," Clay said, "I've been hurt worse playing bridge with my wife."

"Yes, sir."

The general glanced at his wristwatch. "The 1st is supposed to launch our operation in fourteen minutes. Who's in charge here?"

Sessions staggered, and Clay caught him by the arm. The lieutenant may have had a slight concussion. He replied weakly, "Major General Franks, sir, but he's dead. So's everybody else. They nailed us."

Again Clay looked at his watch. He looked up, surveying the damage. He shoved his fist into his pants pocket. A moment passed. Then he said, "We've got thirteen minutes to put this headquarters together and launch the operation. I'm going to act as your divisional commander. Will you help me, Lieutenant?"

"Yes, sir."

"How many signalmen do you have left?"

"Sir, we just got hit and I haven't—"

Clay held up his hand. "I want you to find whoever is left and get a radio set up on the divisional and AEFHQ bands, and I'll also need a ground wire with a green line. And a pack radio for the regiments. This room'll stand for a while, so run the lines and antenna leads right into here."

"Yes, sir." Sessions staggered away. His resolve must have firmed as Clay's charge settled on him, because he was walking more firmly as he disappeared down a hallway.

General Clay moved to the soldier wearing the tourniquet. Clay said, "Looks like you're bleeding."

"Yes, sir."

"Looks like its mostly stopped."

The soldier risked a glance at his arm. "Yes, sir."

"Name, soldier," Clay demanded.

"Corporal Samuel Johnson, sir, 1st Armored HQ intelligence clerk."

"Corporals normally stand at attention when they are being addressed by a general." Clay rocked back on his heels.

Johnson struggled to his feet, pushing himself against the wall and backpedaling until he was upright. His arm swayed loosely. Drops of blood fell to the oak floor. His face was pinched with pain.

Clay said, "That proves you can walk, then. My G2 is trailing me in a jeep. You will see that the maps and charts scattered around this room are in order for him when he gets here. I want you prepared to display positions, and I want you to find General Franks' attack order. We'll work from that."

Johnson may have been bewildered, but he nodded his head with energy.

I followed the general over a pile of stones and masonry into a large dining room. The exterior wall had collapsed outward, and the rose garden was visible through the aperture. A chandelier had fallen onto the table. Crystal facets and broken light bulbs were scattered over the table and floor. A litter team was carrying away another of the wounded, loudly crushing the crystal under their feet. The injured man was a major, and his head and left eye were covered in a blood-soaked bandage.

"Hold there," Clay ordered.

The stretcher bearers stopped immediately. Clay looked down at the wounded officer. "You don't look too bad."

After a moment, the major said, "I guess not, sir."

"It's just your eye, looks like."

"Yes, sir."

340

"Hell, we've all got a spare eye, don't we?" the general asked. "Yes, sir."

"Then get the hell off that stretcher and help me out."

One of the corpsmen said, "Sir, Major Robley here isn't fit to—"

Clay turned to him. "You carry the dead out of here and anyone too hurt to talk. You leave the rest to me. Understand?"

"Yes, sir."

Major Robley pivoted off the stretcher. I helped him to his feet.

Clay asked, "What's your job, Major?"

Robley was in so much pain sweat had formed on his brow and was running down his face from under his bandage. He blinked his good eye. "I'm deputy commander, 19th Ordnance Battalion, 1st Armored."

Clay pursed his lips. "Perfect. You are to bring me up to date on assembly positions."

"Sir, I'm an ammo officer."

"You ship metal rations to all your units, don't you?" Clay asked brusquely.

"Yes, sir."

"Then you must know where they are."

"Yes, sir," Robley said doubtfully.

"Then get into the main room and prepare to brief me."

Clay left the major and made his way further into the ruined building. I followed. In the kitchen we found another officer, a lieutenant who was lying on the checkerboard tile floor. He was on his stomach. A trail of blood crossed the black and white tile. He had crawled into the kitchen. A flying splinter had ripped a trench in his leg from ankle to buttocks. His eyes were open.

"Lieutenant, you look healthy, except for your leg. What's your name and duty?" Clay questioned him.

The lieutenant looked up. "General Clay?"

Bracing himself on the edge of a cutting block, Clay knelt to him. "Your name and duty."

"Lieutenant Chet Benson, liaison officer from the 1st Armored Regiment, 1st Armored Division." His words were chopped with suffering.

"You are going to brief me on the 1st Armored's attack order."

The lieutenant groaned. "I'm going to die, sir."

"You don't have time for that."

Benson gulped air. "I need morphine, sir."

"I can't rely on a briefing from a drug fiend, Lieutenant. A litter team will move you into the main room next to our charts. After we talk, we'll see about a pain killer."

The general made several more stops in the building, weaving around collapsed beams and stones and plaster, putting together his command. Assembled in the main room, the new 1st Armored HQ resembled a field hospital. Many were tended to by physicians and medics as they spoke with the general. Generals Lorenzo and Pinkney entered and immediately posted themselves at the restored map table. Clay wrapped his spectacles around his face.

Lieutenant Sessions met the deadline. Four minutes to launch hour, 1st Armored HQ was connected with its regiments, the remnants of the 4th Motorized, and the Canadians.

Clay paused as Lorenzo did his work over the map. He stepped back. He said to me, "The Canuck, Henry Bisset, and I came up with this counterattack last night."

I was puzzled. "Where was I?"

"You were asleep. I looked in on you, but you seemed comfy, all curled up in your blankie, so I let you sleep."

This was nonsense, but my face burned nevertheless. After the battle of Haywards Heath, I had retired at two in the morning, long after the miserable returns were in. I was exhausted, but General Clay had apparently worked through the night.

Lieutenant General Henry Bisset was commander of the Canadian I Corps. He and Clay had formulated the plan in the early hours of the day and had received approval from ACCSS. They named it Operation Redwood. At dawn orders had gone out to divisional headquarters. Now, after the disaster at 1st Armored's HQ, Clay suddenly had to familiarize himself with Roger Franks' implementation. For five minutes he listened to Major Robley and Lieutenant Benson. Then in the remaining minutes until launch, he issued a stream of orders.

I logged them in my pad and carried them to the impromptu signal station.

Most of Lieutenant Sessions' equipment had been placed on an ornate, leather-inlaid desk that had just missed being crushed by a massive beam. Signal officers were streaming in, bringing more gear and wiring it. David Lorenzo used coins to mark units on maps. The room began to look like a working headquarters.

Just before ten in the morning, the third day of the invasion, Clay stared at his wristwatch and counted off the remaining seconds. Then he said to Pinkney, "Go to it, Jay."

Operation Redwood was underway.

Clay said, "Now we wait."

A moment passed. He said, "The Germans call this maneuver *Einkreisung*, encirclement."

I looked up from my pad, but he was talking to the air around us.

He went on, "The German is going to taste some of his own tactical medicine."

I lowered my pad.

He said, "The Teuton loves this goddamn maneuver. Von Moltke, the brilliant Prussian field marshal, used it at Sedan on the River Meuse in the Franco-Prussian War in 1870. The maneuver is the very symbol of German military prowess, as if they invented it. Like hell. They stole it from Napoleon at Austerlitz."

I should have remained silent. But, no. "Or maybe from the encirclement of the Royalist infantry at Naseby during the English Civil War."

His jaw came out. "Or maybe from Genghis Khan at the Battle of Indus."

I countered, "Or maybe from Hannibal at Cannae."

"Jack, I have to take this crap from Winnie, but not from my ADC, who is five ranks below me and may go even lower."

"Of course, sir."

The general rejoined David Lorenzo. For the rest of the morning, Clay acted as a divisional commander. He made do with his battered ad hoc staff. When Lieutenant Benson fainted, Clay had a medic administer smelling salts, then prop him up at the map table. Clay spoke constantly with regimental commanders, guiding them from their assembly positions to the engagements.

I carried orders to the signalmen and their messages to Clay.

Occasionally, he would return to me, if only because it was more seemly than talking to himself.

At one point, he commented, "Armies move very slowly. That's the shame of it."

Later he said to me, "What the German won't expect is the encirclement as counterattack. They don't think that way."

Still later he returned, his mouth moving before he reached me. ". . . so our aim is to prevent the German from turning yesterday's tactical success into victory. Our counterattack has been launched while he is still dazed from our web, don't you see?"

Operation Redwood was a double envelopment. The Wehrmacht was wheeling west from the beaches. AEF forces were grudgingly but surely giving ground. When Clay gave the order at ten that morning, the Canadians roared south from their position near London, and units of the 1st Armored drove north from the coast, all behind the Wehrmacht's westerly moving line. The maneuver was an attempt to encircle the *Schwerpunkt*, to defeat it by cutting it off.

Clay predicted at one point that morning, "Redwood is going to cut the German throat, Jack."

It should have. RAF Lieutenant Richard Ormsby's ordeal at that moment tells why it did not.

I have mentioned that Ormsby spent many afternoons before the invasion napping under his Spitfire, his squadron too low on fuel and ammunition to go aloft for much training. His unit, 46 Squadron, and a handful of others, had been carefully hoarded, camouflaged under netting away from the RAF's bomb-beaten runways, and were waiting for the moment when the RAF's last line would be committed.

S-Day was that moment. But at the end of the day, 46 Squadron had lost half its fighters. On the third day of the invasion, at the start of Redwood, only four of the Squadron's Spitfires were serviceable. By Ormsby's own count, his Spit's eight wing-mounted .303s had only forty shells in each of their belts. A couple of squeezes of the trigger. The armament officer had promised more, but lately there were more promises than shells.

That morning their squadron's controller had held them on the deck until just before ten. Their orders were to supply ground support for the Canadian divisions about to move south. A preposterous notion, Ormsby thought. There were so many Luftwaffe planes overhead, he doubted 46 Squadron would even get to the Canadians, much less provide them cover.

Ormsby had not been out of his uniform jacket in three days. He had dispensed with his Irving suit because it and his harness fouled the cockpit's wireless leads and oxygen tube. So he flew with the heater on full. He had two kills, a Dornier and, improbably for one as green as Ormsby, an Me 109. His ground crew had not had time to stencil them on the Spitfire.

He was so tired he had begun to see double. The lieutenant blinked repeatedly as, once again, he pushed his hands into his gloves and stepped to his plane. The ground crew pulled back the netting, which had branches intertwined in it. Ormsby climbed onto the wing and reached for the cockpit latch.

Yellow fire burst from the cockpit. Ormsby's hands reflexively went to his face, and he lurched back on the wing. Another blast of yellow erupted from the far wing, then another. The engine housing suddenly foamed with fire.

Ormsby leaped blindly from the wing, landing hard, his right knee smashing into his chin. His arms still protecting his head, he rolled away from his plane. The burbling of the spheres of yellow fire was abruptly drowned out by his fuel tank exploding. The lieutenant was still rolling when the heat washed over him.

He sat up. The gutted frame of his fighter was sinking to the ground, its landing gear groaning as it twisted with heat and weight. The flattened tires billowed black smoke. His friend Captain Allen Best's Spit was obscured by sheets of fire rising from its engine. And the captain's plane was being demolished as Ormsby watched, the yellow orbs of fire breaking out in a trail from the prop to the elevator, tearing away panels of fuselage, ripping away the rudder, then engulfing the craft in flames. A Messerschmitt roared overhead.

A hundred yards north, pocks of earth shot skyward, then raced toward Ormsby as another enemy fighter made its run. The lieutenant pushed himself to his feet and sprinted to a sandbag bunker, then dove over the bags and landed on Allen Best, who was lying on his belly, his head between two bags.

Ormsby breathed deeply until he caught his breath. He said, "Incendiaries."

Another German fighter swept over them, the whine of its engine abruptly deepening as it passed. Best looked up. His face had been pressed with such force against the ground that twigs and grit were stuck to it. He smiled sheepishly. "Christ, they pop."

"Those Luftwaffe bastards love them, don't they?"

All pilots did. The incendiaries' yellow bursts on impact were a deadly aiming aid. And incendiaries seemed artful, laying a brightly lit pattern of destruction across the landscape.

Best brushed sand from his chin. "Well, we've joined the rest of our mates as pilots without planes."

Ormsby stared at his plane, nothing more than a cylinder of churning fire, feeling the loss. He said sadly, "We'll be better off on the ground today, I suspect."

Ormsby and Best were not the only pilots to have just lost their rides. On S-Day, the RAF had 248 serviceable fighters. By the launching of General Clay's Redwood, the number was down to 102.

With the aid of merciless hindsight, it is easy to see now that without Allied mastery of the air, without Lieutenant Ormsby and his companions blazing a trail for armor and infantry, General Clay's counterattack was destined to fail.

Fail it did.

I have struggled with the telling of the next few hours more than any other part of this narrative. I was tempted to omit

346

the incident altogether, but Jerry Ness of United Press recently broke the story, accusing General Hargrave and me of trying to cover it up. Now, with the story out, bludgeoning the general's reputation, I must relate the entire episode, correcting some of Ness's account, confirming some.

I admit to trying to bury the affair. My loyalty to General Clay, which I feel as strongly now as when I served him, demanded no less. In a telephone conversation with me, Ness countered that history insists on more from me, and he may be right.

General Clay's conduct should be viewed from the perspective of the moment. He had just suffered four consecutive defeats: the destruction of the Ranger mission the night before S-Day, the collapse of the channel seawall, the breakdown of his islands of resistance defense at Haywards Heath, and the crushing of his counterattack, Redwood. The Germans were pummeling him.

The trouble was first confirmed when General Hargrave asked me where Clay was. By that time, three in the afternoon on May 31, AEFHQ had retreated to Haslemere, midway between Portsmouth and London, about eight miles east of the oncoming Wehrmacht's front.

I replied meekly that he had gone for a walk.

Hargrave removed his pipe and stared at me. "Clarify that, Colonel."

I cleared my throat. "He's walking in the woods behind the caravan, sir."

"What is he doing there?"

"I'm not sure, General. Thinking, perhaps."

Hargrave's small features became brittle. "Those bastard Germans are slamming us left and right and you're telling me Clay's out on a nature walk? You go find him and bring him back here."

AEFHQ was in yet another manor house, this one on land carved out of a beech forest. The house was barely visible through the ivy that climbed to the roof line. The residence and its low-flanking outbuildings were surrounded by a yew hedge that opened at the north end of the property to admit a winding brook and at the south end to let it escape. A lawn edged the creek. Near the creek was a small pergola, empty of the wrought iron table and chairs that undoubtedly had been donated to the war effort. Sentries were posted on the perimeter of the property.

I crossed the lawn, bypassing General Clay's caravan and the trailered AA gun and the HQ signal company truck that followed headquarters everywhere, and made my way to a gate in the stone wall. The last I had seen of the general, he had walked through this gap in the hedge into the trees.

The trail into the woods was dainty, with nothing rigorous about it. It was a lawn footpath, with borders carefully marked with decorative pebbles. Marble benches were located every fifty feet. The path was lined with hydrangeas and camellias and walls of rhododendrons, which were blooming blood red and dusk purple. The path aimlessly turned left and right for a hundred yards, then the trees opened overhead and the path ended at the bank above a shallow ravine. Below was a narrow pool. Two Canada geese drifted on the flat water. The war could have been a thousand miles away.

A bench overlooked the pond, surrounded by clipped lawn and begonia and lavender. General Clay was sitting there, his hands clasped between his knees. I hesitated, thinking he might be in prayer, as improbable as that was. I had never known the general to give even a passing reference to religion, except in several speeches, "because it makes a good finale," he had said.

I waited fully two minutes. Finally I called out, "General, do you have a moment?"

He did not move, still staring at his hands.

I walked into the opening. "General Clay?"

He seemed not to hear me. His gaze shifted from his hands to the pool below. He bit his lower lip. Otherwise, nothing.

I walked over to him. "Sir?"

No response. I tapped his shoulder. "General Clay?"

He started, then looked up. "Jack."

I stood at the end of the bench, waiting for further response. An alarm inside me trilled when the general turned back to the pool and said nothing more.

I moved in front of him, blocking his view. "General Hargrave is asking for you, sir."

Almost without moving his lips, Clay replied, "Tell him to carry on."

Then the general truly frightened me. He sighed, a long, hopeless, shuddering exhale, one's last breath on this earth. I believed him incapable of such a noise.

"You alright, General?"

After several long seconds, he replied, "Jack, you head on back."

Instead, I sat next to him on the bench. "What'll I tell General Hargrave?"

There was only silence from him.

I was at a complete loss. The essence of Wilson Clay was his energy and willfulness, his stamina and wild intelligence. Yet there he was, brooding and still. He appeared frail. His jaw seemed to have grown the wattles of age. Mottled gray pouches under his eyes were newly prominent. His eyes were glazed. I had never before seen the general's shoulders stooped, as if wearing a back-breaking pack. Without his animation, he seemed a shell of himself.

I tried again. "General Clay—"

"Jack, be quiet. Please."

I sat next to him for one hour and forty minutes. Then military police arrived, deployed by General Hargrave to search for the general. I intercepted them at the edge of the clearing and sent them back. A few minutes later, Hargrave appeared. I tried to cut him off, but he brushed by me and marched to the bench.

"What in hell is going on, General?"

Clay raised his eyes. "I need some time to myself, Alex."

"For Christ's sake, we have a collapsing front. You can think while we try to put it back together."

Clay said lamely, "You carry on for a while, Alex. You'll do fine."

Hargrave was dismayed. "General, we've got to . . ." His words died as he saw General Clay turn back to the pool. Hargrave glanced questioningly at me. I shook my head. Hargrave wheeled about and quickly disappeared down the footpath.

I returned to the bench. Another hour elapsed. The general's gaze switched from the pond to his hands, then back. Otherwise, he was motionless. Each time I gathered the courage to speak again, his despairing stillness stopped me.

I had heard of commanders suffering immobilizing depressions after battle losses. Marlborough was plunged into despondency after the loss of two cities, Bruges and Ghent, to the French in 1708, and was incapable of command until Eugene came to his rescue. After his first defeat in ten years, at the Battle of Aspern/Essling in 1809, Napoleon's mind was virtually paralyzed for thirty-six hours. Now the commander in chief of the American Expeditionary Force had been crippled by defeat and was sitting lifelessly while the battle raged nearby. I was overwhelmed by hopelessness.

General Clay abruptly rose from the bench and began back along the footpath. Aggravated by defeat, his limp rocked him side to side. I followed at a distance. His orderly, Charles Elliot, and his physician, William Strothers, had been watching us from under a tree. Elliot's expression was immeasurably sad. They joined me as I walked behind the general.

Clay disappeared inside his camp trailer. Without an invitation, I entered after him. He sat on the settee and stared at a framed photograph of his wife. And there he stayed for another two hours, as motionless as a headstone.

One journalist has estimated that during the five hours General Clay was immobilized by depression, over two thousand Americans and eight hundred Canadians were killed. My response is that this calculation is sophistry, is "sound and fury, signifying nothing." General Hargrave did carry on, and very well, as Clay was later to conclude.

But sitting in his trailer with him, watching as General Clay was consumed by despair, I slowly became enraged. I could here the bustle of command outside the trailer. The Wehrmacht was undoubtedly closer by the moment. And here was the American commander, glassy-eyed, his hands clasped together. Forlorn and pathetic.

His slight groan, as if he had just been injured, when there were thousands of truly injured Allied soldiers nearby, set me off. I rose from the wood chair across from him and yelled, "General, you need to get off your ass."

His head jerked up.

I shouted, "You've got an army depending on you, and you're sitting here doing nothing."

His eyes dug into me. "Jack, get out of here."

I was not to be put off. "Sir, you are needed."

Moving with a lineman's quickness, he rose from the settee, grabbed my shoulders, spun me around, and pitched me through the caravan's door. Like a drunk tossed out of a saloon, I landed on my belly.

Colonel Strothers and Corporal Elliot helped me to my feet. Seething and humiliated, I dusted off my uniform.

I will not admit to being crazed with anger, as my next act suggests. But, then again, no one with an ounce of brains would have done what I did. It was dangerous and insubordinate. "And it made you look like a lunatic," Strothers added later.

I ran toward a perimeter sentry. "You, Corporal. General Clay needs your help."

The guard started toward the trailer.

I said, "He needs ten or twelve of your best men, right now."

"Yes, sir." He blew his whistle.

HQ company sentries ran from their posts on the outskirts of the manor grounds.

Carrying their M1s across their chests, ready for anything, they gathered around me as I started for Clay's trailer. I improvised, "Headquarters is bugging out again. We have to leave the trailer, and we don't want the Germans to get their hands on it."

"Yes, sir," the sergeant answered. He glanced at one of his men, as if he might have a further clue.

When we reached the caravan, I ordered, "You men line up along this side of the trailer. Hook your hands underneath. When I give the order, lift and shove. Got it?"

"Yes, sir," the sergeant dutifully replied.

Colonel Strothers demanded, "Jack, what are you doing?"

The sentries arrayed themselves along the west side of the trailer, the side with the door.

"Ready?" I called out, grabbing the step under General Clay's door. "One, two, three, heave."

The trailer was hoisted to shoulder height, then with grunts and shouts from the sentries, was toppled onto its side. The trailer landed heavily, followed instantly by the crash of chairs and pots and the general hitting the inside wall.

"Thank you, Sergeant," I said. "You and your men are dismissed."

They hurried away, talking animatedly among themselves.

"May I dismiss myself?" Strothers asked politely.

I nodded. He fairly sprinted away. Then I grabbed my hands behind my back, stretched my backbone to its limit, and awaited my fate.

I did not wait long. General Clay pushed open the door, now on the topside, and pulled himself through to a sitting position. His cap was over an ear, and he pushed it into place. He looked around.

His eyes came to rest on me, and he said, "You'd better tell me my trailer was just hit by a Luftwaffe bomb."

"I'm afraid I can't, sir. This was done on my orders."

"Are you goddamn bucking for a section eight, Jack?"

"I'd be in pleasant company, wouldn't I, sir?"

He glared at me. His face may have changed color a time or two. Then he abruptly brayed with laughter, long and loud and convincing.

He swung his feet up through the door, crawled to the edge of the caravan, and slid down to the grass, laughing all the while.

He looked at me again. "Jack, I'm going to court martial you for attempting to assassinate your commander. You'll help me with the paperwork, won't you?"

"Of course, sir."

"Good. We've got some commanding to do first, though." He led me into the manor house.

Marlborough emerged from his short depression inspired

and went immediately on to his tactically brilliant victory at Oudenarde. Napoleon rebounded from his mental paralysis to lead his troops to victory at the Battle of Wagram.

General Clay roared back, too. The feat for which he will always be remembered was yet in front of him.

19

English courage when confronted by invaders has long been the subject of fanciful speculation. In A.D. 793, the author of the *Anglo-Saxon Chronicle* wrote that when the Vikings were rumored to be on their way, "Dire forwarnings came over the land . . . , and miserably terrified the people." Written long after the event, this can be little more than conjecture. In 1771, Captain Guy Carleton forecast that "amidst the first panic terrors" upon the appearance of a French fleet on the horizon, "The people will naturally fly." The French never came, and the people never flew.

In truth, no people are less alarmed or less easily cast down by reverses than the British. A mad rush, with Londoners choking the roads, sweeping away all in front of them in a frenzied and fearful stampede, never materialized. Instead, Londoners met the approaching disaster with their usual phlegm.

With the German horde at hand, British imperturbability was vast and, to me, unfathomable. Let me give a few examples. After the war, I spoke with Clyde Lamb, of Lamb Brothers, the Bond Street tailor. I asked him if he had given thought to fleeing the city. He made a show of furling his brow and staring at the wall in thought before answering, "I might have, had I not promised Sir James Stamford his four suits by the end of the week."

I asked Professor Fenton Swain of the Natural History Museum in South Kensington why he was not tempted to abandon the city. Swain was the noted paleozoologist who had painstakingly over seven years reconstructed the bones of the dinosaur *Diplodocus carnegii*, measuring over eighty-five feet long. Astonished at the question, he replied, "What, and abandon Dippy?"

One episode was recounted by the *London Times*. The woman was unnamed by the newspaper, but among her circle was easily identified because the article carried the titles of several of her paintings. Apparently she could not determine a way to spirit her artwork out of the city, so two days after S-Day, she rushed into Sotheby's and demanded of their lead auctioneer, Powell Prescott, that he immediately auction off her Pre-Raphaelite collection, which included John Everett Millais' *Garden of the Lady* and William Holman Hunt's *The Stable of Christ*. According to the *Times*, Prescott removed his spectacles and said, "Madam, to sell them now would be unseemly."

Simon Durwin admits he had hoped to profit from the war. Durwin was the owner of a leading London wine shop, Durwin Wine Merchants on Brompton Road. He had kept in reserve hundreds of cases of his best product, waiting for the inevitable spiraling prices caused by war shortages.

"I waited too long," he told me after the war. "I was pinched by my own greed, don't you see?"

Durwin was tormented by his dilemma. "In my cellar I had the rarest Chateau Lafite and Chateau Margaux, the finest years. I had sixteen bottles of sixty-year-old Dom Pérignon. I had two thousand bottles of priceless . . ." His voice diminished as the memory bit him. "And after General Clay's reverses, I knew German soldiers would soon be drinking the lot of it. It would be the drunken melee of the conqueror, an unthinkable blasphemy against those precious vintages."

The wine merchant considered destroying his collection. "I actually had a hammer in my hand, intent on descending those steps and smashing each and every bottle. And then a better idea struck me."

Durwin hastened down into the cellar and carried up the Dom Pérignon. He stepped into the street and passed them out one by one to surprised passersby. To each he said, "For the days to come."

In the next three hours, he handed out his entire inventory. There was no rush from Londoners, no crowd with grasping hands thrust forward. Each took a bottle, nodded thanks, and carried on. I spoke with a number of recipients of Durwin's largess. The bottles proved to be needed restoratives in the days ahead.

Elizabeth Stanhope's mother, Beatrice, had labored on her daughter's wedding for six months. As the joyous day approached, so did the Wehrmacht. Beatrice feared the celebration would not be attended by any of the hundred invited guests. She could hardly blame them. She, too, was tempted to run in front of the invaders, who had landed two days before the planned event.

The wedding was to be in the Chelsea Old Church, a portion of which dated from pre-Norman times. The nave, tower, chancel, and chapels were added over the centuries. In 1528, Sir Thomas More remodeled the south chapel, and all but that chapel had been destroyed by Luftwaffe bombs. But just that chapel, with its glorious history and its bomb blast dust covering everything, would be sufficient for Beatrice Stanhope, if only her friends would fill it.

Fill it, they did. Of the hundred invitees, eighty-two attended. The wedding, with its rented cardboard cake for lack of sugar and flour, was a giddy success. Beatrice was doubly proud of the newlyweds when they postponed their honeymoon in the Cotswolds because they did not want to appear to be fleeing the city.

There were over forty thousand horses in Greater London early in the war. Thirty of them were owned by Jasper Anson, who was the proprietor of the Highpark Stable near Hyde Park. He employed ten stable boys and claimed his quarter horses were the finest for let in the city.

"No hobbling nags under my roof, I will tell you."

The business had been in Anson's family for four generations. Above the stable was a warehouse of bridles, halters, and harnesses, most not used since the automobile had come to London.

His horses' fate was clear to Anson. "Some German mess sergeant was going to push them through a meat grinder and stuff them into sausage sleeves."

So two days after S-Day, Anson began giving them away. "Anyone who needed a horse got one."

Although there was no rush north, many London citizens—those who suspected German security services would soon be searching for them—knew it prudent to leave. Few cars and trucks had gasoline. Anson let it be known that he could make a few lorries useful again.

He told me, "Quarter horses aren't draft animals, but they'll do for a while. I put together twelve hauling teams, using old harnesses, some dating from the Crimean War, back when they were used on horses hauling artillery."

"Last I'd see of them, my quarter horses would be pulling a loaded flatbed lorry, a family in the cab, all their possessions on the bed, and the driver perched on the bonnet trying to manage the reins."

Anson admitted it was an odd sight. He stayed behind. "I had to look after my stable, even if it was empty."

Clara Lowell had obeyed when ordered to "Dig for Victory," and had planted a vegetable garden covering every inch of her yard near Osterly Park. Gardening was not her only contribution to the war effort. She had also been a member of the WVF, the Women's Voluntary Service, a civil defense organization which, among other duties, aided in finding homes and clothes for evacuees.

"We called ourselves Widows, Virgins, and Spinsters." She laughed. "But no one else dared."

Most of her garden was still too green to harvest just after S-Day, and she feared the Germans would commandeer her produce. "So after months of lovingly tending my plantings, coaxing them from the ground, watering and feeding them, I ripped them all out of the ground, weeping all the while."

Elbert Royden debated leaving London, but a wager kept him on his street in Mayfair and at his shovel and wheelbarrow. The morning after the first Luftwaffe bombs fell on London, early in the war, Royden and his neighbors gathered in his parlor and vowed they would never surrender their street to German explosives and that they would cart off every stone and pile of mortar and sweep up each speck of dust that might land on their street for the duration of the war. They bet themselves a bottle of Highland malt whiskey.

Many weeks Royden and his friends worked every evening until midnight, back-breaking labor with crowbars, shovels, wheelbarrows, and brushes. When I asked Royden why he did not desert the city, he replied in the tone I had become accustomed to, "Who would have continued our work on our street?"

I report here that at the end of the war, Royden's avenue had lost three townhouses on one corner and four in the middle of the block. Other than those gaps, the street was in pristine condition. No mounds of rubble, no dust. Planters were in bloom, cobblestones were brushed, and windows were clean.

Royden concluded, "The Glenlivet made the entire effort worthwhile."

By his own figuring, David Woodley lifted over four hundred thousand buckets of water during the war. "At the end of a night of it, my arms would hang down my sides like limp rags. I would not be able to lift a fork the next morning, could hardly shave myself."

Woodley was a member of the London Fire Brigade. He was once a sailor, as were most brigade fire-fighters. He had trained endlessly on their new pumper. "It was a thing of beauty, a Dodge, made in America, ruby red, with brass nozzles and chrome plating on the mountings. We treated it like a royal lady."

In May 1941, Woodley's fire station in Chelsea was hit by a Luftwaffe bomb that demolished the pumper. "Could not be salvaged. We pitched the scrap metal to the Ministry of Works. There was no replacement to be had, not with the RAF needing Spitfires. So we fought the fires with buckets."

Night after night, Woodley organized bucket lines among brigade members and pressed civilians. "I truly think we were more symbolic than anything else. Not much a bucket brigade can do against an entire city block on fire."

If he was powerless against the blazes, why didn't he flee London? I asked after the war.

He replied with the assurance of a man with a mission fulfilled, "We had nothing else, so we fought the bombers with symbols. It was an important fight, and I stayed for it."

My personal lesson on British perseverance came from Rose Hadley. She was a Cockney, born within the sound of the Bow Bells, who proudly listed her trade as "washer woman." Once a week Corporal Elliot dropped off General Clay's and my laundry at her Cheapside shop. During our trip to London on the day before the invasion, Elliot drove by her shop to pick up the last batch of laundry. He returned to my office to say that Mrs. Hadley's small business had been destroyed by fire and that she was nowhere to be found. He had seen her washing machine crushed under fallen rubble. We had grown fond of Mrs. Hadley.

Just when I thought Elliot might become teary, I heard this thunderous voice call out, "'Allo, darlin's."

Elliot spun to see Mrs. Hadley stepping into the office, dragging a child's wagon filled with neatly folded uniform shirts and trousers.

The corporal cried out, "Mrs. Hadley! You're OK!"

He rushed to her and clasped her in his arms.

She giggled and squirmed out of the embrace. "Ah, go on with you. It's nothing your mother wouldn't do." (As with the Germans I interviewed, I'm translating. Her actual words were "Awr, gerwom wiv yer. Nuffink yer muvver weren't do.")

She had salvaged an old washing board, used a door as an ironing board, heated her irons over a fire in a pit dug in the debris, and was making deliveries in a borrowed wagon. She bade Elliot good-bye with "You Yanks like your shirts clean, I know that much."

For me, Mrs. Hadley best represented London spirit in its time of crisis. Small courage was shown in quiet ways, thousands upon thousands of times each day.

We know now that a primary goal of the German High Command was to generate terror in the city and to start a massive, destabilizing exodus of frightened citizens that would leave London empty. It never came to pass. As General Clay seemed on the verge of losing his battle, Londoners had already begun winning theirs.

As far as I can determine, only one arrow was fired during the invasion. Roger Leeds, the elderly president of the Worthing Archery Club, let it fly, and as a result, he and the rest of Geoffrey Hurst's guerrillas were added to the timeless scroll of English heroes. Today, ask any schoolboy in England to name his idols, and he'll likely reply, "Geoffrey Hurst and Roger Leeds, and maybe Robin Hood." Indeed, Fleet Street likened Hurst's soldiers to Robin Hood's band of merry men.

"I laughed at Leeds and his bow all those weeks of training," Captain Hurst told me after the war. By then he was Sir Geoffrey. "The old bugger didn't tell me he was the European archery champion three years running in the 1920s."

By S-Day, Captain Hurst's guerrilla cell had matured and was served by two signalmen, a clerk, and a storeman. They were supplied with a light ration of high explosives, ammunition, and booby traps. They had also been provided a base.

"Other strike forces—that's what we were called by General Stedman, and I credited him with a sense of humor—had underground dugouts that had been excavated, roofed, and furnished with bunks and ventilation by the Royal Engineers. Ours was less opulent. It was an enlarged badgers' sett in an abandoned chalkpit. I suppose badgers had lived there for fifty years. We walled off half their burrow and lived next to them. I've had worse neighbors."

In their burrow, the guerrillas waited as the Germans rolled by overhead. "It was dark as pitch in there, and that old fool Roger Leeds kept poking me with his longbow. Panzers above, and one of my men was carrying a bow and arrows. I wanted to bawl."

Hurst became a convert that night. The bow was made of yew and was six feet long. It could send a goose-feathered arrow three hundred yards with accuracy. "But Roger was less than thirty yards from his target."

His target was a Wermacht sentry patrolling a home north of Worthing. The sentry's squadron had collapsed in their bedrolls after the long channel crossing and the day of battle on English soil. The German guard was walking a random circuit around the grounds, his rifle hanging limply in his hand.

Hurst told me, "Just as he passed a poplar tree in front of the house, Roger's arrow hit him, right through the neck, with such force that it pinned him to the tree. The German didn't make a sound, just hung there limply and died. His rifle dropped to the grass."

Gallant Robin Hood may not have behaved quite as Captain Hurst then did. His service knife between his teeth, Hurst crawled across the grass to the house's front door. He carefully pushed it open. There were no lights inside. He heard the muffled breathing and turning and whimpering of exhausted men at sleep. The Wehrmacht infantrymen were scattered about the main room, two on davenports, the remainder on a Persian carpet.

Hurst moved silently to the first German. He gently put his hand over the sleeping soldier's mouth and slit his throat. The man jerked and tightened, but made no more commotion than did his sleeping neighbors. After a moment, the guerrilla captain inched further along the carpet, passing by the next German, to the third enemy soldier. His knife worked again, its steel blade a soft glimmer in the darkness.

Hurst spent the next ten minutes dispensing death and granting life in an alternating pattern. His work done, he dragged himself through the front door, knowing Roger Leeds was covering him from behind a tree. The guerrillas escaped, the only casualty being Hurst's stained clothing.

I have read an OKW report on Hurst's action, written by the deputy chief of the Wehrmacht Operations Staff, Colonel Hellmuth Hayn. The survivors of Captain Hurst's attack awoke, terrified and aghast, each of them sandwiched between comrades whose necks were laid open. Their horror quickly spread to other German units. In Wehrmacht units near Worthing, all soldiers were put on watch-and-watch, where fully half the infantrymen were on guard at one time. Fear of the night became a contagion.

Geoffrey Hurst told me, "The Wehrmacht had not anticipated irregular warfare behind their lines, nothing like us, not so soon. Modern warfare is terrifying, and they had expected to move into regions where the English occupants were numbed and confused and preoccupied with surviving. The Germans hoped there would be little to fear behind their lines."

They were wrong, with Captain Hurst and his men about. The Wehrmacht's 4th Motorized Infantry Regiment, 20th Motorized Division, had landed in the second wave east of Brighton. One of their motorcycle squadrons was rushing to the front, a parade of ten motorcyles arrayed in pairs, along a lane near Storrington. They sped into Captain Hurst's trap.

"We had never set off one of our fire barrels because of the shortage of petrol. General Stedman's ordnance officers promised they would work, and we took their word on it."

Hurst blew his whistle, and four of his men yanked the chords on the Flame Fougasses, driving small explosives charges into the barrels, which ignited the mix of lime, gasoline, and tar.

"They were like volcanoes, shooting out huge spumes of fiery molten liquid. The road was bathed in it. The Germans disappeared under the sticky, flaming mess. For a few yards, the motorcycles kept going, trailing fire. Then they went down, every one of them, caught in pools of fire, billowing flame and smoke. Several gas tanks blew. The road looked like a frying pan, sizzling and popping. The drivers flapped their arms and screamed, but the goo stuck to them, burning into them, twisting them up. It was a sight to curdle the blood."

The assassination of Major General Albrecht Feldt was much cleaner. Feldt was commander of the Wehrmacht's 20th Division, which landed in the second wave. Ever thorough, the Germans had brought their own currency. Feldt, whose troops had suffered from the Flame Fougasses and Hurst's work with the knife, posted a reward of five thousand British occupation pounds for the capture of the guerrilla leader. On the third evening of the invasion, a local woman came forward, claiming she could name the guerrilla commander, that he was a neighbor who lived in Worthing.

The informer's name was Adrienne Small, thirty-two years old, a waitress at the Steyne Gardens Hotel in Worthing, who had overheard parts of a conversation in the hotel's restaurant just before the invasion. She was delivered to Major General Feldt at his field headquarters near Harrow Hill.

I interviewed Major Gerhard Wellner after the war. Wellner was General Feldt's aide. He and several other 20th Division staff officers were standing around the general when Adrienne Small was brought to him.

"An informant may not otherwise have merited the general's personal attention," Wellner told me, "but General Feldt had been enraged by the guerrilla incident, the throat cutting. I served him for four years, and I never saw him so angry. He was taut with it. When General Feldt unsnapped his holster cover, I thought he was going to shoot her outright, without even questioning her."

Wellner described the waitress. "I remember her hair best of all, for good reason as it turned out. Strands of it were in ringlets to her shoulder, but most of it was tied loosely behind her neck, quite breathtaking, brunette with traces of steel and straw colors mixed in. She had large eyes, freckles, and was rather frail. Her blouse was torn from the weapons search of her, I suspect. One of her eyes was blackened. I remember thinking she should have been frightened, but her eyes were lifeless."

The general barked, "Tell me what you know. Who leads the irregulars? Be quick with it."

"I want my money first," she whispered.

Feldt nodded at Wellner, who withdrew a bundle of currency from an attaché case and passed it to her.

The woman turned the packet in her hand, squinting at it. "I've never seen money like this before."

"It's occupation currency," Feldt said, reddening at her insolence. His balled fist tapped the butt of his Luger.

She read from the top bill, " 'British Occupation Pound.' I don't know if five thousand of these will buy a loaf of bread or a home."

His mouth curling down and his fist rising, General Feldt stepped closer to the woman.

Major Wellner told me, "That's when it happened. She was so quick she must have practiced and practiced the move. Her hand shot to her head to pull out the comb that had been holding her hair in place. It had tortoise shell tines, but attached to it was a blade the length of a finger. In one smooth, angry motion she brought it around and jammed the blade deep into General Feldt's eye socket. He collapsed instantly."

The knife had plunged through the socket to the German's brain. He was dead before he was horizontal.

"One of the general's guards immediately brought out a pistol and emptied the clip at her. She fell over General Feldt's body."

Wellner shook his head. "General Feldt's death was a great loss, to the Wehrmacht and to me personally. I still miss him. He was a good soldier and commander, a man troops were proud to follow."

The major added wistfully, "But perhaps it is just as well he did not live to see what was to come."

Adrienne Small was one of Captain's Hurst's guerrillas. I asked Hurst if this had been a planned assassination.

"Planned to the last detail."

I was intrigued. "Except for her escape. You must have known what would happen to her."

The pain on Sir Geoffrey's face made me regret my allegation.

"We had a plan to get her out," he said. "But she was dead before we could do anything." He breathed deeply, then added, "I haven't told you that I married Adrienne a week before the invasion."

It was Captain Hurst's nature that he would extract a payment in kind from the Germans. Later that day General Feldt's deputy ordered a reprisal for the general's murder. Thirty Storrington villagers were dragged from their basement hiding places by soldiers of the 20th Division's headquarters company.

Forest Grayson was among the captives. He recalled after the war, "The Germans prodded us with their rifle stocks toward the wall, yelling at us in their awful language. I was so frightened the fellow next to me, John Derwin the baker, had to take my arm and help me along."

The villagers were lined up along an ivy-covered wall near the Anglican chapel. "We were the old, the lame, and the toothless. Not much of a retribution, really. They shoved us back against the wall. A Wehrmacht armored car watched over the operation, its machine gun pointing at us."

Captain Hurst gave the specifications. "It was a Horch armored car, a four-by-four, with a crew of three and an MG 34."

Grayson said, "Then the Germans formed a column in front of us, their rifles at the ready. I honestly cannot remember if I was weeping, or whether it was John Derwin. As I got older, I had begun to pray that I would meet my end with dignity. This wasn't it."

A lieutenant marched up. "He was full of purpose, that one. He yelled an order, and the soldiers straightened, their rifles at their sides. Then he gave commands, and the rifles came up. I was light-headed with fear, and I grabbed the hand next to me, Derwin's maybe, or maybe it was the pub owner Matthew Trahern's. And then, by God, the German soldiers just began disintegrating. That was my impression. Their heads popped open, their arms tore away, gaps opened in their chests, and they all spilled over backwards, kicking and bucking."

The armored car's machine gun had opened up, cutting through the firing squad.

"And I must be truly be old," Grayson said, "because I don't remember the sound of it."

Captain Hurst added, "There was plenty of sound inside the armored car, I can assure you."

Hurst and his men had found the armored car at the edge of town, with its hatch open and its crew inattentive. With a pistol in his hand, Hurst had leaped up to the engine housing, then dropped through the hatch.

"We had a ride, quick as a wink. But it was tight in there, with three of us, and the three dead German crewmen on the car's floor, and Roger Leeds's goddam longbow poking me all the time."

Forest Grayson told me, "Well, I didn't know it was Captain Hurst at the time, of course. But we learned soon enough, the whole town did. All of England did. He sure made the Germans jump, didn't he?"

Hurst's team and the other guerrilla forces in southern England were a costly diversion to the Wehrmacht. The Germans were forced to tie up many times the guerrillas' number trying to protect themselves and locate guerrilla bases. But dash and daring could not fully recompense the guerrillas for their lack of men and supplies and arms. Seventy percent of them died before the battle for England ended.

English civilians could be likened, with apologies, to the hair on a dog's back. The invaders landed, and the English rose up with acts of defiance great and small.

Ava Singleton, who had earlier been surprised to find that the paratrooper in her apple tree at the Goldings was a dummy, had surprises of her own in store for the Germans. They were in her pantry.

"My mother taught me to can fruit when I was a lass. I put up preserves every year. I cannot tolerate fruit canned in a factory. Stawberries, raspberries, I preserve them all, nice as ninepence."

Like all other Britons, Mrs. Singleton had known the Germans were coming for many months. "So I canned some deadly nightshade berries. Made preserves out of them. I added raspberries to ease some of the tartness."

I asked, "And you put them on shelf next to the strawberry preserves?"

She nodded. "But I labeled them in ink, plain as day. Each jar—there were six of them—had 'Nightshade Preserves,' on it. If whoever took those jars could not read the king's English, he deserved what he got, and I wouldn't fancy his chances."

Apparently none of the soldiers of the Wehrmacht's 5th Infantry Regiment's *Infanterischulzkampanie* (a specially designated artillery unit attached to the regiment) could read English. On their way to the front the soldiers looted Mrs. Singleton's pantry and spread her preserves over their blackbread ration.

Three of them died in agony. Another four were returned to the Continent on a hospital evacuation ship.

Mrs. Singleton added, "Serves them right, stealing from an old woman's pantry."

Coal miner Allen Lewes had spent two days walking and stealing rides from passing trucks, escaping his Northumberland coal mine and the Essential Work Order that had kept him there.

"I didn't really know where I was, just looking for the war so I could be part of it."

Lewes wandered south until he found himself behind German lines. When I spoke with him, he went to some length to appear to have been bumbling and lost, when in fact he moved with calculation and purpose, intent on inflicting damage on the enemy.

"I had in mind joining some crack British army unit. Me, a coal miner straggling in from the north. It strikes me as laughable now. So I found myself behind the German lines."

I asked how one simply wandered behind the front.

"I went from burned-out house to burned-out house, always heading toward the smoke."

He had no weapons, no training. "I was a bit angry, though," he told me. "The bloody gall of those people, crossing the channel and landing on our soil like they owned it."

Lewes waited until night. "I figured that burning gasoline down the hatch of one those panzers wouldn't help them any. So I siphoned petrol from a lorrie into a gin bottle."

The coal miner crawled through thickets to reach the tank, moving no more than a yard a minute, knowing there must be sentries around.

"Holding this bottle of petrol, a box of matches in my trousers pocket, staying under the bushes, it was slow progress. And I couldn't see anything except this black metal mass in front of me, darker than the night. I could hear one of the panzer's crewmen snoring from inside the turret, so I knew the hatch must be open."

Night magnified sounds, and Lewes thought every twig he snapped would bring the enemy running. "I finally reached the tank and gripped a tread, then levered myself up the tank. I climbed over its trackguard, then onto the deck, then I stood alongside the turret. The hatch was open. Holding the bottle between my knees, I lifted the matches from my pocket and struck one against the box. I struck and struck it. It wouldn't light. My crawl through the damp underbrush had made them all sodden."

The Ausf E tank and its crew were safe, for the moment.

"So down I went. I couldn't see anything, and my pants got caught on a spare track link stowed on the front. I freed my leg, then slipped down to the ground. The German kept up his snoring."

I interviewed Lewes in a pub in Newcastle. He sipped his ale, then used his glass to point to others in the establishment. "A lot of these Geordies were stuck underground during the invasion. Not me."

He ordered another ale. "Now, Mr. Royce, you would think that a box of matches would be the easiest thing in the world to find. But it took me three hours."

Lewes visited four destroyed farm houses looking in the rubble for matches. He searched through fireplace utensils and in kitchen drawers. Finally, in the fifth he found a pottery jar where the family stored them. "I must have walked ten miles. Then back I went, the same route, through the stickers and thickets, this time with the matches in my shirt pocket wrapped around a handkerchief. Up the tank I went."

The match fired on the first strike. "It sounded like a rasp on iron. But that German kept on snoring. I hauled back with my hand and threw the bottle through the hatch. I heard it crash, and I heard one of them inside yell. I dropped the match into the turret. Then I lit two more as fast as I could. I never saw flames inside the tank, because I didn't want to wait. And I never saw smoke, because it was dark. I jumped down and sprinted away, too afraid to look back. I never learned what happened to that tank."

After the war, I tried to ascertain what Lewes could not. I deduced that the miner carried on his one-man irregular war in the area of the Wehrmacht's 1st Mountain Division. I spent two days studying the division's after-action reports. Sure enough, an Ausf E, commanded by Lieutenant Gregor Marcks, 1st Battalion, 15th Panzer Regiment, attached to the 1st Mountain, suffered an interior fire, killing Marcks and his crew. The report concluded the fire was caused by a gasoline bomb.

I thought Lewes would be ecstatic when I relayed my discovery to him.

Instead, he scratched his head and said, "I've come to think lately that miners who stayed underground contributed as much."

Vicar Richard Richman had already killed one German with his Austin Twelve, running him over like a mole on the road. Two nights later he was roughly evicted from his chapel by a Wehrmacht infantry colonel. I had done my homework here, also, and was able to tell the vicar it had been Colonel Joachim Scheringer of the 14th *Panzeraufklärungsabteilung* (armored recon unit), 35th Infantry Division. Sheringer used the chapel as a field headquarters.

"I watched from the choral pews in the balcony," the vicar told me. "The colonel was with six or seven of his staff. They spread their maps over the communion table, shoving aside the goblets and candle holders, treating them as if they had no meaning. I thought I had left my anger on the road, with that German I had run my auto over. I hadn't. Again, I was gripped by an unholy anger."

Richman descended the stone steps from the balcony. The recon unit's heavy and light armored cars were scattered about. "One had backed through the picket fence into the cemetery next to the chapel, pushing over headstones, some two hundred years old."

The priest stepped outside, along the gravel path toward the cemetery. Wehrmacht medics were tending the wounded under a tent near the graveyard. Several of the injured soldiers had been quickly stripped of their uniforms and provisions.

"A small pile of clothing and weapons lay next to the tent. I looked left and right. Soldiers milled about. They saw my white collar and perhaps thought I was there to give last rites, and paid no more attention to me."

They should have. The vicar removed a stick grenade from the pile of discarded clothing and weapons. Blood dripped from its wood handle. He quickly shoved it under his tunic and walked back to the chapel.

"I knew the colonel was standing under my stained glass window, and the realization of what I had to do crushed me.

369

That window dated from 1770. It portrayed Christ as a shepherd gathering his flock, and at the edges were geometrical medallions, many quatrefoils and lozenges, in red and blue and purple and green. It was beautiful to behold, an inspiration to all my faithful, the pride of the parish."

The vicar twisted the grenade's handle, then launched it at the rose window. He missed.

"It hit the stone frame around the window, and fell back, landing at my feet with a soft plop in the grass. I was terrified."

He snatched it up, wound up like a cricket bowler, and released it. This time his aim was true.

"To see the grenade smash through the window broke my heart."

It did worse to the 14th *Panzerauklärungsabteilung*'s staff. Colonel Scheringer was killed instantly, as were three of his staff. Four others were wounded.

Still appearing to be his pious self and ignored by the soldiers who rushed toward the chapel to investigate the explosion, the vicar strolled into the weald.

"I hid in Agnes Smathers' cellar. She is the woman to whom I regularly administer last rites. I'm pleased to report she survived the war and will probably outlive me."

Other civilians called themselves to arms. Peter Rathbone was a beekeeper near Royal Tunbridge Wells. Dressed in his protective gear, he found a paper wasp nest under the eaves of his barn, tore it off with his gloved hand, walked fifty yards to an armored personnel carrier, shook it furiously, then tossed it into the open hatch.

His neighbors, with whom I spoke after the war, called it a foolish waste. A dozen Wehrmacht infantrymen were stung badly, but Rathbone paid with his life, shot in the back as he turned to run from the APC.

Wendell Thorley had learned his lesson about saving petrol the hard way. He was a machinist with his own shop and six employees. Because he was an essential worker, he was alloted extra ration points. Several months before S-Day, he had been stopped and required to prove his journey was necessary and that he was on the shortest route. He was on his way to the cinema. He was prosecuted, then acquitted by a compassionate judge. But the humiliated Thorley viewed the prosecution as a claim by His Majesty's Government that he was not doing his part in the war effort.

From then on, he saved every drop of petrol he could, siphoning it from his automobile and storing it in a thirty-gallon drum. He swore he would put it to good effect some day. During the third night of the invasion, Thorley added five cups of metal shavings to the barrel, then rolled it to the petrol station near his shop. He left it near the pump, then hid in the glade across the lane. Next morning, four Wehrmacht motorcycle troops stopped at the station. The pumps were empty, but the fuel in the barrel smelled fine. They poured it into their tanks.

"I ran after them," Thorley told me. "It took me a while to catch up with the buggers, but there they were, strung out along a quarter mile of road, each soldier kicking his starter or kneeling alongside his motorcycle, trying to find out the problem. Those shavings had stripped their pistons. I still laugh about it."

The Moulten sisters would not claim to be as inventive. Edith and Edina Moulten were identical twins, Edith the older by seventeen minutes. They were widows in their late sixties who had taken to calling themselves by their maiden name after both husbands had perished, which they did within a month of each other. Both had silver hair and glittering, astute blue eyes. Their animation and their enjoyment of life and each other pared years away from them.

Edith was a telephone operator, an essential worker who was not moved north. Edina, who taught piano lessons in their cottage on the outskirts of Horsham, would not go without her. Both were secret port tipplers, drinking three or four glasses each evening after the last student departed. The sisters had seen the shortages coming and had stockpiled several cases of the fortified wine in their cellar.

A trap door under the throw rug in the sitting room led to the cellar. They hid their few silver serving pieces there. It was a cool place, ideal for storing summer fruit.

When they heard artillery, the twins climbed down into the cellar to wait out the danger. They could not pull the rug behind them over the trap door. Less than six hours later, the door was yanked open by a Wehrmacht infantryman.

"I have never been so frightened," Edith recalled. I was interviewing them in their new flat in Horsham. "There he was, with a blackened face and big boots, his rifle pointing down at us. Edina here had taken to the drink a little early that day, so she fared better than I did."

Edina gently slapped her sister's knee. "A scoundrel, you are, sister."

Edith went on, "They yelled '*Rause, rause,*' at us. I don't speak German, but I knew well enough what they meant. Edina and I started to climb up, and they pulled us the rest of the way through the door."

"None too gently, either," Edina clarified. "There were only two of them, both carrying rifles. Then," she clasped the broach at her throat, "they threw me onto the sofa. I almost broke my leg."

"You did not come close to breaking your leg, dearie," Edith interrupted.

"Then the leader—he might have been a corporal or a major, I would not know—descended the stairs to the cellar and called out something. The other followed him down, and they opened one of our bottles of port. I could hear them chortling and carrying on."

Edith's voice broke as she added, "They just left us there, forgotten, two helpless old widows."

Well, not quite helpless. The sisters acted with the special intuition twin's share. They did not say a word to each other. Their piano was an upright on rollers. They leaned into it.

"I pushed so hard I thought my bridgework would pop out," Edith told me. "But I knew we could move it, because every six months we did so to dust the floor."

They rolled it three feet. Just as the piano reached the cellar, Edith threw the hatch into place. The twins pushed and pulled, and a pair of piano legs rolled into place on the hatch.

"We heard them yell, and we heard them hit the underside of the hatch with their rifle stocks. But they were trapped."

I knew the answer from reading about it—the Moulten sisters were received as heroes by the king after the war—but I asked anyway, "Then what did you do?"

Edina replied, "I had never favored our window curtains, had you, Edith?"

She giggled. "No, not at all. So we set fire to them. Then to the sofa, then to newspapers we were collecting for salvage. We left the cottage just in time."

Edith completed their story. "Soon the roar of the fire drowned out the Germans' screaming. We heard the pinging of the piano strings as they snapped from the heat. Our home burned to the foundation. We lived with our brother in Crawley until the war ended. We miss that little cottage. But perhaps less so than we should, knowing there are two cooked Germans in the cellar." She chuckled, "Cooked, and basted in port."

These accounts have been representative samples, no more dramatic than a thousand others. English civilians did not take kindly to the Germans, and throughout Kent and Sussex they extracted their small tolls from the invaders.

20

"When did she begin to love him?"

The British historian Joseph Windham asked me the question after the war. He was working on a biography of Lady Anne Percival's father, Earl Selden.

I answered rather testily that she never did love General Clay, that she was incapable of the emotion, that the very notion was preposterous. Lady Anne did not love, she devoured. And if she appeared smitten, it was only because she possessed a singular talent for presenting herself as she wished. Her infatuation was an act to suit her purposes, murky as those purposes were.

Windham replied, "Now that you've vented your spleen, I'll ask again. When did she begin to love him?"

If love existed, it must have had a starting point, and I can recall several times when I may have witnessed its inception in Lady Anne.

It may have been at a British Army military hospital in Glasgow, which we visited during one of the general's countless tours before the invasion. The hospital, a somber brick structure built as a woolen mill 150 years before, was filled with soldiers wounded in the North Africa campaign. Lady Anne had been appointed to something called the Women's Hospital

Advisory Committee and claimed it gave her the right to join us. On that day she led us into the long-term convalescence ward. British soldiers struggled upright in their beds or turned their heads toward us. A few rose unsteadily and saluted the general. They grinned at the honor. General Clay loudly greeted them, then walked slowly along the line of beds, speaking with them one at a time, shaking hands, returning salutes, patting shoulders.

He came to one soldier who was staring at the ceiling. A sheet covered him to his neck. He rapidly opened and closed his eyes and wet his lips in a mysterious syncopation, but seemed oblivious to our visit. Clay stopped at the end of his bed. Lady Anne, the British colonel who was the hospital director, and I gathered around him. Clay asked, "Tell me where the German got you, soldier."

The wounded man did not respond, but a serviceman in a bed across the aisle called out, "The Germans had nothing to do with it, General. The chap is taking a few weeks off from the war, is all. A bit of a holiday."

Another soldier, with a leg elevated in a cast, said loudly, "He's supposed to be shell-shocked, general. But he eats fine, whatever is served. And he reads his mail. And you know how dreary it is on the front, sleeping on rocks and cactus, and having to put up with those pesky Germans."

Someone else shouted, "Pigeon-hearted bastard."

General Clay pulled at his chin. He lifted the chart from the foot of the bed and glanced at it. Then he leaned closer to the shell-shocked soldier. He said in intimate tones, yet sufficiently resonant for all to hear, "I've kept this a secret for decades, Private Sidwell, but this same thing happened to me in the Great War."

A chorus of laughter came from the British soldiers.

One shouted, "Sure it did, General."

"Right-o, General," said another. "And I'm the Prince of Wales, just as soon as I can convince my doctor."

The soldier with the elevated leg chortled, "You're a real tonic, General. A regular Ben Lyon."

Lyon was the radio comedian who appeared with his wife, Bebe Daniels, on the show *Hi Gang!*

Clay grinned at them, but held up a hand. "Let me finish." He turned back to Private Sidwell. "It didn't happen during the first artillery battle I was in, but the second, which I've always found curious. I was a battery officer, and we were trading rounds with the German. The sound was unbearable. It just collapsed my will. I was shaking so badly I could hardly give the firing sequence. And then one of my pieces was taken out by German artillery, splattered my gunners all over French soil."

General Clay stood stiffly to his full height. He gazed at the ward wall, his mouth turning down. He seemed lost in the remembrance. "And then I just sat down on the edge of a crater and stayed there. I couldn't move. I was taken to a hospital in Rouen and stayed there for three weeks."

Lady Anne stared at him, indiscreetly, I thought.

"The dunderheads in the army didn't understand the injury back then, and I would've been drummed out of the service if Alex Hargrave hadn't covered for me. He lied on all sorts of reports and finagled the doctors at the hospital into doing the same. To this day, only four or five people know what actually happened to me, and where I was for those weeks."

He turned to the wounded soldiers. He put an edge of mock belligerence in his voice, "And now you Tommies know, so don't go talking it around, or my reputation will be shot."

They called out, "Yes, sir."

"I was hurt badly, but there was no blood. Same as this man here."

"Yes, sir."

The general may not have convinced them, but at least they quieted. Private Sidwell, blinking and running his tongue over his lips, gave no indication he had heard Clay. We moved down the aisle between the beds. The general spoke briefly with dozens of wounded soldiers. All the while I felt the deflected heat of adoration from Lady Anne, who at one point stumbled over a lamp cord because she had been unable to remove her eyes from the general.

I add, with admitted petulance, that I have searched records of the British war government and auxiliary organizations, and find no reference whatever to the Women's Hospital Advisory Committee. I suspect she invented it to accompany him. The committee may not have been the only invention that day. I thoroughly searched General Clay's records from the first war, and find no mention of a stay at a hospital in Rouen. Either Alex Hargrave superbly covered up the incident, or General Clay concocted the story on the spot at the Glasgow hospital.

This hospital tour may have been when her love began, or it may have been when General Clay and Lady Anne visited the lambing station on the earl's farm. The general knew nothing about sheep and may have thought he was about to witness a shearing. As always, I followed at their heels.

The station was a squat barn with one wall open to the pasture. Stalls were filled with straw. The spring scent of alfalfa and the bleating of the Hampshire ewes and their newborn filled the barn. Three farmhands touched their caps to Lady Anne.

She led us along the sheepshed. "Have you ever seen a lamb come into the world, Wilson?"

The general looked sharply at her. "Born? I've never seen anything being born."

"It's an unforgettable experience," she said.

The general shook his head. "I've gone a long way out of my way to avoid watching anything being born."

"I thought you spent your childhood in the farm country," she chided.

Clay replied, "My father was a banker, not a farmer. He had no stomach for this kind of thing either, the coward."

Lady Anne exchanged a few words with one of the hands. The worker nodded and led her along the shed. We followed to a lambing pen, where another farmhand was tending to a ewe. He clucked and stroked the ewe's head.

Lady Anne said, "May we watch, Bart?"

"Of course, ma'am." Bart was about sixty years old and was wearing suspenders and pants tucked into his boots. "She's about ready to drop. Just a few moments now."

The ewe was on her side, her head in Bart's hand. A rear leg was raised slightly. The animal lowered her head to lick herself, then returned it to Bart's ministrations. She bleated feebly.

"What's going on here?" the general demanded.

"Here it comes," Bart said. He reached down, prepared to help if needed.

"There's the lamb's head," Lady Anne said. "Look, its eyes are already open."

"You're doing just fine," Bart cooed. "There's a doll."

Fascinated, I leaned against a post at the edge of the pen. I had seen kittens being born, but nothing else. No mistake, it is a bizarre process. Out came this wet and slimy wad, not recognizable as anything alive or cherished.

Lady Anne said, "I visit the sheep station every season, and love to watch . . ." Her voice wavered. She touched away a tear. "And every time I recall chances lost, of how my life might have been different, perhaps children."

Lady Anne Percival as a mother was not an image that easily formed.

The lamb lay on the straw. Already it was raising its head and trying to lift a front leg. The ewe stroked her newborn with her tongue, cleaning and nudging it. Bart beamed.

Lady Anne pursued her theme. "I've often thought that had I been born into a commoner's family, or had my schooling been less rigid, or had I not chased off to the Continent, my life would have been more fulfilling." She exhaled slowly. "Wilson, do you ever have second thoughts? Do you ever wonder about another life, one you chose not to live?" She turned away from the ewe and lamb, searching for his eyes.

General Clay had disappeared. I turned with her, looking for him, a bit alarmed. I seldom had him out of my sight and was not comfortable when he was. I followed her down the aisle, looking left and right. Our pace quickened.

We found him sitting on a bale, his face as white as the ewe's wool. His mouth was slack and his eyes were fogged. He was panting. His voice was a weak tremolo. "Jack, it's your goddamn job to make sure I don't see things like that."

"Yes, sir."

He stood unsteadily, bracing himself against a pen gate. "I mean, Jesus, I signed up as a general, not an obstetrician."

"Yes, sir."

Lady Anne put her hand under his arm to support him. He leaned into her and let her lead him out of the sheep station. I walked after them, but I stepped in a pile of sheep dung and had to stop and scrape it off my shoe using a pen slat.

I caught up to them at the door. She was still holding his arm and was gazing up at him. Neither spoke. She smiled at him in a proprietary way. When he turned to her, I could see the chagrin on his face.

As we neared her car, she said, as sweetly as I ever heard her say anything, "What a big baby you are."

So the sheepshed may have been where she began to love him. Or it may have been at the country home of Arthur Stedman, who was hosting a reception for General Alfred Alexander, commander in chief of Joint Army Operations. The home was Isselhurst Castle in Kent. Two red brick turrets rose above a random array of Elizabethan and Tudor buildings. The estate was surrounded by apple and cobnut trees and by one of the premier gardens in southern England.

The garden was strictly formal, with geometric enclosures and axial paths. The areas were named the East Courtyard, the Nuttery, the Spring Garden, and the Rose Garden and were planted so that each area was particularly resplendent during one season. At that time of year the Spring Garden was filled with hellebores, peonies, lilies, and pots of blue clematis. The finest in Kent, the gardens offered a reprieve from thoughts of the coming battle.

Lady Anne must have thought them competitors. My clearest memory of her startling beauty is from that evening. She had gone to extraordinary lengths, it seemed to me, to eclipse her surroundings, both the gardens and the other guests. Because of the war shortages of soap and perfumes and cosmetics, many English women thought it unpatriotic to bother with one's appearance. Lady Anne defied that notion altogether.

That evening at General Alexander's home she wore a black silk dress that flared in even a slight breeze, its folds marking her passage by languorously wafting behind her. The dress was gathered around her waist by a black eelskin belt. Suspended from her neck was a diamond that Alexander's ADC told me was named the Christiana Star. She carried a clutch ornamented with black beads and a spray of diamonds. Her sable hair was pulled behind her neck by a black ribbon. Her shimmering green eyes stole the Christiana Star's glory.

She and Generals Clay and Stedman had gathered at the bar in the Spring Garden. Stedman sipped a highball. Clay spoke with his hands behind his back. Across a narrow table from them, a bartender arranged glasses and utensils and bottles of liquor and seltzer, occasionally mixing a drink for a guest who approached and made a request.

Talking with Alexander's ADC, I had wandered too far from General Clay. I crossed the grass toward them, passing Clement Attlee and Lord Lindley and his wife. General Sutton of Fighter Command and his American counterpart General Ward Wallace were talking in another corner of the Spring Garden.

This next happened quickly. As I neared General Clay, I heard him say, "I never lose an argument. My rank of general assures that."

She smiled and said, "You lose quite every argument you have with me, Wilson."

General Stedman pulled a pipe and a packet of tobacco from his jacket pocket. He chuckled, "Wilson, you don't have the strength to win an argument with Lady Anne. I doubt anyone in the kingdom does."

She nodded at Stedman for the compliment and persisted, "Doubtless you have an easy time with most people you meet, Wilson, because your rank allows you to dominate. I dare say that a quarrel among equals daunts you."

"Such as this quarrel?" Clay asked, an edge in his voice.

"You have not had the need to develop wit or humor or the art of the polemic, not when you can yell at your inferiors, and thus end all discussion."

Stedman's eyebrows rose. This was an uncomfortable spat. He had just joined Lady Anne and General Clay and had not heard how it began. Neither had I. Stedman looked around for a gracious escape.

Clay lifted himself on his toes. "Lady Anne, your ignorance of battle tactics assures you will lose this argument."

"Changing the subject is a desperate ploy on our bumbling American friend's part, don't you think, Arthur?"

Clay said, "Every commander knows there can never be too many projectiles in battle or in an argument."

With that, General Clay swiftly reached across the table for a bottle of seltzer. He brought it up, aimed it by tilting it back, then squeezed the handle.

A jet of foaming seltzer shot out of the bottle's spigot and instantly crossed to Lady Anne. Water surged onto her, entirely hiding her face, then cascading down over her dress and shoes. Clay kept his finger on the trigger, and the torrent flowed and flowed, drenching her and falling over her clothing to the lawn. Droplets splashed away, a few landing on General Stedman's uniform sleeve. The bottle finally hissed, and the stream sputtered and bubbled to an end.

Lady Anne's mouth was open and her hands were held away from her hips. Her hair was plastered flat against her skull. Water trickled off her cheeks and her nose and ears. Her makeup ran down her face. Her silk dress looked like a damp washrag, a shapeless mess. Her handbag was on the grass. She could not utter a word.

Neither could General Stedman nor Clement Attlee nor the bartender nor any of the others.

Wilson Clay calmly returned the seltzer bottle to the table and said, "It appears I have just won that argument, does it not, Lady Anne?"

He marched away and I followed. If the more we love, the nearer we are to hate, as La Rochefoucauld said, then this may have been the moment Lady Anne began to love General Clay.

Or it may have been at her father's funeral. Earl Selden died five days before the invasion. The service was performed at the family chapel. Generals Clay and Stedman attended, then walked with the family to the burial plot. Mist fell in long, trailing curtains that hid surrounding hills. Mowing of most cemeteries had been forgotten for the war, so the grass was long, and it soaked my pants to the calves. The first Earl Selden, who died in 1798, was buried nearby, the headstone speckled with moss and the engraving made shallow by age.

With the gasoline shortages and with memorial services having lost their novelty because of the war, few attended the earl's funeral, no more than forty people. We huddled around the hole in the ground and listened to the bishop's brief words. The casket was made of cherry because metal was too dear to put into the ground.

Anne Percival was stricken. She stood apart from other mourners, wearing a black wool coat with an upturned collar that rose to her ears. Several friends approached her to put a hand on her arm or to whisper a few words, but she might not have been aware of them. She stared only at the casket. Several times she sagged forward, as if the effort to stand were too much, and would catch herself with a quick step ahead. General Clay did not approach her.

There was nothing august about the affair, held out in a rural graveyard, with the thick, drenching haze and the almost rudely abrupt service. Even I, an American not attuned to the protocol of English nobility, felt this small ceremony was insufficient for an earl, who had served with distinction in the military and as a military theoretician later in life. His daughter may also have sensed the inadequacy of the parting, adding to her grief.

As pallbearers reached for the lines to lower the casket into the ground, a U.S. Army truck crested the hill to the east and rolled toward the cemetery. It was a 7.5-ton Mack with a tarpaulin-draped box and a white star painted on the door. The truck stopped at the graveyard. General Clay nodded.

American soldiers carrying M1s jumped from the back of the truck. A lieutenant climbed down from the cab and waved them into a line at the edge of the plot. The pallbearers slowly lowered the casket.

Lady Anne's eyes moved to the soldiers. The lieutenant snapped an order, and the line of ten GIs came to attention. At an order, they brought their rifles up, pointed at the clouds.

"Ready, aim, fire," the lieutenant ordered.

The rifles crackled.

"Ready, aim, fire."

They sounded eleven times, bringing needed dignity and recognition to the ritual, a gift to Lady Anne from the general.

The lieutenant ordered the weapons lowered. The soldiers stood at attention while the bishop ended the ceremony with another reading from the Bible.

Lady Anne shed her first tears for her father during the rifle salute, and that may have been when she began to love the general.

As I look back now, I realize that I have tried to diminish in my mind Lady Anne's importance to the general. But Wilson Clay was a man bound by duty, and she did not sway him from it. My last visit to her home, Haldon House, proved this beyond all doubt. I will detail what I learned there later in this narrative.

Adolf Hitler's plan was to dismantle Great Britain. Two thousand years of national evolution were to be reversed. The realm's institutions were to be torn down, its society extinguished, its history suppressed, its people driven into vassalage. The kingdom was to be reduced to a colony.

The führer had counted on the terror of his coming to begin the disintegration. Frightened to their national soul, the British would disassemble their heritage themselves, abandoning it, destroying it, fleeing with it, hiding it, renouncing it. The cement of British national identity would be dissolved by the time of his triumphant march into London.

Hitler's singular mistake of the war was to misjudge British character. As General Clay once delicately put it, "The Brits sometimes act like they've got corks up their butts, but they are steadfast, I'll give them that." This solidity and refusal to desert their birthright manifested itself time and time again.

Victoria Haselhurst, who had witnessed the fire bombing of Norwich and had begun a long walk toward her home in Ipswich, was evidence of this trait. She had slept that night in a barn with a dozen other Norwich refugees. The morning of the invasion she began south again.

"By midday, I was exhausted," she told me after the war. "My dress was soaked through, my shoes were falling apart. I was soiled and hungry and angry and frightened."

The roads had filled with troop trucks and tanks of the British II Corps rushing south. Long lines of displaced civilians walked both ways, north and south, no one knowing the direction of safety.

"I spent half the time lying in ditches alongside the road because German airplanes kept hitting the convoys. Every time I climbed out of a ditch, I would be covered again with stickers and weeds and mud."

AACCS had determined that restricting movement of reinforcements to the hours of darkness would mean they would arrive too late. The drawn-out lines of British armored vehicles and trucks simply had to endure the Luftwaffe. Mounted AA guns fired back with little effect. High British losses were inevitable. Fields were shortly strewn with burning wrecks that had been pushed off the roads to allow other vehicles to pass. Smoke rose across Norfolk and Suffolk in evenly spaced columns marking the roadways.

"Most all vehicles were moving south," Victoria Haselhurst recalled, "but one lorry in olive and brown camouflage rolled toward me coming from the direction of London. The road was narrow, so it had wheels on the shoulder of the road as it came. I could see the driver through the windscreen. He wasn't wearing a uniform, which I thought peculiar. At that moment, I heard an explosion from behind me and I leaped into the ditch. An elderly fellow landed on top of me and shouted an apology as he crawled off. Others crowded the ditch."

I asked, "What kind of planes were they?"

"I wouldn't know," she replied.

"Strafing or bombing?"

She laughed lightly. Her blond hair had grown out from her war cut and fell almost to her shoulders. "I have no idea. I pushed my head into the mud in the ditch and did not lift it until the explosions ended."

When she arose—it might have been five minutes later—the north-bound truck was upended. Its cargo box had been ripped open. The truck was on fire, along with a burning Bren gun carrier and a Leyland Hippo truck that had been hauling a Cruiser Mark III tank. Craters had been blown into the roadway. Twisted fragments of the vehicles were spread over the fields and road.

Haselhurst told me she should have heard the cries of the wounded and should have rushed to aid them, but the glittering from the roadside pebbles at her feet transfixed her. She lowered herself to pull a sparkling object from a torn black velvet bag.

"I recognized it instantly," she told me. "Any of the king's subjects would have. It was the Imperial State Crown. I carefully lifted it to my eye. It was lighter than I would have thought, but I had to squint to look at it, so bright was the reflection off the stones."

The crown was worn at all state occasions except the coronation, for which the monarch wears the St. Edward's Crown. The Imperial State Crown was set with over three thousand stones, including the Black Prince's ruby (given to the prince by Pedro the Cruel of Castile after the battle of Najara in 1367), the Stuart sapphire (first seen during the reign of Edward IV in the fifteenth century), and the Second Star of Africa (one of the nine stones cut from the enormous Cullinan diamond in 1908).

"And here this lass from Norfolk had it in her hand," she recalled with a bright smile. "I was dumbstruck."

"What did you do?" I asked.

"Why, I tried it on. When else would I be presented with that opportunity? The king must have a larger head than I, because it fell to the bridge of my nose. Then I began to think wearing the crown might not be appropriate, so I removed it."

By then other refugees were scrambling after pieces of the crown jewels. The Royal Scepter, containing the 530-carat Star of Africa was found by a Norwich automobile mechanic. Intricately worked bracelets and plate were found in the ditch. Gold spurs made for Charles II's coronation were recovered. The King's Orb, dented but whole, was found in a furrow by a Norwich waitress. The Imperial Crown of India, made for George V to wear at the Delhi Curbar in 1912, was pulled from the burning bed of the truck by a public school student.

"A man wearing a smith's apron found a finely wrought sword. I thought the bomb blast had destroyed it, but learned later it was the Sword of Justice, which had always had a broken blade."

Haselhurst also found the jeweled Sword of State, but an elderly woman pulled it from her grasp. The sword had been damaged and several diamonds and rubies were left behind in the dirt. Haselhurst scooped them up.

"Within just a few minutes, all of it had been gathered. It had been a furious rush. We acted like looters."

They were not looters. An Austin open-tourer command car found the wreckage. Major General Randolph Gilmore took it upon himself to collect the jewels, his ADC keeping an inventory.

The result of the collection may be the subject of English song a thousand years from now. Not one item was taken from the scene. The refugees lined up at Gilmore's automobile and one by one handed over the treasures. The crowns, swords, scepters, orbs, spurs, and all the rest were deposited with the general, as were individual stones and pearls knocked loose from their settings. A number of jewels were not recovered until later in the day, when an entire acre of pasture was sifted by a regiment of British army soldiers directed by Edward Anson, the Oxford archaeologist.

One stone, and one only, was not found, a three-carat diamond from a crown made for Queen Victoria in 1887. The English now believe as a tenet of their faith in the monarchy that that diamond was not meant to be uncovered, that it was fated to commemorate the event by lying in that Suffolk field forever.

Self-proclaimed witnesses to historic events grow in number as the years pass. More people later claimed to have heard Lincoln's Gettysburg address than could have fit within the range of his voice. The fall of the Bastille was allegedly witnessed by more Parisians than could possibly have crammed themselves into the nearby narrow streets.

So it has been with the King's Ruse, as it was later named by the press. I made sure I spoke with a witness who knew what he was talking about, RAF Captain R. G. Essex, who flew the fabled Dakota from Croydon.

"I was not told of my mission until thirty minutes before take-off," he told me after the war. "I pride myself on a steady hand, but, truth to tell, I became a bit agitated when I learned who my passenger would be."

The passenger was to be His Royal Highness George VI, and the flight was to be to Dublin, then to Greenland, and on across the Atlantic. The monarchy was to be removed to Canada for the term of the occupation.

The king and Winston Churchill have given their versions of their meeting, and they are for the most part identical. At midnight of the first day of the invasion, the prime minister requested an audience with the king, who received him immediately. Royal residences in London had all been destroyed or damaged, so his highness was staying in an apartment at Hampton Court Palace, fifteen miles southwest of London. The palace had been a favorite residence of British monarchs for centuries, but Queen Victoria had opened it to the public in 1851. The palace had been reclaimed from the public when Buckingham Palace was destroyed.

The momentous meeting occurred in the palace's great room. King George knew in advance why Churchill had come. The powers of the British monarch have been in flux since the Magna Carta and are not yet precisely defined. Neither of them could predict the outcome of their discussion.

After brief formalities, Churchill said, "Your Highness, the War Ministry has determined it is no longer safe for you to remain in Great Britain. We ask that you now fly to the Commonwealth of Canada, there to remain until the invader has been repelled."

"I will share the fate of my people, Prime Minister, so I must refuse your request."

"We had no doubt you would, Your Highness. I am charged with pointing out, however, that your reign, and indeed the monarchy, may end within a few days if you refuse."

"I must refuse," the king said.

Churchill increased the stakes. "Your capture or death would be a mortal blow to your subjects. To remain here would be a disservice to them and to our efforts to win this battle. Your duty is to leave your beloved island."

"My duty—"

The prime minister brazenly interrupted, "As plainly as I can state it, your duty is to leave."

That convinced King George, or so it seemed. He stared balefully at Churchill a moment, then nodded. Twenty minutes later he departed for the airbase. His queen and daughters, Elizabeth and Margaret, would escape to Canada on a different plane.

Captain Essex resumed his account. "I was still putting the plane through its preflight when his highness boarded. He immediately entered the cockpit. I attempted to rise, forgetting that I had my straps on. He put a hand on my shoulder and pushed me back. My copilot, Captain Woodley, could not remove his eyes from him."

The king then disappeared into the cabin to strap himself into a seat.

The Dakota waited for the escort fighters to take off, then rolled to the end of the runway. By then, several dozen Royal Air Force pilots, crewmen, and mechanics had heard that the king was taking one of their transports. They ran to the edge of the runway, waving and saluting. This was the crowd that would, by individual bragging rights, swell beyond credence in later accounts.

Just as Captain Essex pushed the throttle controls forward and the Pratt and Whitney engines roared, King George reappeared in the cockpit. "Captain, I want you to roll this plane to the end of the runway, then stop it there."

"Sir?"

"I intend to get out."

"But, sir—"

"Do not forget with whom you are speaking, Captain."

"No, sir."

Captain Essex told me, "Well, I had my orders, and I had my orders. I chose the latter."

The Dakota rushed forward, and midway down the runway

began to slow. The plane halted just short of the end of the strip. Captain Woodley helped the king with the ladder. He descended to the concrete.

Essex recalled, "After his highness told me what to do, I thought this must be some sort of plan, some subterfuge to fool the Germans, and that there would be a limousine waiting at the end of the runway to whisk his highness away. But there was no automobile, and no one waiting for him. There was no plan, apparently. He just walked across the concrete onto the grass, alone, and disappeared into the darkness, to the cheers of the RAF onlookers, who knew very well what they were witnessing."

One can imagine the surprise of William Reed, a carpenter who lived near the airbase, when the king of Great Britain and Northern Ireland knocked on his door and asked for a bed for the night.

Reed told me after the war, "The king wouldn't let me waken my daughter, Hannah, to give him her bed, so he slept on the davenport in the sitting room. I found an extra blanket for him."

Asked about his decision to leave the airplane, the king mischievously explained after the war, "I decided I outranked a prime minister, even a Mr. Churchill."

Evelyn Blaine determined that her small part of British heritage would not fall into German hands and that to allow Wehrmacht troops to bivouac in her cottage near Shepherd's Close would be tantamount to trampling on the Union Jack. When the artillery barrages came within earshot, she began distributing to refugees the priceless foodstuffs General Clay had given her several days before.

She told me, "There was an endless stream of people passing my door, some leading heavily burdened horses, some carrying a grip in each hand, some with nothing but an extra coat over an arm. Tommy and I started giving out boxes and bags of food. We must have made a hundred trips between the cottage and the road carrying it all. We'd receive a smile or a nod or a brief word of thanks. Some were too dazed to reply, and I'd just tuck a bag of food under an arm, and they would walk on. Soon General Clay's gracious gift was gone. I saved one tin of ham and a small bag of apples for Tommy and me."

Mrs. Blaine returned to her sitting room for the last time. She took a piece of paper and a pen and wrote a note to her husband, Lieutenant Jeffrey Blaine.

"The letter had only three sentences. I told him we were traveling north, that his son and I would be at the Marble Arch in London each and every Sunday at noon until he found us, and that I loved him."

She put the letter into an envelope and wrapped it in waxed paper, then placed it in her mailbox near the road. Then she told Tom to remain near the mailbox while she finished up in the house. It took her little more than five minutes to push her furniture into the center of the sitting room. From her sewing box she removed the cloth strips and patches she had hoarded over the months to mend their clothing. She made a small pile of them under her husband's favorite item in the house, a well-worn wicker rocking chair. She lit a sulphur match and fanned the flame until it caught on the fabric.

She remembered, "I stood in the doorway until the furniture was well ablaze. By the time I reached the mailbox, smoke was pouring out the windows. I could not see through my tears, so my son took my hand and led me away, and we joined the others fleeing north in front of the invaders."

Mrs. Blaine was one of many Kent and Sussex citizens who put the torch to their homes and belongings. The pall of smoke that hung over England from the channel to London during those days was not so much from battle as from the acts of thousands of civilians who destroyed their homes.

Some have said English citizens individually adopted a scorched earth policy, burning in front of the invaders so as not to provide them with shelter or sustenance. But I think they resolved that if they could not take with them their mementos and photographs and Bibles and family histories, all their treasured belongings, all the items that singled them out as English and marked their passage through this life as British subjects, they would destroy those possessions rather than allow the invaders' hands to soil them.

Here, too, in ways perhaps less grand but no less pro-
found than the king's heroic gesture of remaining in England
or the refugees' gathering up the crown jewels, the English
proved that their heritage would not be frightened away from
them, that they would hold onto it fiercely, if only in their
memories.

21

The prime minister deserved to be shaken. Instead, he stood near his chair in the war cabinet room, imperturbably chewing on his cigar, one hand casually in a jacket pocket.

"A deliberate assassination attempt by the Nazis, I think," Churchill said. He could draw out the word "Nazi" until it sounded odious. "Had I been sitting here, it would have crushed my head."

A plaster slab the size of a truck tire had dropped onto his chair, snapping off the backrest. The wall clock had fallen to the concrete. Other chunks of plaster lay about the room. One of the bell-shaped glass lamps that had been suspended from the ceiling had shattered. AACCS members swatted at the glass and plaster on the green cloth before placing their folders on the table. Dust was thick in the air.

"Your head is your least vulnerable spot, Prime Minister," Clement Attlee said, lowering himself into the chair near Churchill.

Thirty minutes before the meeting was to have begun, a five-hundred pound bomb had gutted the government offices above the cabinet rooms, leaving only a twisted steel frame and a mountain of rubble. Debris filled King Charles and Great George streets. Several trees in St. James Park had been blown down. Royal Engineers had quickly cleared the stairs leading to the basement war rooms and had assured the Defense Committee that the hole in the ground was still sound. Telephone lines had been quickly reconnected.

The Flying Buttresses found their places. I once again sat behind Clay. Generals Barclay, Alexander, and Douglas, Lords Lindley and Erskin, and the other committee members took their seats. Many coughed against the dust. Churchill tilted his chair until the plaster fell off. He had been drinking tea in his quarters down the hall when the bomb hit. His coat was still wet from the spill. He carefully lowered himself to the seat, leaning forward so as to not lose his balance.

The prime minister's face was a dispassionate mask. Only the dark stains under his eyes hinted at his sleeplessness and anxiety. He uselessly tapped his damp cigar on an ashtray and said, "It is the last day of May. The Germans have been on our island now for three days. I want to know the state of our preparations to throw them off. We'll begin with your situation report, General Clay."

Clay rose quickly and walked to the map of Sussex and Kent. I could tell he was moving with a rigor he did not feel, that his back, as straight as a dagger, was aching, and that only with concentrated effort could he remove the limp from his gait.

He said, "Discussions of throwing the Wehrmacht out of Great Britain are a bit premature, Prime Minister."

Churchill pointed his cigar. "Don't trouble me with trivialities, General. The Germans' returning to the sea whence they came is as inevitable as tomorrow's sunrise."

"Yes, sir."

"Tell me where they are this morning, then."

Clay brought up a hand. "The Wehrmacht front is fluid due to the eruptive nature of its attacks. But generally the line as of 0700 today runs from Guildford southwest almost to Chichester in a great bow. We still hold Bognor Regis, Littlehampton, and Worthing, since they have been bypassed inland, and the German is behind them."

"And your northern defensive positions?" Churchill asked.

"The line runs east from Guildford to Royal Tunbridge Wells, then across Kent to Faversham. My 5th Infantry still holds the area from Canterbury to the North Foreland, largely because units facing it are being diverted for the push to London."

"In other words, the invading host has captured three-quarters of English soil between London and the channel."

"Yes, sir."

"Perhaps seventeen hundred square miles of this treasured isle."

"Yes, sir."

Churchill pinched his nose. "And more by the moment."

General Alexander said stiffly, "In fact, the Wehrmacht is within twenty miles of this meeting."

Clay went on, "Our intelligence is spotty, but we believe now that fifteen divisions landed between Dover and Brighton. Their main thrust continues to be from their wheel, heading northwest to encircle the city clockwise."

The general continued for several moments, reporting on estimated strengths of the enemy divisions. He then summarized, "We have bloodied them, Prime Minister. We are quite sure that our resistance at Haywards Heath came as a surprise, as was our Redwood counterattack."

"But both failed utterly, did they not?" Lord Lindley asked. "The Germans are still on the march."

Churchill cut in, "What are your casualties, General Clay?"

"My 1st Armored has suffered fifty-five percent casualties, and I should take it off the line."

Alexander said tartly, "The enemy is advancing faster than your litter bearers can run to the rear."

"Two of the 1st's armored regiments have dissolved, as have a field artillery battalion and an armored infantry regiment. Normally tank losses are six times personnel losses, but we've been hit so hard that our troop loss is much higher. The Canadian divisions are heavily involved alongside the 1st, but they too are taking heavy casualties."

Clay continued for a few moments, listing the devastation to his units. The 4th Motorized and 2nd Infantry divisions had been mauled, but some of their regiments were still operational and were retreating with some order north toward London, fighting with tactical counterpunches as they pulled back. The 35th

Infantry, which had taken the brunt of the German XIII Corps beach assault between Dungeness and Folkestone, existed only on paper. Its commander, Major General John Hammond, had been killed, as had his deputy, Major General Mark Keyes, and the chief of staff, Colonel Henry Culligan. Colonel Walter Pelovik was in charge, but could not be contacted to be told so.

With casualties approaching fifty percent, the 2nd Armored was retreating in confusion behind Tonbridge, almost within Londoners' hearing range of artillery. Clay continued by saying that his soldiers were inflicting damage on the enemy, that the Wehrmacht was not slicing through England unmolested, that the Germans may have fallen behind their own schedule, and that their objectives were proving harder to attain than OKW had anticipated.

AACCS Chief of Staff Allen Barclay asked pointedly, "But, General Clay, slowing them does not mean stopping them, does it? They are still advancing apace?"

"Yes, they are still moving forward."

Clay returned to his chair. Gloom settled over the room as thick as the dust from the bomb blast. The meeting next heard from General Stedman on prospects of reinforcing the southern front. Elements of the British XI, IV, and II corps, so carefully placed along the eastern sea wall to halt the anticipated invasion from across the North Sea, were moving south, but Stedman said transportation facilities had been so badly damaged by Luftwaffe operations that progress was sluggish. Many British army units were reduced to walking south.

Churchill asked, "They will arrive too late, will they not, General Stedman?"

"Sir, it would take two weeks to move those corps south and into position, even under neutral conditions. With the Luftwaffe controlling the skies and with rail lines and bridges out, a longer time will be needed."

"We don't have two weeks," the prime minister said softly. "Our men are going to be too late."

The meteorologist, Group Captain Richard Swarthmore, reported next, moving to his map of the channel and carrying a clipboard. He pushed from his eyes an errant lock of hair. "Prime Minister, the low pressure system which I outlined at our last meeting continues to move our way. We have every indication from outlying reporting stations that a summer storm is gathering."

Swarthmore glanced at his clipboard. "Seas off Land's End are already six to seven feet with winds up to eighteen knots. This system will continue to move west, with predicted conditions at the German routes across the channel at level three to four winds with a thousand-foot ceiling."

As usual, several Defense Committee members peppered Swarthmore with questions about the reliability of his forecasts. He replied that monitoring stations reporting through the Air Ministry and the Admiralty and the U.S. services at Widewing unanimously predicted declining weather conditions.

After the meteorologist was excused, Admiral Parker Gilford, commander in chief of the Allied Naval Forces, said, "The Kriegsmarine will have increasing difficulty resupplying the troops ashore, and further waves of troops will be slowed."

There was discussion as to tonnage the German Navy would be able to land in the anticipated L5 gale. The estimated 150,000 enemy troops in England would require 1,500 tons of supplies per day. The Wehrmacht would surely suffer shortages, but the officers unanimously believed weather-imposed logistical problems would not significantly slow the enemy's advance before it took London.

Churchill said finally, "Even the weather is too late."

Reports were given by General Douglas and Admiral Gilford on the status of air and sea activity. Their services, or what remained of them, were being constantly pressed. They offered little good news.

Then Alfred Alexander motioned for the floor. He stared at his notes for a moment before saying, "General Clay, you said your 1st Armored had taken fifty-five percent casualties. When there are few alternatives, a division need not be immediately replaced until it has suffered seventy percent casualties."

From my position, I had a good view of the back of Clay's neck, a reliable indicator of his humor. It reddened. His words were clipped, "What is your point?"

Alexander said, "Can you say with certainty that the American soldiers under your command are putting forth their supreme effort?"

Clay glared at Alexander. "That is delicately phrased, in your noble English tradition, isn't it, General? What you are asking is if my soldiers have their hearts in it, if my soldiers think this goddamn country is worth their American hides?"

"General Clay, those who fight in their own territory do so with metal in their backs. Your troops are in a foreign land and—"

Clay broke in, his voice clipped with emotion, "My soldiers, those wonderful men, have built their wall of the dead. I can ask no more of them than that."

Silence fell on the meeting. Every British officer there knew Clay's reference to the most famous incident of the Battle of Agincourt in 1415, where the dead reportedly lay in six-foot-high stacks.

Churchill said quickly, "We meet again this evening." He rose from his chair.

Several Defense Committee members glanced tensely at Clay, then at Alexander. As Churchill gathered his documents, Alexander cleared his throat and said, "Prime Minister, there is a matter of command I wish to raise."

As is always the case, one commander finds himself at the hard point of the enemy advance. To that officer belongs the fame and veneration or the condemnation and loathing. General Clay had yet to show mastery of any field. Recrimination had not often surfaced among these professionals, but with losses mounting and London in peril, it was inevitable. With apparent reluctance, the prime minister lowered himself to his chair.

Alexander had thin, bloodless lips, perfect for handing down a sentence. "I do not make this recommendation lightly, Prime Minister, and I do so fully aware of the sacrifice made by American soldiers. But General Clay has overseen the loss of our southern counties. Now that the enemy is at the gates of London, it is time to change the watch. I recommend that we ask President Roosevelt to remove General Clay from command."

There was no movement in the room, not a cough, not a

rustle of paper. The undulating, weak sound of an air raid siren on the street above filtered into the cabinet room.

Churchill formed a steeple with his fingers. He stared morosely at Alexander.

Arthur Stedman said, "That is premature, General Alexander."

Churchill shifted his gaze.

Stedman added, "The German would be at Picadilly were it not for General Clay's defensive maneuvers. His holding back regiments of his 35th Infantry and 4th Motorized from the sea wall—"

Barclay cut in, "Directly contradicting his orders from the committee."

Stedman's hand hit the table. "It has been absolutely decisive in slowing the Wehrmacht."

"And then there is the raid by your so-called Rangers," Alexander said. "Frankly, I was shocked to hear of it."

Lord Lindley said, "We were perfectly stunned by the news."

"Not only was it ill-conceived," Alexander explained, "but you did not consult with anyone else in this room."

Stedman again argued for Clay. "We do not yet know the consequences of the raid, General Alexander. Even though it was not successful on the surface, it may have thrown confusion into the Wehrmacht command."

Alexander gave the smallest glance to Stedman, his subordinate. "General Stedman, your dogged defense of General Clay can be excused this time, since you have not as yet been apprised of Bletchley's conclusion that the German headquarters for the invasion was nowhere near Holland, but in Normandy, and that the Rangers' target building in Flanders was part of the ruse. The lives of those American soldiers were entirely wasted."

Stedman was finally silent. So was General Clay. I could not see his face. This news must have been crushing.

Clay was to say later that he had been right about General Stedman, that he indeed turned out to be Clay's Eugene of Savoy, his Stonewall Jackson, "not on the battlefield, as I had thought, but at that meeting."

Alexander continued, "But I am speaking of more than mere

competence." He turned again to Churchill. "I am also speaking of stability. Not your reckless shooting of a Lee Enfield at that Messerschmitt, not your rash flight over the invasion beaches, both of which can be excused because some folly is par for Americans. But, General Clay, we have reports that you were incommunicado for a number of critical hours yesterday."

Several in the room nodded.

With his eyes, Churchill dispensed permission to speak. He looked at Clay.

The general said, "Would you rather I did not deliberate about tactical moves, General Alexander?"

"You could not be reached. You cut yourself off completely, an utter abandonment of command."

"I will not give a premature order. I insist on reflection. Yesterday I needed time alone to—"

Alexander shouted, "The issue is your health."

Clay launched himself to standing and jabbed a finger at the British general. "You dare to question my sanity?"

Admiral Fairfax answered, "We need to investigate yesterday's incident, General. Until then a replacement commander is in order."

Alexander said in his steel voice, "I will not have the fate of this nation dependent on someone who may be having difficulty with his mental processes."

The admiral added, "And you, General Clay, would not hesitate to strip command from someone who had floundered, who had failed in his mission."

Churchill slapped the table. "That's enough, gentlemen." He took in the entire room, left to right. "General Alexander, I heard those rumors, but have no solid evidence of any instability on the part of our American friend here. I agree with Stedman that General Clay has accomplished an admirable delaying action, given his inexperienced troops and limited resources. He will remain in command."

Once again he pushed himself up from his chair. He said, "We meet again this evening. Good day, gentlemen."

The committee members returned papers to briefcases, gathered their pipes and cigarettes, and pushed themselves away from the table. A few spoke among themselves. Alexander glanced at his knuckles for a moment before rising. He had suffered a defeat, but was not one to do so quietly. He rose from his chair and left the room. The Buttresses paired themselves with their commanders and followed them out.

General Clay remained seated, his palms flat on the table. His eyes were locked on the prime minister as Churchill walked to the door. A patriot to his soul, Wilson Clay's first allegiance was to the Stars and Stripes. But at that moment, I believe, he silently pledged himself to Winston Churchill. In light of what was to come, this allegiance will forever be the subject of heated controversy.

From the beginning of the war, British civilians had been called on to sacrifice and to endure. They did so willingly, with devotion to cause and country and with the certainty that righteousness exalts a nation. But many thought their years of noble abnegation were insufficient and idle, at least when compared to their servicemen's hardships.

English civilians were impatient to spring into the breach, at least according to General Clay. "They were taut with it, ready to rush out in some crazed display of defiance to the German invaders."

British journalists have taken to calling the populace's two spontaneous and heroic acts of resistance the Day of the Barricades and Second Dunkirk. My postwar correspondence with American and English historians indicates the labels may stick. General Clay and I knew of these communal endeavors as they were occurring. I suggested to Clay they were nothing more than hysterical charges at windmills.

He shook his head and asked, "Jack, do you know who said, 'Even when the likelihood of success is against us, we must not think of our undertaking as unreasonable or impossible, for it is always reasonable if we do not know of anything better to do'?"

I narrowed my lips in thought, then replied, "Buffalo Bill Cody?"

400

"Jesus H. Christ, Jack, sometimes I think you are on the moon and I'm down here running the war myself. It was Clausewitz."

He ended the argument by saying that the Day of the Barricades and Second Dunkirk were simple operations, that brilliant military ideas are usually simple, and that I was always simple.

As events transpired, we were both half right. One of these exploits would play no role other than as a stirring lift to morale. The other would be crucial to the outcome of the invasion.

The Day of the Barricades was an impulsive revolt against the inevitable. The Wehrmacht was closing in on London. The city's streets would soon be echoing with German jackboots.

"The very idea of Londoners allowing the Hun to pass freely into our city was repelling," David Woodley of the London Fire Brigade recalled after the war. "We weren't Parisians, after all. We had more fire in our bellies."

Attempting to avoid a bloodbath, the War Ministry had issued instructions that Londoners were not to attempt to stop German armor. "Who made the decision to barricade the streets?" I asked the fireman.

"I know only that there was a rush into the streets all across the city. Hundreds of thousands, maybe a million of us."

Woodley made good use of his experience organizing bucket brigades. "I'm proud to say I had fifteen hundred people working under me. Quite the captain this old sailor was, if I may say so."

With crowbars and picks, Woodley's huge crew tore up King's Road. Cobblestones were harvested in swaths from the street, requiring longer and longer lines of citizens passing them forward. The street stones quickly grew to a mound, then to a mountain the height of a two-story building.

"It was the hardest work of my life, passing rocks right to left," Woodley remembered. "I tried to lead my troops in song to lift their spirits. The only tune that came to mind was 'God Bless Charley, the Man Who Invented Beer.' It worked well enough, and we sang with gusto."

When the wall of cobblestones was judged sufficiently high, several iron window railings that the Ministry of Works had missed were cut apart, then placed as pikes atop the stones.

Woodley told me, "Largely because none of us had ever seen a panzer regiment in action, our new stone barricade looked impenetrable. We limped to our homes for dinner, exhausted, every muscle aching. I could not lift my arms to open my flat's door or even to knock on it. They were utterly spent. I butted the door with my head until my wife let me in. I had a sizable blue bump on my forehead the next day."

He may have taken offense when I grinned, because he added in the tones of a martyr, "So you can put in your book that David Woodley did not escape the war unscathed."

George Portman was a veteran of the Somme, where he served with the Royal Fusiliers (City of London Regiment). The regiment was originally raised during Monmouth's Rebellion in 1685 from the Tower of London's existing garrison. Portman told me, "Our unit was known to be singularly difficult to remove from positions we had set to hold."

Portman claimed to be an authority at receiving artillery shells. "The Fusiliers took our share in the Great War. Surviving it makes you an expert."

When he joined the thousands of Londoner's excavating a trench and tank trap in Hyde Park, he immediately saw their folly. "They were digging under trees."

I admitted I did not know the danger of placing a trench under trees.

"Neither did they. So I whistled between my fingers and gathered a few of them around. They were using garden hoes and coal shovels, all these fine Mayfair and Belgravia ladies, some wearing evening gloves up to their elbows. They had mud streaked on their faces, and their hair was damp with sweat. One woman was wearing a string of pearls over a leather apron probably borrowed from her gardener. Quite a sight. Another woman dug while her chauffeur waited on Carriage Road, the door of her Rolls Royce open for her return."

Portman and I were sipping ale at the One for All Pub in London. He went on, "I told them our unit had learned the harsh lesson at the Somme. A nearby squadron was in a foxhole in an orchard. They were under the low branches of an apple tree. I was posted along an embankment near a road and saw what happened and will never forget it. I heard the shell coming in and looked up. The shell stuck the tree, which acted as an airburst. The fragments shot straight down like a grenade, killing six soldiers in the hole."

What did the Hyde Park diggers do? I asked.

"I give them credit. They shuddered at my description, but I didn't hear one groan or see one mouth turn down. They just marched fifty yards away from the trees and began to dig a new trench parallel to the old one."

I had never seen a television receiver before I came to London. Hugh Young, owner of Marylebone Radio and Electronics, assured me there were over twenty thousand of them in London before the war began. He lived in a flat above his shop.

He told me after the war, "Our barricade was assembled in great haste, in a frenzy, really. We were swept up in the urgency of it all, and our efforts were fanned by fear and defiance. People emptied their flats of furniture to pile it in the street."

Desks, dressers, bookshelves, mattresses, and rolled-up rugs were thrown onto the heap. Hanging flower pots, commercial display racks, closet doors, an antique secretary. Young remembered a long and varied list.

"My neighbors were offering their all for the barricade, and I could do no less. One at a time, I carted out my television receivers and tossed them onto the mound. Twelve of them, their glass screens shattering as more furniture was thrown onto the pile.

"You lost your entire inventory?" I asked.

"You would have to have been on Marylebone Street to understand our fervor for that barricade."

Philip Little was a bus driver who recalled for me his blockade. "We made the barricade with what we knew best, our double-deckers. Me and Arthur Johns and James Sullivan and Harold Bass parked them side by side on Bishopsgate. You couldn't have squeezed a leaf between them."

I asked if a panzer couldn't easily have pushed one of the double deckers out of the way.

"That was our next thought. So we flattened all the tires."

"That still doesn't seem enough," I commented.

"Then we filled the buses with rubble. Stones and bricks and beams. They sank to their axles."

"Even that doesn't sound like enough."

"Well," Little said, "then I bashed out the front window and sat in my driver's chair with my old Lee Enfield, waiting for the bastards."

Sidney Blasingale sold gas-proof dog kennels, manufactured by the People's Dispensary for Sick Animals. "They cost four pounds, and I hadn't sold many. I threw two dozen of them on the barricade, glad to be rid of them."

Douglas Harlow owned the Victoria Street Cinema. "I was losing money because of the fourteen fire-watchers I had to employ. The cinema's wide, flat roof seemed to attract the incendiaries, and the fire-watchers had to sit up there every night. Then I made the mistake of showing *Opened by Mistake*, which had a bad-luck reputation because three cinemas showing it had been bombed. The long queues normally in front of my cinema disappeared. So I directed my fire-watchers to rip out the rows of seats and add them to the barricade."

Martha Hudson rushed out of her flat to find a barricade being constructed of thirty-gallon drums carted from a nearby Thames dock. Her neighbors' plan was to make a wall of them, then fill them with water for weight. Hudson urged that many of them be filled with petrol instead. An immediate rush ensued to siphon the tanks of automobiles and trucks. Where a siphoning hose was not available, gasoline tanks were pierced with a nail or a screwdriver, and the spilling gasoline was collected in jars. Most autos were low on fuel, but slowly, jar by jar, six of the barrels were filled. Gasoline-soaked rags were inserted into the bungholes. "You Americans are fond of barbecues," she told me after the war. "My neighbors and I had one planned for the first Germans we saw."

The Day of the Barricades produced several anomalies, to my mind, but perhaps not to an Englishman's. London was awash in bomb rubble, yet many of the blockades were of automobiles and furniture and material ripped from standing buildings. Perhaps Londoners were saying, "We'll give it our best," and their best was items of value. Many of the barricades were made of what had until then remained intact.

Another peculiarity, possibly explained by their history as an island fortress, was that at the center of the concentric circles of barricades was not the seat of government, the Houses of Parliament, but the Tower. Some unspoken historic pulse, sensed by all, decreed that the ancient citadel would be London's last stand. Fireman David Woodley said, "England would fall only when the invader had planted his wretched banner atop the White Tower."

Winston Churchill later told General Clay that Second Dunkirk will be recorded as one of the celebrated marches of all time, maybe the most celebrated.

Clay, who by then should have known better, said, "Surely not as great as Alexander's march to Thebes, 240 miles in thirteen days."

The prime minister looked up from his tea. He wore an expression of tired indulgence. "As great, and as great as Hannibal's winter march over the Alps in 218 B.C."

"But not as great as Scipio Africanus' masterly march from Utica up the Bagradas Valley."

Churchill came back with, "As great, and as great as Harold's march from York to Battle in 1066."

"But not as great as the march of Napoleon's Grand Army to the Rhine, eighteen miles a day."

"Greater, and as great as Marlborough's march to the Danube, the finest military maneuver of the 1700s."

Clay hesitated, cast his eyes at me as if I would help him, then sputtered something about the insignificance of precedent. In high color, he reached for the tea.

Churchill chuckled. "You keep coming back for more, Wilson. Your determination is to be admired. And pitied."

Both would agree that Second Dunkirk was a marvel of tactics by those who knew nothing of tactics. No one knows who started the land bridge, but I interviewed several candidates after the war.

Lewis Stout was a wheat farmer with two hundred acres near Hadleigh, just inland from Ipswich. As soldiers from the 165th Infantry Brigade, 55th (West Lancashire) Infantry Division, filed past, some in armored personnel carriers, others on trucks, but many walking, Stout stood by the road and ladled water from a barrel on the bed of his truck to refill canteens.

"Our lads were exhausted and were marching on only their pluck. I served in the Great War, and I marched across France, and then back again. My feet have hardly recovered. So it struck me that in this day and age, no soldier should have to walk until he enters battle."

The farmer abruptly lowered his ladle and shouted, "You Johnnies climb up here, and I'll drive you as far south as my petrol will hold."

Stout hauled thirty infantrymen to Chelmsford, almost to London. "Each one of them shook my hand as he left the lorry."

Another farmer, Joseph Warren, witnessed a Luftwaffe strafing run tear up a Bedford three-ton truck's engine. "By the time I rose from my cover behind a stone fence, the truck had pulled over. The driver pointed out to his lieutenant holes in the bonnet. The bullets had gone clear through the engine block. But I thought, this truck is still good, mostly."

Warren ran to his barn, started his Austin tractor, and quickly drove it to the front of the Bedford. "The soldiers saw my purpose and used a chain to attach the tractor to the lorry's axle. Then I told them to harness my two iron-wheeled hay wagons to the back of the truck. So we formed a road train and with a whoop, they climbed on."

The farmer transported an entire company of the Royal Norfolk Regiment eighteen miles to the south, until the tractor's fuel tank was dry. He said proudly, "My boys went on to win five Victoria Crosses, more than any other regiment." At the end of the war, the regiment presented Warren with their Britannia badge, and he was wearing it on his wool cap when I spoke with him.

Peter Penry was a coal driver at Kingston upon Hull, on the Humber River. He filled his truck with soldiers of the 201st Infantry Brigade, Yorkshire County Division. "I carried them all the way to the Chilterns. But I hadn't had time to clean my truck, you see."

When the infantrymen climbed down, their uniforms were covered with coal dust. Their faces and hands were smudged. Some of them were spitting it out.

"I said I was terribly sorry," Penry recalled for me. "But one sergeant told me that I had just saved them their supply of burnt cork. They marched away, quick as you please, looking more like chimneysweeps than soldiers."

"I had a rural practice," Dr. Calvin Shields told me, "with visits up to fifteen miles away, so I had an iron-clad reason for obtaining all the petrol I needed. I had a full tank for Second Dunkirk."

Shields drove a Vauxhall Ten. He picked up six soldiers of the 131th Infantry Brigade, 44th Home Counties.

"They told me they had lost their platoon's medical officer to a Luftwaffe fighter," he explained. "So when we got as close to the front as an automobile could, I parked the car and followed them in, carrying my black bag. Their lieutenant said he hoped they wouldn't need me, but was glad for the company."

Walter McWhety was surprised when soldiers of the Wessex Infantry accepted his offer of a ride south. "I am a mortician. I was driving my hearse. They didn't hesitate, just climbed right in. Made something of a joke of it."

The mortician almost came to blows with the sergeant sitting next to him. McWhety would not explain the short detours he made as they drove toward London. He told me after the war, "I knew the location of every cemetery in that part of the country, and I didn't think it right that Tommies heading for the front in a hearse should be driven by graveyards. Bad for morale and all."

The sheriff of Nottingham, Charles Doane, also found himself avoiding fistfights. He stationed himself at the south end of a bridge over the River Trent, and refused to permit refugees fleeing north to cross.

"I knew from the Great War that all bridges must be one way, toward the front. There were too many soldiers and too many vehicles crossing the bridge to congest it with civilians rushing away from the battle. But I almost had a riot on my hands."

Delbert Dolby owned a bicycle shop in Coventry. He rolled the bicycles onto the street and gave them away to soldiers of the 133rd Infantry Brigade, Home Counties Division. He told me, "To tell you the truth, I did not mind seeing them go. Those bicycles compared poorly with prewar models. There was no chromium on them, and they were painted black, every inch. There were no three-speed gears. Even the handlebar bells were tinny." Dolby said the soldiers were nonetheless happy to receive the bicycles.

Through her cottage window, Joan Kerry watched British soldiers marching south. "An endless column, and they were so tired, tramping on and on. I wanted to help them, but felt useless, until my eyes fell on my violin."

Kerry belonged to the Leicester String Quartet. "I played lead violin. My neighbor Dalia Jennings played second, and Terrance Barton, the chemist, played the viola. Our cello player was in the Royal Navy."

She ran next door and ordered Dalia Jennings to grab her violin. She telephoned Barton, and he appeared within minutes, carrying his viola. The three of them joined the marching column.

"I asked the first soldier I came to the name of his regiment. He said they were the Yellow Bellies. I learned later it was their nickname, because their first colors had a yellow ground. He must have seen my confusion so he clarified by saying they were the North Lincolnshires. So I asked the name of their regimental march. The soldier, a sergeant I think, replied it was 'The Lincolnshire Poacher.' "

Kerry looked at Dalia Jennings and asked, "The Lincolnshire Poacher?" Jennings shook her head, as did Barton. They had not heard of it. Kerry told me, "Mind you, we played Mozart and Bach and Schubert. I had never played any music with the word 'poacher' in it, I was quite sure of that."

She asked the soldier to hum it. He did, and several other infantrymen joined him.

Kerry remembered, "Regimental marches aren't the most

complicated of music, but they certainly are thrilling. We swung into it gaily, the three of us."

The Leicester String Quartet, minus one, marched fifteen miles with them, as far as the musicians' legs would go. With the quartet setting the tempo, the Lincolnshires' pace quickened, and their hearts hardened to the task ahead.

The Lincolnshires were no strangers to the forced march. The 10th Foot endured a 120-mile march across the Egyptian desert in 1801, for which it was awarded the Sphinx badge. This regimental badge was awarded to the Leicester String Quartet after the war. Joan Kerry stitched the design—a Sphinx atop the word "Egypt" atop a banner on which was the regiment's name—onto a flag, and it now appears on a pole next to them at all their performances.

Mary Branscomb was a Red Cross volunteer, an American who had been assigned to dispense doughnuts and coffee to British units in the north. She and her crew of Doughnut Dollies operated a mobile canteen, called a clubmobile, a Ford van that opened to serve refreshments. "We gave doughnuts to them all, and what an education it was for a Seattle girl like me. We served dashing Polish cavalry officers, who had colorful uniforms from the last century, and knew only two English words, 'girl' and 'bed,' and always used them together. And Norwegians with their fresh faces and all that blond hair. And the French, who really were gallant, kissing our hands and everything."

Branscomb saw the sweep of troops south and immediately offered her clubmobile as part of the caravan. "You can imagine my distress," she told me after the war, "when eight soldiers of the 4th Highlanders boarded the van."

She paused in her story for my reaction, but I had none.

She repeated emphatically, "The 4th Highlanders."

When I shook my head, she replied, "Why, we were warned about the 4th Highlanders from the minute we arrived in Great Britain. They were a notoriously rowdy Scottish regiment, the bane of us innocent American girls."

What happened in the canteen? I asked.

"Well," she said, "nothing at all. They were dead tired and

so anxious to get south that they sagged to the floor of the van and didn't say anything at all, or do anything at all, except eat all the doughnuts."

I teased her, "To have the 4th Highlanders all to yourselves and them too fatigued to raise a finger must have been a cruel disappointment."

A touch of color graced her cheeks, then she smiled. "A little disappointing, I must admit."

Woodrow Smith's ancestors had been blacksmiths since before records were kept. "I believe that's how we got our name, Smith," he told me. His shop was near Cambridge, and I visited it after the war. The building was under the dark shadow of an enormous oak tree. The day I found him was bright with sun, and when I entered his shop I could see nothing but the fire in the forge. His son manned bellows. Smith's anvils and hammers might have been two hundred years old. He told me he had also begun repairing automobiles and lorries but regretted it, preferring to shoe horses.

He said, "I was working on a tractor wheel, trying to straighten it, when a tank brigade began rolling by. My shop filled with dust as their treads dug up the road. My boy and I walked to the door to watch them pass. Just then one of the brigade's Mark VI tanks broke a tread, and the tank drove right off the tread, its road wheels sinking into the road, and the tread gathering behind it."

The 20th Armored, 6th Armored Division, was critically short of parts, as were all British Army units. The tank commander crawled out of his vehicle, and, cursing mightily, ran his hand along the tank's front hull, where spare treads should have been stowed. Too hurried to push the disabled Mark VI off the road, the line of tanks behind him detoured around it, crushing the fence and rose garden of the home across from the blacksmith's shop.

"I wandered over to the tank to examine the tread. Then I said to the tank commander, a sergeant, 'I can repair this.' He looked at me as if I had just granted him a pardon."

Smith rolled his cutting torch to Donald George's dump-truck, towed to the lot in back of the shop two days before so the blacksmith could replace a universal joint. He cut a re-

410

placement tread out of the truck's bed. Within forty minutes, Smith had sized and drilled the steel and installed it on the track.

"The tank commander saluted me, and he and his crew were on their way. And the next day, when I told Donald George how the hole in his lorry bed came to be, all he did was congratulate me for being clever."

Thousands of private vehicles and their drivers were offered to the British Army. The civilians viewed themselves as part of the lineage of citizen armies dating from the time of Cromwell.

At the front, hearing of the vast march south, General Clay thought it would fail. "The Luftwaffe is going to tear them up."

German fighters took their toll on the English caravans, but far less than Clay had anticipated because most German aircraft were providing air cover at the front and because of the volunteers' dispersed routes.

Still, General Clay reflected the common wisdom on that day when he said, "We won't last until they get here. The British reinforcements will be a day late and a dollar short."

22

We were in the Cub when General Clay turned to me and held up a palm, fingers apart. "Jack, soldiers hold in scathing contempt commanders whose armies seep like sand through their fingers. And those commanders' names are quickly lost to history."

Lost, except to generals such as Wilson Clay, who study their humiliation and shudder at their fate.

He said, "Cadorna and Kerensky during the Great War and Gamelin of this one, so recently at the head of once-formidable forces, have already been forgotten."

As the Germans ground toward London, Clay feared he was about to join them. The condition of the American Expeditionary Force that Sunday will long be debated, with Clay's detractors claiming it was still fairly robust. They paint him as unduly pessimistic, on the verge of panic, mistakenly believing that his army was dissolving. I was with him during those hours and will report fully here. I gained an idea how ludicrous stories about a controversial man originate.

Not even his critics deny General Clay had an unerring instinct for appearing where the action was hottest. The general insisted on visiting the front. "I cannot order soldiers to bear risk without sharing it," he said.

From London we flew to headquarters of the 1st Armored Regiment, 1st Armored Division, arriving at ten in the morning, the fourth day of the invasion. The regiment had initially rushed east toward the invader, but once the Wehrmacht wheeled into them, it was forced to retreat. When we marched into his tent, we found Colonel Alan Hebert packing his duffel bag. His jeep driver was waiting with the engine running. The colonel pronounced his name "Ay-Bear." Enemy shelling was distressingly close, and the ground shivered under my feet. Hebert's shaving mirror swayed on the tent post.

An artillery veteran once told me to keep my mouth open during close shelling, lest my eyeballs pop out from a concussive blast. He may have been yanking my chain, but to be on the safe side I parted my mouth and left it that way. Doubtless I resembled a moron.

Clay said, "Colonel, your last report didn't lead me to believe withdrawal was indicated. Explain your retreat."

Perhaps startled by Clay's unannounced appearance, Hebert stammered that the 4th Battalion had vanished and that he was without information on survivors, but presumed most were either POWs or casualties. His 3rd Battalion was pulling back in order. He was awaiting a report from his 5th Battalion and was going to meet with its commander at new headquarters at the rear.

General Clay questioned him. I am not a tactician, but overhearing them, I gained a clear impression from Hebert of puzzlement and passivity.

Clay demanded, "How many hours of ammunition remain?"

"I'm working on that, General. I'm waiting for—"

"And fuel reserves?"

His eyes flicked to the card table that served as his desk. "I've got Lieutenant Maynard checking on it, sir."

"Franks ordered your brigade's fuel to be resupplied by the 123rd Armored Ordnance two hours ago. Where is that convoy?"

"We are not in contact with them, sir," Hebert answered. He spoke with a Louisiana drawl.

Small arms rattled nearby, followed by the blare of a heavy machine gun. A soldier yelled, but I could not make out his words. I heard the hollow bark of a mortar salvo.

"Colonel, I am relieving you of command."

"Sir?" Hebert's face was devoid of surprise. Apparently out of touch with the bulk of his command and ready to flee to the rear, he may have known it was inevitable.

"Where is your deputy?"

"Lieutenant Colonel Greeley is in the signal truck."

Greeley opened the tent flap and entered at that moment, followed by a signal officer.

Hebert resisted. "Isn't this something only my CO, General Franks, can do?"

"Franks does what I tell him," Clay said, turning to the lieutenant colonel. "I'm ordering you to speak candidly. What has been wrong with Colonel Hebert's command?"

Greeley made a small sound in his throat before saying, "At this time, sir, I don't believe we have a choice but to pull back. But it seems our regiment is doing so a bit docilely, and with some confusion."

Clay nodded. "Command of the 1st Armored Regiment is now yours. Pull it together."

We left the tent. In light of General Clay's widely known dislike of things French, a rumor circulated after the war that Hebert was cashiered simply because of his insistence on the French pronunciation of his name. This story ran in the *Spokane Times*, which Clay regarded as his hometown newspaper. I credit Associated Press with refusing to distribute this calumny. Nevertheless, the invention was accepted as truth by the credulous, stoking the controversy to come.

To my consternation, we then drove toward the sound of gunfire. I wanted to remind Clay he was a general, deserving of a desk, away from bothersome rifle fire, with his aide. The road was rutted, and my rear end received a pounding. We passed American APCs and artillery tractors going the opposite direction.

Clay said, "Goddamn retrograde operation, Jack."

Our driver, Corporal Hubert Turner of the Royal Sussex Regiment, was home from Africa with a hand injury. He had

414

told us it was a scratch and should not have put him on the hospital ship. I glanced at his right hand. He was missing three fingers. A Sten gun was tucked behind his feet. He had confided to me, "I'm not yet done with the Germans."

The clamor of weaponry could be heard above the jeep's engine. Clay pointed south, and we turned along a row of trees. A column of AEF troops marched raggedly toward the rear. When they saw the general, many looked away. We passed dug-in soldiers and two Shermans using a stone fence for cover. Shells hissed overhead. A hundred yards to my left, a fire ball erupted from the ground. Near it a cottage was burning, the flame whirling overhead.

Clay pointed again. We turned toward a squad of soldiers using a road embankment as a breastwork for their jeep's pintle-mounted machine gun. Two soldiers were crouched behind their weapon, while a lieutenant leaned into the bank, binoculars at his eyes. Five others also rested against the embankment, their M1s pushed into the grass atop the slope.

Corporal Turner drove right up to the jeep. Clay hopped out, and I followed.

"Identify yourself," Clay ordered.

"Lieutenant Bill Smolowe, 6th Armored Infantry, sir." He was about twenty years old and had a shaving nick on his pink chin, and the look of an innocent.

A burst of rifle fire sounded from a glade beyond the burning cottage. A plane flew overhead, but smoke obscured it.

"What's out in front of you, Lieutenant?" Clay asked.

"Sir, we think the enemy is over in those woods and maybe in the brush thicket in front of the trees."

Clay bit crescents into his cheeks. "Why the hell aren't you letting them have it?"

"Sir, we aren't sure what their movement is at this point."

"Jesus H. Christ, Lieutenant." Clay brushed aside the gunner, grabbed the handles of the machine gun and pulled the trigger. The gun roared. Flame shot from the barrel and empty shell casings flew, some bouncing off my ankles. Clay slowly pivoted the gun as he fired. A private fed the metal link belt, hand over hand. When the 110-round belt was gone, Clay spun the gun's handles to the lieutenant.

"Fire on infested areas, Lieutenant. If you wait to see the enemy before you fire, you'll get his bayonet up your ass."

The lieutenant nodded glumly.

"Get going, then."

While the feeder hooked in a new belt, the lieutenant took the gunner's position and lifted his leg to brace it against the side of the jeep. When the feeder nodded, the lieutenant yanked the bolt, then fired. The din rattled my teeth.

Clods of dirt jumped from the bank. A machine gun always attracts return fire. The infantrymen ducked. One of them pulled a grenade from his belt and held it in his hand, studying it. Clay jumped to the ground. Bullets cut the air all around.

He crawled up the embankment to the soldiers. "Men, you've got to fire your weapons."

"Yes, sir," several said.

A mortar round landed on the other side of the embankment. The ground trembled and dirt and brush rained on us. I think I was losing my hearing. I held my helmet on with both hands, as undignified a position as I've ever assumed.

One of the riflemen looked at me and asked, "You a lawyer or something?"

Clay said, "Men, after the Battle of Gettysburg, some Springfield rifles were found with as many as a dozen charges down the barrel."

I wanted to yell at him, "For God's sake, General, not now!"

Clay lectured, "In the noise and fire of battle, the soldiers just forgot to fire their rifles."

"Yes, sir," came from some of them.

"Now I want you to climb up there and fire. Marksmanship is a lot of crap. Fill the air with lead."

They did so, firing repeatedly, their M1s sounding like toys next to the constant bawl of the M2 HB on the jeep. Clay waited until they began to change their clips. He used the lieutenant's binoculars, then yelled over the bellow of the machine gun, "You men are firing too high. Too much front sight. Fire low."

One of the soldiers looked over his shoulder at the general.

Clay yelled, "Your ricochets will frighten the German, and they do a lot of tissue damage when they hit."

416

The infantryman turned back to his weapon. Clay patted him on the back and slid down the bank.

We returned to the jeep. Corporal Turner was gone.

Clay said as he lifted himself to the seat. "I figured that Brit wouldn't last as my driver. The minute my back was turned, he ran forward and is now giving the German hell with that Sten gun he thinks I didn't see. I wish I had a thousand like him."

I drove us away from the line, my boot against the firewall. The story that General Clay spent the day acting as a rifle instructor, lost in the tiny technique of aiming an M1 while the island burned around him, is a blatant exaggeration. He was showing himself at the front. He said later, "Soldiers will not follow a man they think will let them die alone in the field."

The general had three command trucks, which were mobile signal stations. They were three-quarter-ton 4×4 Dodges, called officially T 214-WC 56s, and they looked like enlarged jeeps. The trucks were armored and crowded with radio and coding equipment and maps. Whenever they pulled off a road, the driver raised three antennas. Dodge supplied the same chassis as a weapons carrier.

Because Clay usually travelled in the Cub, he posted two of the Dodges at roughly the corners of his command and one in the center. Each truck had a branch AEFHQ staff, including signalmen, G2 officers, sentries, mechanics, and drivers. We called them AEFHQ West, Central, and East. Whenever we touched down after the invasion, the nearest truck would either be waiting or would rush toward us. We did not use them often prior to the German landings, because Clay typically flew directly to divisional or regimental headquarters. They proved their worth after S-Day.

I go to some lengths to mention them here, because their existence was a secret, so much so that journalists who now suggest Clay abandoned his command for the field were not aware, and probably will not be aware until they read this narrative, of the mobile command vehicles. Nor do they know of the many times that day General Clay and I went inside the vehicles. That morning after the visit to the 6th Armored

Infantry, Clay and I spent the next fifty minutes inside Command West, during which he received or reviewed forty-three messages and issued sixteen signals. I still possess my notes as proof.

Then we set off again in the jeep. A map was on his lap. A jeep with a mounted Browning followed us. The general said to me, "We need to make a brief stop. Ordnance isn't getting to the 27th Field Artillery."

Moments later he directed me to cross a field toward a grove of trees. I was within fifty yards before I saw white stars that seemed to hang in the underbrush. Trucks were hidden there, almost invisible in their olive and brown camouflage, a white star on each door. To the east, across a shallow valley, a brace of Stukas, dots on the clouds, was diving out of the sky. I could not see their hapless target.

Clay was out of the jeep before I had it stopped. He carried a sheaf of orders. He called to the driver of the first truck, a General Motors deuce-and-a-half. "Name and unit, soldier."

The driver, a corporal, peered out the window. When he recognized Clay, he hurriedly threw open the door and jumped to the ground to salute. "Sir, Milton Cook, Bravo Company, 19th Ordnance." He remembered his cigarette, and spit it out.

Clay demanded, "Why aren't you provisioning the 27th Field Artillery? I've got a copy of your goddamn orders in my hand."

The corporal glanced at the line of trucks behind him. The crews were trotting toward us. The 19th Ordnance was newly raised. It resembled a high school class.

A lieutenant reached us first. He said, "Sir, I wanted to wait until the sky was clear of the enemy. We're carrying explosives. An incendiary into one of these trucks would end us all."

Clay pointed into the cab. "Get in there, Corporal Cook, and move over." He turned to the lieutenant. "If you wait until the Luftwaffe goes home, you'll be under these trees until geese crap pearls."

The general climbed into the seat. The displaced driver looked doubtfully at him. Clay stamped on the starter pedal. With a growl, the GM lurched forward. I hastily jumped onto the running board and held onto the window frame. We rolled out from under the tree canopy into the field. The Stukas had disappeared. Smoke rose from their target, spreading across the ground like waves in the increasing wind.

Clay drove furiously. I glanced behind us. The column of trucks was following, five or six of them. Clay twisted the steering wheel, and we turned east, across deep furrows. I bounced crazily on the running board.

All war may be foolish, and some aspects of war more foolish than others. But the most asinine report that came out of the invasion, bar none, stems from that brief truck ride. The *Los Angeles Tribune* interviewed Corporal Cook after the war, then reported in an article that at times of stress General Clay would lapse into baby talk, that he would revert to his infancy. United Press picked up the story. An article in the *Birmingham Sun*, down in the land of Baptists, bless them, gave the general the benefit of the doubt by speculating that perhaps it was a biblical tongue rather than baby talk.

The entire account stems from that moment when the general turned to me and said through the truck window, " 'Arf-made recruities, Jack, 'arf-made recruities."

I nodded knowingly, but had to look it up later. Corporal Cook did not hear the general correctly, or perhaps he just did not know the poem. Clay was quoting Kipling: "When the 'arf-made recruity goes out to the East, / 'E acts like a babe an' 'e drinks like a beast, / An' 'e wonders because 'e is frequent deceased / Ere 'e's fit to serve as a soldier . . ."

The general was referring to the youth and inexperience of his soldiers. I state categorically that Clay never spoke baby talk and am perturbed that I must even address such a breathtaking absurdity.

Clay frequently quoted Kipling. His favorite during the invasion was, " 'There are only two divisions in the world today: human beings and Germans.' "

We soon reached the remaining guns of the 27th Field Artillery. A battery of 105mm howitzers was already hooked up to its tractors and was pulling out. One of the guns was on its side, enveloped in fire. Three bodies had been pulled from the flames, then forgotten. Another battery was still firing. Its officer ran up to Clay. He was a lieutenant with his face blackened by cork, even in broad daylight.

"Report, Lieutenant."

He was out of breath. He swallowed quickly several times. Howitzer blasts seemed to split my head.

"Letelier, 27th Field Artillery, sir. We're laying them direct. No time for correction data or aiming points."

"Good for you."

"I've got an enemy armored regiment along my sights, but I'm down to six or seven rounds for each piece, sir."

Clay said, "I heard you had those goddamn German tankers by the balls, so I brought your shells, personally."

The lieutenant beamed. "Yes, sir. Thank you." His right hand was covered with blood. I could not tell if it belonged to him or one of his artillerymen.

"You stay at your guns. I'll get the stuff to you."

The lieutenant sprinted back to his battery. Clay directed the truck crews to distribute howitzer shells, which took only several minutes since the ordnance squadron was extremely anxious to depart. Between the bone-jarring noise of our artillery, I thought I heard the distant grind of panzer engines coming closer.

Clay led the convoy away. He said to me through the window, "I like that artillery officer's grit, Jack. See that he is decorated."

"Decorated with what, sir?"

"Christ, I don't know. Whatever you think is appropriate. And you find the name of the battery officer who was pulling out his howitzers, and you bust that chickenshit and put him on the boat."

"Yes, sir."

I later gave Lieutenant Letelier a bronze star, and I never found the fleeing artillery officer. I didn't look hard, because if I could have, I would have been on his tractor seat next to him.

When we returned to cover, Clay gave orders to the ordnance lieutenant, who nodded eagerly, either inspired or chagrined by the general's visit. Shortly thereafter we were again in the Cub.

Clay was peering at a map when Terry Norman said, "General, there's some trouble below."

"You got that right," Clay replied without looking up.

420

Clay tipped the Cub's wing to give Clay a better view. The pilot said, "I mean, right now, right below us."

Clay pushed his nose against the window. "Those men are going to be blind-sided."

I looked out the window. We were just east of Reigate. Below, three tanks were about to crest a tree-topped hill. I could not tell from their colors, but I presumed they were panzers. They were fanning out as they neared the summit. One tank pushed over a small tree and rolled on. Beyond the hill was a fleet of Canadian I Corps vehicles: several scout cars followed by three tanks and a dozen APCs and trucks. They had pulled off the road. A number of officers were conferring near one of the scout cars. Blue diesel exhaust hung over the convoy. The Canadians were about to be ambushed.

Norman said, "We don't have time to patch through a radio warning, General."

Clay replied, "Then let's go sit on that German armor."

The pilot grinned fiendishly, and the bottom seemed to fall out of the Cub. We plunged toward the ground. I gripped the back of Clay's seat so hard my knuckles turned white.

The general said mildly, "Jack, you've got some of my uniform in your fist there."

With an effort, I opened my hand.

We dropped toward the panzers. The terrain rose with sickening velocity. Just when I could make out the black cap of the German tank commander in his hatch, Norman pulled back the stick. The Cub's struts groaned, or it might have been me. I glanced at the gauges. We were passing 180 miles an hour. Norman had once told me, in a fit of rancor about being deprived of a Mustang, that the Cub would fall apart if it ever broke 150. The fuselage creaked and the engine howled.

Norman banked the Cub into a tight circle over the panzers. He wagged the wings. With each roll the wings were almost perpendicular to the ground. My throat was packed with bile.

Around and around we went. The panzers were beneath me, then seemed to soar out of sight overhead. Then again they appeared below, to race away out of sight beyond the top of the Cub's window. Intent on their prey, the German tank crews may never have known we were over them.

The Canadians saw us, though. Their tanks turned on their axes to cover the three-man antitank crews who ran toward the hill. Even at our height and despite Terry Norman's gyrations with his plane, I could see their recoilless rifles. The Canadians disappeared into the trees fifty yards from the panzers. Norman calmed the plane. I swallowed and swallowed, desperately trying not to vomit down the back of General Clay's neck.

We saw a flash, followed by smoke filtering up from the trees below.

Norman said, "One panzer down."

"Let's get going, Captain," Clay intoned. "We don't have time to direct traffic all day."

I learned later that the Canadians successfully ambushed their ambushers. The three panzers never made it out of the woods. The Canadians of the 3rd Battalion, 2nd Armored Infantry, did not suffer a single casualty during that brief engagement.

It would have been unlike General Clay not to mention his role in the affair, so he sent the Canadians' commander, Henry Bisset, a telex: "General Bisset: I waved the wings of my plane at some of your soldiers this morning. Simple courtesy dictated a return salute, even from Canadians. s/Clay."

Bisset's return telex read: "General Clay: My soldiers did salute you. Did you not smell it? s/Bisset."

We landed near Tonbridge, where AEFHQ Central met us. We spent an hour inside the truck. Again I take pains to mention that Clay received thirty-eight messages during this time and issued fourteen, all dealing with redeployment and resupply of his units. He also held radio conferences with the Defense Committee. Generals Girard and Lorenzo were also at the station, deliberating with Clay. When he spoke directly with the prime minister, he asked for privacy.

I therefore never had notes of that conversation, despite the insistence of several historians that I destroyed them.

When we emerged from the truck, we were surrounded by American soldiers, their rifles across their necks or hanging limply from their hands. Their uniforms were disheveled and a few were missing helmets or packs. It was a sea of haggard, frightened, defeated faces.

Clay waded into the soldiers. He called out, "What in hell are you men doing?"

None of them said anything. None broke pace to the rear. They would not look at him.

The general grabbed one of the infantrymen by his shoulders. "What's your unit, soldier?"

The reply was meek. "2nd Battalion, 38th Infantry Regiment, sir."

Clay held the first soldier by his uniform while he roughly handled a second, jolting him to a stop. "What's your unit?"

"2nd Quartermaster, 2nd Infantry, sir."

"And you?" Clay demanded of another infantryman.

"2nd Recon Troop, sir."

"Do you men know where the goddamn front is?"

No one said anything. The only sound was the shuffling of boots and distant artillery rounds. One of the soldiers was using his rifle as a cane. Another wore his arm in a sling. One infantryman was leading another who had a blood-stained bandage over his eyes.

Clay marched back to the truck. He grabbed a trenching spade from the pack of a passing serviceman, then smacked the flat of the blade against the command truck's hood. He struck it several more times until he had their attention. The infantrymen turned to the general, reluctantly it seemed. I doubted they would be receptive to a rousing pep talk.

I consulted with David Lorenzo before transcribing here General Clay's next words. The general's brief oration to the river of men drifting past AEFHQ Central has been used against him. I wanted to check my memory of it against Lorenzo's. We agree on the following.

General Clay yelled, "Your men's units are mixed, and that means you are running in disarray, doesn't it?"

He was not expecting an answer.

"I didn't give the order for any of your units to fall back as far as Tonbridge. That means you are fleeing your posts. I didn't bring you soldiers over here for you to walk away from your duty. Don't you SOBs know that it's cheaper to hold ground than to retake it?"

Again Clay was met with silence. Surly silence.

"And I goddamn guarantee you that I am going to retake what you've lost."

His gaze singled out a soldier. "You, where in the goddamn hell is your M1?"

The soldier muttered something.

The general ran at him. He fairly lifted him off the ground by his collars. "It is a dereliction of duty to abandon your rifle." Clay spun to me. "Colonel, notify 2nd Infantry MPs to arrest this man, and anyone else found without his personal weapon."

Lorenzo and I cannot deny that General Clay was in a fury.

"Your units are still at the front, but you soldiers have left them. Deserted them." He drew a line in the dirt with his foot, like a boy challenging another to cross it. Then he turned again to me, the dispatcher of his orders. "Colonel Royce, you are to post headquarters company MPs along an east-west line right here. Any soldier crossing that line toward London without his unit will be dealt with summarily."

That is the phrase he used, both Lorenzo and I recall clearly: dealt with summarily. I state emphatically General Clay did not say they were to be shot. Some analysts have gone so far as to assert that Clay established drumhead courts, that firing squads roamed between London and the front.

I personally issued the order over General Clay's signature. It directed military police to detain suspected deserters. No more, no less.

The soldiers stared at him balefully. Clay's jaw was thrust forward and his fists were on his hips.

One soldier, a corporal with a bloodstain on his sleeve, made a step to cross the line.

Clay said in a chilling voice, "Son, you had better believe that I am worse than the German."

The corporal hesitated, inhaled loudly, then turned back. It is also patently untrue that Clay barked Frederick's famous phrase, "Dogs, would you live forever?"

As if a DI had called an about face, the beaten formation of

424

stragglers turned around and began treading south, again to face the invaders.

General Clay's day up to that hour has been set forth with particularity, beginning with the morning War Ministry meeting in London until the showdown with his own soldiers near Tonbridge at three in the afternoon. I have done so to dispute irresponsible hearsay reports that the general had forsaken his command to fight as a common soldier, that he turned viciously on his own troops, that he was touching upon madness.

There is no question, though, that General Clay was achingly aware his army was disintegrating. His place in the military history he knew so well would be as an utterly defeated commander.

I personally investigated the death of Lady Anne Percival. In light of the charges bandied about regarding her and General Clay, I decided to dig and pry and then reconstruct her last moments. I will be called ghoulish, perhaps deservedly so.

Earl Selden's home had been heavily damaged by artillery fire. My guess is that a shell entered the leaded glass rose window above the great hall and detonated inside against one of the masonry arches, bringing down the center of the building. Another shell streaked into the servants' wing. Defenders must have made the manor a redoubt, because bullet pocks etched the exterior brick and stone in long strings and swirls. Inside the main entrance, a fragmentation grenade had scoured the slate floor and the hall woodwork with metal shards. The door had been ripped from its ancient iron hinges and was lying across a flattened yew near the walkway.

Although I visited the manor house a month after the battle, it had remained untouched since the combatants had departed, except for the quick visit by the burial service. Nothing had been looted or further overturned, nothing picked through by collectors or the curious. Much of the county was in ruin. Earl Selden's ancestral mansion shared the same end as hundreds of others and as thousands upon thousands of more modest homes and shops. At the time of my visit, there were too many buildings destroyed and too many lives dashed for the recovery to have begun. The remains of the manor house stood unsteadily, empty and silent, in sorrowful contrast to the scintillating conversation and wild flirtation I had witnessed here.

I pushed aside splintered panels to make my way through the hall. Glass crackled under each footfall. A Chippendale giltwood mirror lay on the floor, the wood in a dozen pieces scattered around the floor, and the glass shattered. An oyster walnut-veneered longcase clock was on its side, the pendulum hanging out of the open case. A painting lay face down, its gilded gesso frame cracked. I lifted it and saw a portrait of an earlier earl, whiskered and frowning, but with an amused cant to his eyes. I could see Lady Anne in the portrait. I placed it on an exposed nail and carefully leveled it.

A beam had crushed a buffet in the dining room, but the china closet was intact. Not a plate or serving dish or sauceboat had been broken. A fire had begun in the main kitchen and spread into the servants' kitchen. The stoves and coolers had been blackened. Wallpaper had curled and peeled with the heat. The fire may have been extinguished using the two buckets near the door. It appeared a grenade had been lobbed through the window and landed in a sink. Porcelain fragments covered the kitchen tile, and exposed water pipes rose from the floor like bent fingers.

I wandered next into the library, where General Clay and the earl had spent so many hours. I righted the globe. A bookshelf that had been against an outside wall had been overturned by a blast that had punched a hole into the room. Books were spilled across the carpets. The earl's display cases were on their sides, the glass in long shards. His treasured Wellington letters were scattered about. I took a moment to gather them, finding sixty-two, and put them in his desk drawer. One leg of the Bosendorfer piano had collapsed. The instrument was at a sharp angle to the floor, looking undignified. A soldier had fired up through the window, raggedly serrating the hammered copper ceiling.

I searched the building until I found Lady Anne's chambers, which were comprised of a bedroom, dressing room, study, and bathroom. Her rooms were more girlish than I would have

426

imagined. The wallpaper was patterned in pink and green flowers, and a settee was covered in pink velvet. One wall of the study had been entirely covered with framed photographs from her youth. Most had fallen to the floor. They showed her in riding habits posing on numerous horses. There were bays and chestnuts and a palomino. She must have gone through horses like she went through men.

Her bedroom was dominated by a mahogany four-poster bed dressed in silk damask. She was not known to use this bed often. I peered into her closet, pushing hanging clothes along the bars one at a time, regaining a sense of her. I looked through an armoir and a William and Mary chest of drawers and a plumwood highboy, fingering her intimate items, feeling like a voyeur. I poked through several jewelry boxes. Necklaces and earrings, many with diamonds and other stones, were still in the small drawers. I realized I was delaying my search, putting off what I feared to discover. I snapped the drawers closed, and walked into her study.

Lyle Foote of the burial service had told me he had found her body in front of her rococo-styled desk, which I found out later was from the time of Louis XV, complete with the stamp "ASSNAT," standing for "Assemblée Nationale," indicating it had been confiscated from an aristocratic house during the French Revolution. Foote believed the concussion of a bomb or artillery round had blown her back, toppling her chair and spilling her onto the Chinese rug. Or, he said, the window frame hit her, or the cross beam that had cut her desk into halves had also crashed into her.

Foote said, no, he had not inventoried her effects. "Too many corpses to get under ground before they bloated to have time for the niceties."

Her inlaid mahogany chair was on its side near the desk. A crystal inkwell was turned upside down on the rug, and a blue stain had spread under the well. I lifted one end of the beam and pivoted it away from the desk. The blotter was curved like a ladle from the weight of the beam. I opened several drawers until I found a small packet of letters from Wilson Clay. The cancellations showed them to be from dates earlier than I was looking for, but I put them in my jacket pocket. I continued to search through the side drawers, examining letters and mementos, bits and pieces of a life. I felt that at any moment, Anne Percival would appear in the doorway, scold me for being a nosy child, and slap my fingers.

The last place I looked was the center drawer, buckled by the beam. I tugged it several times before parts broke free. I pulled out pencils, stamps, paper clips, and, finally, the letter I had presumed existed.

An envelope was stamped with the AEFHQ logo. On it also, in General Clay's handwriting, were her address and the words, "HQ Signal Co., hand deliver immediately. Clay."

I pulled the letter from the envelope and unfolded it. It read in full: "Anne, I beg of you, leave Haldon House for London this hour. For the sake of your country and mine, my plans cannot be altered. Wilson."

Then, after ten more minutes of searching, I found her response, which she either did not have the inclination or the time to complete. The sheet of paper had been blown into her bathroom, perhaps by the blast or by a later wind through the broken windows, and was near a basin stand. Her stationery was a bond so heavy that a pen might have caught in the coarse fibers. I could not tell from the condition of the paper if she had wadded it up to throw it away.

Her letter read, "Wilson, You will destroy England to save it. I will never leave Haldon House. I am the price you will pay if—" The letter was unfinished.

So my questions were still unanswered by their last correspondence, and that is why I had her body exhumed and examined by a Scotland Yard forensic pathologist. I admit I did not go through channels. I did not even attempt to find surviving members of her family to ask permission. I believed then, and still believe, that the demands of a precise record of the war demanded that I plunge ahead with the ghastly task. I convinced Henry Bartholemew, the pathologist, and Lyle Foote, the gravedigger, to assist me.

Foote walked us to the cite at the corner of the earl's winter garden. England had far more bodies than coffins. Despite her wealth and standing, Lady Anne had been wrapped in a blanket and lowered into a pit. Foote said she must have released her servants, because hers was the only body found in the manor. Foote, Bartholemew, and I dug with gardeners' tools. The others dealt with corpses as their professions, and worked quickly, but I gingerly hacked at the ground.

Foote's shovel scraped the blanket. "There she is."

They continued with their shovels, but a putrid scent escaped the folds of the blanket, gagging me, and I had to climb out of the pit and watch them work.

Foote wore overalls and a watch cap. He was about forty years old, but his face was prematurely creased and sagging, perhaps from the nature of his work. Bartholemew wore a suit shiny with age and a key chain across his stomach. He had left a black leather bag containing his tools and an apron at the side of the pit.

As they lifted her from the ground, Bartholemew reassured me, "She's been here only a month. Even for an amateur like you, this won't be too bad."

He was wrong. They carried her body to the manor house.

The pathologist said, "With her dead four weeks, I won't need a blood gutter around the table. Let's use the dining table."

She was laid out and unwrapped. I saw her hair, glistening as it always had, but when my eyes moved to her face, I had to look away and grab the table edge for support.

Bartholemew pulled a pair of gloves and several tools from his bag. He wrapped the apron strings around his waist and tied them in front.

He passed me his notebook. "You take notes, Colonel."

I did, with a trembling hand.

He cut away her clothes, then said, "Desecrated muscles and deteriorated skin indicate death occurred about a month ago, as believed. Her joints are intact. There is considerable abdominal viscera rotting, with its odor."

I was embarrassed for her, lying on her table, stripped of her clothes, shed of all the careful constructs of her life, her dignity, even her humanity.

Bartholemew said, "She had a both-bone fracture of her

right arm. The radius and ulna are virtually severed by an impact that pierced the skin. Her right clavicle has also been fractured."

He poked and peeled for a few more moments. I gradually discovered that I could watch this morbid process. The memory of Lady Anne became disassociated from the mound of decomposing flesh and bones on the table.

I asked, "Would those injuries have killed her?"

"Yes, if she received no care."

Then I asked the question for which I had exhumed her. "Did she die before she received those wounds?"

He replied, "Any break produces a blood collection called a fracture hematoma. The blood clots, then the cells turn into a fibrous clot, a tannish, sticky substance like glue. The body deposits calcium there to repair the break. No evidence of that here."

I took notes.

Bartholemew continued, "And a fracture tears periosteum off the bone. Had she been alive when these breaks occurred, there would be blood around the fracture ends."

I looked up from the pad.

He concluded, "There is no blood. Her circulation was well stopped when her body received this trauma. She died of something other than these fractures, something other than the explosion that tossed her study and knocked her off the chair, something other than the falling beam, which may have hit her."

Then I knew how she died.

Lady Anne had been sitting at her desk at five o'clock that afternoon, May 31, 1942, the fourth day of the invasion. I had come to understand her sense of herself, and she may have had the windows open as a dare and an invitation. There were several books about the room, so she may have been reading, or she may have been writing the letter to General Clay.

As Foote told me, "She was dressed for evening when I found her, just like you see her clothes on this table. Ready for the ball. Black dress and pearls. I didn't even remove her earrings. Too busy."

There she sat at her desk, braced by her ineffable calm and

steely purpose, when the invisible cloud drifted in through her windows. She inhaled the poison several times and silently slumped forward onto her desk.

That is how I think of it, out of newly found respect for her memory. But Haldon House had been enveloped by the nerve gas tabun, and her death more probably involved vomiting, involuntary defecation and urination, and body-wrenching seizures.

She died in agony, as did thousands of her countrymen at that same hour.

23

The Luftwaffe had manufactured its Scapa Flow victory decorations before the operation. The medal depicted the black, upended bow of a sinking Royal Navy battleship in a bronze circle. The Luftwaffe—the entire Fatherland—was besotted with medals. Even so, *Oberleutnant* Franz Stenzel was proud of his Scapa Flow medal. He and his weapons officer, Fritz Cohausz, had pinned theirs to their jerkins just after receiving their new Stuka.

Staffel 4, II *Stukageschwader* (Stuka squadron), had been providing ground support from the captured RAF aerodrome near Guildford with endless dive-bombing missions in front of armor and infantry. Stenzel was rummy from his labors. Twelve sorties already that day, and almost five hours of daylight still remained. Each time, he returned with empty bomb racks and gun belts.

They were empty yet again as he banked for an approach to the airfield. Southern England had been blanketed by smoke since his countrymen had arrived. From Stenzel's vantage, it seemed that hardly a structure in Kent and Sussex remained whole. Smoke rolled away from most of them.

Stenzel said into his mask, "I'm becoming an expert on

smoke. Black smoke from vehicle oil fires. Gray smoke from fires that are still churning. White smoke from dying fires."

"Kindly keep your eye on the road, Franz," came from Cohausz.

They sank toward the runway. Smoke rolled across the concrete. Stenzel wondered at it, because firecrews should have quickly extinguished fires hazardous to air maneuvers. He nodded when he saw a fire truck near the north end of the runway. They were working on the blaze, but it would be a stunt landing, as difficult as his ditching in the North Sea a few days before.

He lowered his flaps. It appeared that some of the squadron was about to take off. The planes faded, then materialized in the haze. Mechanics were clustered around one of the Stukas. Perhaps an engine failure was holding up the entire squadron. It was unlike Stenzel's squadron leader to allow delays. Perhaps it was the smoke. The *Oberleutnant* stuck his oxygen mask back over his nose and mouth. He motioned for Cohausz to do the same. He didn't want the indignity of greeting his ground crew with a racking cough.

They glided toward the airstrip. Stenzel nudged his stick with his knees. The rolling smoke and the sock at the far end of the runway indicated the wind was blustery. The pilot could feel it in his controls. The haze parted, and he was startled by the closeness of the runway. The Stuka bounced, cracking its pilot's teeth together. "A perfect three-point landing, four times," he told me after the war.

He throttled back, and his Stuka slowed. He guided it toward a fuel truck waiting for him. He would undoubtedly return to the sky in moments.

Cohausz said, "I hope the controller lets us leave the cockpit. I've got to pee."

Stenzel drew his plane nearer to the other planes and gave a thumb's up signal when he recognized Schwartz at the controls of the nearest dive-bomber.

"I had not noticed anything remarkable, but suddenly everything was wrong," he recalled. "Schwarz was leaning forward over his stick, motionless. Another pilot lay on his wing. The crew of mechanics, who I had thought was repairing a plane, was prostrate on the ground. No one moved."

Stenzel turned the plane toward the hangar, the north portion of which had been heavily damaged before the invasion. A dozen, maybe twenty, Luftwaffe pilots and crew were sprawled before the opening as if they had been cast out of the structure by a strong wind.

"And only then did the color of the smoke register on me. Not black or grey or white. It was a faint yellow-green."

Cohausz realized it also. He yelled, "Get us out of here, Franz."

Stenzel does not remember making any firm conclusions about the haze passing before him like veils, but he spun the Stuka around and headed for the end of the runway. With a hand, he pasted his mask against his face. He glanced west. He saw no fires, only the ominous haze. Bodies of the fire-crew were scattered across the pasture. He threw forward the throttle.

A moment later they were again airborne. Ground support required arming twice for every fueling. His last touchdown had been for bombs and shells. They would soon be low on fuel. For thirty minutes they searched behind friendly lines for a landing zone free from the green smoke. They could not find one.

For the second time in a five days, *Oberleutnant* Stenzel put a Stuka down in the sea. He and Cohausz were rescued by a hospital ship an hour later, but not before Stenzel lost his Scapa Flow medal as he scrambled out of the cockpit and jumped into the channel.

All Wolfgang Kleber knew about England he had read in translated Sherlock Holmes stories. The land was a place of bog and murk and unstable people. The hand of God had helped Kleber up the beach, but now, deep within a Sussex forest, God had disappeared, leaving him with the exhausted survivors of his platoon.

Because trucks could not penetrate the woods, the soldiers were acting as mules. Wurmbach was laden with a tripod. Detmers was carrying the mortar and Busse its base. Busse stumbled over an exposed root, almost sinking to the undergrowth.

Luth was burdened with ammunition boxes. Bringing up the rear, all Kleber carried was his pack, respirator case, rations, and rifle.

Kleber had yet to see a bog or any murk, but the woods were eerie enough, with the trees rustling in the wind and the muffled sounds of explosions coming from all directions. He hoped the platoon leader knew where they were; unable to see more than ten meters ahead, Kleber had no idea. When the soldiers in front of him disappeared in the trees, Kleber increased his pace. They were descending a wooded ravine.

The English woods at last fulfilled Kleber's Sherlock Holmes–fired expectations when a turbid haze reached for them from between the trees, following the contour of the land, descending into the ravine.

"It came at us in long cords, winding around tree trunks as it poured into the small valley."

Clutching his face, Luth fell, buried beneath his ammunition cases. Detmers screamed, "Gas! Gas! Get out—" His words were choked off as he sank to the ground.

"I thought God was finished with me, but I was wrong," Kleber told me after the war. "Burdened with equipment, my friends were thirty seconds slower than I in opening their gas mask cases. And they were deeper in the ravine, where the clouds were thick. They began spitting and gagging, and that made them fumble with their equipment. I had mine on, tight over my face, before any of them."

Detmers, Buse, Wurmbach, and the others in the platoon died of suffocation within minutes. Wolfgang Kleber sat in the woods alone for two days.

"I almost went mad with thirst, because I was afraid to remove my mask."

He did not know the phosgene persisted in the forest less than a quarter of an hour.

Lieutenant Del Mason did, but hoped not to have to test the knowledge. Mason was the practical joker with the flour near Royal Tunbridge Wells. He commanded a battery of 4.2-inch mortars. His CWS platoon had been held in reserve, always retreating, but at that hour had been rushed to the line. Mason had received the next order with disbelief, and in a breach of decorum demanded confirmation from Lieutenant Colonel Rhone, rather than asking Company C's captain. Rhone radioed "Obey your orders," so the lieutenant broke open the canister cases.

Mason admits his command of the battery was a fumbling, myopic affair. "It's tough to see out of a gas mask, with the glass misting over. And I had on rubberized boots and gloves, and a cape over everything. It was stifling and awkward. It felt like I was wading in a stream. Everything slowed down. And I was shaking with what I was about to do."

Mason tested the wind, then checked that the battery crew was buttoned up in protective gear. He could hear the roar of battle beyond the ridge, perhaps four hundred yards away. He gave the order. His crew, looking like beached seals in their gas cloaks, let the phosgene shells fall down the mortar throats. The mortars yelped. Working like machines, his crew lifted shells and let them plunge, lift and drop, lift and drop.

"Then, maybe four minutes later, the unseen battle over the rise quieted, as if someone had placed a muffling blanket over the area. I felt sorry for the bastards, really."

Sergeant Gottfried Pfaffinger yelled into the turret voice tube, "Left forty, Erich, then steady."

Yet his *Panzerkampfwagen* trundled straight ahead, plowing over an apple tree, then another. Pfaffinger thought he had seen a target just west of the orchard, glimpsed between curtains of smoke.

"Erich, left forty," the sergeant shouted over the wail of the engine, "and be quick about it."

The tank rumbled straight ahead, deeper into the orchard. Pfaffinger wiped the vision block. The apple trees were old and gnarled, with their branches propped with poles.

"And the fog, of course, the fog, rolling between the trees."

Pfaffinger was from Freiburg and had a Swabian accent, which to other Germans sounds lisping. "I remember thinking England has fog too, like we do."

Pfaffinger told his loader to investigate. The loader disappeared into the belly of the tank and never returned.

"Then I looked below," the sergeant said during the interview. "There was a green, cotton haze in the driver's com-

436

partment. I squinted at it. My hull gunner was slumped over the radio, and Erich Ruhland was being held up only by his steering levers. His gas mask container was opened, but he hadn't had time to get it out. He might have yelled, but I couldn't hear him over the noise of the engine. My loader was there also, fallen to the deck. The poison had entered through the vent and had settled below and didn't rise."

The tank commander frantically climbed back into the turret and threw a mask at the gunner. They wrestled them on, then abandoned the tank.

Pfaffinger and the gunner ran through the orchard, searching for a way out of the deadly cloud. "Through the haze, I saw another panzer that had butted against a high stone fence. The tank was tilted almost upright on the stones, its treads whirling uselessly away, like a wind-up toy. Its entire crew must have been surprised by the gas."

Pfaffinger furled his brows a moment, then told me, "You know, that's my most frightening memory of the war, the utter hopelessness of that panzer, grinding futilely away at an English garden wall."

Flugmelder (Aircraft-Spotter) Rolf Ruckteschell had been at sea for six years. On the fourth day of the invasion, he was aboard the naval supply vessel *Dithmarschen*, lying three miles off Brighton. The ship was transporting rations and ordnance. Channel weather had deteriorated over the prior twenty-four hours. *Dithmarschen* was stalled off the coast because the surf had severely slowed the resupply operation.

"I remember having to lean into the port rail against the wind." Ruckteschell told me after the war. "I had gained some knowledge about weather, gazing at the sky all day looking for British airplanes, which was the easiest duty in the Kriegsmarine, because the Royal Air Force was about out of planes by then. But I had never seen anything like that fog, not on the channel or the North Sea, not anywhere."

Brighton was still held by Allied troops, as the Wehrmacht was avoiding cities as too costly to take. German units had pivoted inland behind the city.

Ruckteschell said, "The fog began at the eastern edge of the city, and the blustering wind quickly carried it east along the shore and over the breaking waves. The haze drained the coast-line of perspective."

The spotter raised his binoculars. "Then I saw the artillery burst over the beach, with grass-green gas erupting from the shells while they were still airborne. I could see some of our barges and landing craft vanish into the cloud, too late to reverse engines and pull back, their crews already dead."

Ruckteschell added, "I hadn't been ill since my first days onboard a ship, years before. But I was sick then, sick for my fellow sailors disappearing into that lethal mist."

When General Stedman read the first draft of this manuscript, he brought to my attention a gap in the narrative. I had yet to touch upon the German invasion command. The reason was pardonable, I thought: I had not yet found any survivors. After my conversation with Stedman, I spent another two weeks searching Germany for a witness to the Wehmracht forward command. I found one, Corporal Joachim Zenker, who had been a sentry posted to von Rundstedt's Army Group A headquarters. Under von Rundstedt was the entire Wehrmacht invasion force except those units hitting the British VI Corps at Lyme Bay west of the Americans.

Army Group A's headquarters that day were at a country house near Wisborough Green, southwest of Horsham. The house was in an elevated position near the hamlet and in the middle of a five-acre garden. The house was thirteen miles east of the furthest German advances. It was also fourteen miles, one hundred yards, east of the U.S. Army's 13th Field Artillery Brigade.

Corporal Zenker guarded the home's front gate, once wrought iron, he guessed, but removed and contributed to the British war effort. He walked idly back and forth between two brick gate posts, a Schmeisser submachine gun hanging from a leather strap over his shoulder. Zenker had never seen anything like this country house, with its paddock, grass tennis court, chapel, and five secondary cottages. The corporal had not been inside the main house. "To be under a roof was not my position in the Fatherland's war effort," he told me after the war. "I stood in the wind, just looking at the place, knowing that inside huge decisions were being made by von Rundstedt, who nodded at me once, I think."

Corporal Zenker's view of the house was along a hundred-yard driveway, which was bordered by azaleas and lady's mantle in front of purple-leaf maples. "I could see right down the drive to the front entrance, where more sentries were posted among scout cars and a few black sedans."

The artillery shell hit midway down the drive. "An enormous explosion. I jumped a meter off the ground. I expected to see a crater the size of a tank in the ground when the smoke cleared. Well, it cleared, and there was nothing to see."

Zenker debated leaving his post at the gate to investigate. Moments later, the guards at the door were on the ground, "scratching at the pebbles, as if digging a foxhole with their hands, and kicking. I decided I'd better have a look."

The corporal ran toward the house, passing the blackened ground where the shell had landed. When he saw the maples were still standing, instead of blown over by the blast, he knew the nature of the shell, though not the nature of the chemical, tabun, the nerve gas that cannot be smelled or seen. He removed his gas mask from its canister on his service belt. "I'd only put it on three or four times in drills. Never comfortable with it. I wasn't even sure it worked."

He passed three sentries, now dead from suffocation induced by the gas. He peered into one of the sedans. Its driver was spilled sideways on the seat, still twitching and jerking. Zenker pushed open the house's door. "The heaviest door I've ever opened, I thought then. But I discovered that a major had fallen against the inside of it, his legs splayed out in front of him. I pressed my mask to my face. Bodies were everywhere, in front of maps pinned to the wall, draped over desks, one officer hanging out a window. Several were still having convulsions. Vomit was everywhere. An aide had opened a case of gas masks, but hadn't had time to issue them or get one on himself. Five or six of the masks were at his feet."

Von Rundstedt was wearing his modified piped field service tunic. Instead of collar patches normally worn by a field marshall, he favored the parade uniform collar patches worn by infantry officers below the rank of general. In his hand was

439

his interim-stab, the everyday version of his field marshal's baton.

"And he was dead, all that Prussian military grandeur, very dead," Zenker recalled. "Trying to breathe, the field marshall had clawed a hole in his neck with his fingers. Two of his fingers were inside his neck. I wondered who would lead us now."

The 13th Field Artillery Brigade was the only unit capable of delivering the shell that far behind enemy lines, so the origination of the killing shell was not hard for me to figure out. The gas shell had been delivered courtesy of a 4.5 Gun M1, which weighed six tons and fired a fifty-five-pound shell. The gun was near the tiny village of Bramshot, and von Rundstedt's headquarters was about two hundred yards inside the gun's maximum range.

I spoke with one of the brigade's battery officers, Lieutenant Dennis Pritchard. He said, "CWS companies were shelling them close in, and we had a number of big gas shells, so we decided to hit their reserves. I figured, why let our heavy shells go to waste? Why not give some anonymous German assholes some time-on-target? I didn't have target coordinates. We just raised the barrel and let them have it."

In other words, the shell that devastated the Wehrmacht command was a lucky shot. Pritchard was unaware of his gun's accomplishment until I told him after the war. He was then a shoe store manager in Moline, Illinois. He replied, "The hell you say." And that's all he said. "The hell you say."

I witnessed General Clay give the order to use phosgene and the nerve gas. The suggestion by the British historian Forbes Wooden that I have denied giving interviews about the event to boost sales of this narrative is specious and undeserving of comment except to say that I was determined to have my recollection appear in its entirety, not edited to support one hardened viewpoint or another.

The most controversial question of the invasion, and perhaps of the war, was with whom did Clay consult before deciding to use the gas? I do not know. I have a theory, which I will press on you later in this chronicle, when all my evidence has been set forth.

The first I knew of his decision was the instant he gave the order. AEFHQ's forward headquarters that hour, 4:45 P.M., Sunday, May 31, 1942, was near Woking, twenty miles southwest of the City. The western edge of General Clay's command was at Woking. Beyond that lay the British V Corps. If the Wehrmacht had pushed west beyond that town, tactical decisions regarding defending against the German encirclement would have passed to a British corps commander.

So Clay ordered the chemical shelling just before such a decision would have been taken out of his hands. Many post-invasion critics say it was never in his hands.

Headquarters near Woking was in the barn of a destroyed country home. Present were I Corps's Alex Hargrave, the 2nd Infantry's Burt Jones, G2 David Lorenzo, and others.

When signalman Captain Branch called out, "General Clay, General Alexander on the wireless," Clay growled, "What does he want?"

Branch's head came up from his equipment. "I'm a lowly captain, sir. It's not really my place to ask the C in C of Joint Army Operations what he wants."

"Ask him anyway. He'll expect no less from an American."

After a moment, Branch said, "Sir, he wants to discuss transfer of field defense command to General Durward of British V Corps."

Clay said, "Tell him I'm unavailable."

"Sir?" Branch asked in a pleading tone. "He's right here on the line."

"Tell him I'm out using the two-holer." Clay turned to me. "Alexander could get under my skin, given enough time."

I followed the general toward Alex Hargrave. Midway, Clay stopped and his hand shot out to brace himself on a bale of hay, as if he were faint. His knees were shaking.

I quickly stepped to him. "Sir? You okay?"

He might not have heard me. He took a long breath, then began again toward Hargrave. He said. "Alex, I'm ordering Yellow Boy."

United States Army lieutenant generals do not like to be heard to gasp, but that is precisely what escaped Hargrave. "Yellow Boy?"

"Right now. Pass it through."

"General, do you have the authority for such an order?"

"I'm your superior," Clay said in a wintry tone. "Do as I tell you."

Hargrave's small features were a blank of perplexity. He breathed stertorously. "General Clay . . . Wilson, do you realize what you are doing?"

"Fully."

"You will be the first commander in this war to break the 1925 convention against its use."

"Pass the order to your divisions, Alex."

Hargrave gripped the upturned fruit crate that was acting as his desk. "I must ask to see your authorization from General Marshall or the president in Washington or from the prime minister."

"Are you failing to discharge an order from me, Alex?"

Generals Lorenzo and Jones were motionless near the barn door. The field telephone dangled from Captain Branch's hand.

"Let me see the command from Washington or London, sir," Hargrave said, holding out his hand.

Clay at that moment resembled a brawler. Chin down, shoulders bunched, fists clenched, neck thick and corded. He said in a voice dark with both rage and regret, "Alex, for failure to follow an order of your superior officer, you are relieved of command."

Hargrave said softly, as if in the presence of the dead, "Don't do this, Wilson."

"You are dismissed." Clay turned to the door. "Burt, are you still following your commander?"

General Jones replied stiffly, "Yes, sir."

"Then you are promoted to I Corps commander. Issue Yellow Boy to your units. Tell me when it is underway."

"Yes, sir." With a last glance at Hargrave, Jones rushed to Captain Branch's signal station.

Hargrave whispered, "For the love of God, don't do this, Wilson. Think of what you will release upon the world."

Clay spun on his heels. As he brushed by me, he said, "Follow me, Colonel Royce, immediately."

I hurried after him to one corner of the barn. That command, to follow him, was the most urgent he gave me during the invasion. I feared he was going to test me as he had General Hargrave.

I had forgotten that I was nothing but his sounding board. He squared himself, nodding toward Burt Jones who was bent over a radio with Captain Branch. Clay fairly snarled, "You know why I've gone to Yellow Boy, don't you, Jack?"

I was breathless from the spectacle of a commander ordering use of an outlawed weapon and from General Clay's taut dismissal of his friend of three decades. "Sir?"

His voice softened. "When the crap begins to fly in Washington and London, no one is going to listen to anything I have to say."

"What?"

"I think I've caught the German celebrating, Jack."

"What?"

If I weren't such a scrupulous reporter, I would make myself sound brighter throughout this narrative.

"The German has had his way for four days now, and he has begun to celebrate. He can't help it. It's human nature, loath though I am to credit the German with that. History teaches the danger of celebrating early."

Then I understood him. He was going to justify himself before the court of his aide-de-camp, who was known for paroles and concurrent sentences.

"The kaiser lost his head during the first hours of the Somme in 1918 and raised the hurrahs of victory."

I wanted to search for a box of gas masks. I couldn't remember if I had ever been issued one.

"And the Austrian Archduke Charles after the victory at Aspern/Essling was so elated he became incapable of decision."

I asked in a rush, "Sir, do we have gas masks? Where do we keep them?"

Clay continued, "And the Hessian, Colonel Rall, was so over-confident that he was dead drunk when Washington was cross-ing the Delaware toward him."

"Maybe the quartermaster would know about the masks. I don't think I've ever had one on."

"Jack, for Christ's sake, you aren't listening. Forget about the goddamn gas mask a moment."

"Yes, sir," I replied dubiously.

"Overconfidence will throw a commander off his pace, Jack. Just before the battle, Napoleon said Waterloo would be a picnic. Bonnie Prince Charles had an unfounded belief his five thousand followers were invincible, and they were destroyed by the English in 1746. And you wrote about Burgoyne in that interminable thesis of yours. So you know that he was enthu-siastic before Saratoga and that the colonials destroyed his army."

My God, was that German gas from a retaliatory strike com-ing through the barn door? No, just dust blown by the wind.

"The German has had his way too long. Do you get my point?"

"What?" Maybe General Lorenzo knew where our masks were. He seemed to know everything.

"The German is overconfident. He has allowed himself to stray about three feet too far from his gas mask. So I've got him by the balls."

Burt Jones left the signal station and walked toward us.

I said, "By the nose is a better metaphor in this case, sir."

As a courtesy to you, the reader, I have omitted many of General Clay's historical references from this narrative, al-though, I admit, it may not seem that way. This one is included in full because it struck me as forced, a bit frantic. He was pitiful and poignant, thinking he had to justify himself to me.

Jones said, "The orders are out, General Clay. The first shells are on their way."

When Jones had retreated, the general said, "Jack, the Great War showed that if troops are expecting a gas attack, casualties are less than two percent, but if the enemy is surprised by chemicals, the casualty rate is seventy to ninety percent."

"Yes, sir."

"And I think I've surprised them, don't you?"
Indeed he had.

Poison gas does not discriminate in favor of civilians, of course.

The Haslemere Savings Bank was managed by John Lind. Haslemere is midway between London and Portsmouth. Wehrmacht troops had passed through the town while Lind and a teller had hidden in the bank's cellar. When the scattered firing and artillery bombardment had lessened, they cautiously climbed up to the ground floor to peer through the window to the street. Several other civilians had ventured out. There were no Germans to be seen, until a three-vehicle convoy rumbled down the street. They were armored cars, Lind decided, and clearly German, since he saw a coal scuttle helmet poking from one of the hatches.

Then an apple-green vapor swept down the street as if it were the armored cars' exhaust. Lind told me, "Early in the war, the greatest fear was of gas. I knew instantly what the cloud was. Bertie and I ran into our old Chubb vault and closed the door. We waited as long as the air in the Chubb held out, about an hour. Then we emerged. The gas had vanished, but it was an anguishing sight that met us."

Lind stepped outside onto the sidewalk. Five bodies lay there. "I knew most of them. Mrs. Able, the butcher's widow. Peter Smythe, a carpenter. Harold Laidlaw, our solicitor. Others, all dead. I started running along, stopping every few steps to turn over and recognize the dead. It was a grisly business, Haslemere's citizens sprawled along its lanes. And I thanked God I had sent my wife and child north."

Near Reigate, the Heavy Rescue Service found three greyhounds inside Paul Lewis's Anderson bomb shelter, which he had constructed to be virtually air-tight. The dogs were alive and hungry. The bodies of Lewis and a fourth greyhound were ten feet from the shelter's entrance. He had attempted to save one too many of the animals.

Alfred Sedgwick remembers his survival with remorse. He and eight other pipefitters and machinists heard screams from outside their Reigate Waterworks machine shop. He recalled, "One look, and we knew what was what, the poison cloud coming at us with the wind."

Sedgwick and the others ran to the back room where the gas masks had been stored for three years. "In 1939, there were more masks in Surrey than people. But they had been shuffled around over the years. And the eight of us found only two of them, stacked in their buff-colored boxes. Only two."

Sedgwick and the others drew lots, using lengths of wire. "Reggie Merrill and I drew long ones. Six of our friends did not. Dreadfully frightened, they ran from the shop, trying to keep in front of the cloud. Their bodies were found a stone's throw from the waterworks. I've never forgiven myself for not finding a better way. I feel as if I sent them to their deaths."

I asked Sedgwick what that better solution would have been.

He shook his head. "Something. Anything. I'm alive, and they're dead. It doesn't seem right."

Maude Bruce was a nurse in Reigate. "We had just placed the last of the wounded and ill from our small hospital on lorries. One moment our town was full of retreating American soldiers. The next moment they had disappeared."

Enemy armor and infantry skirted the town on their march north. She saw them at the edge of her village, glimpses of panzers and camouflaged trucks barely visible in their own dust. Firing came from everywhere.

"It was too late for me to escape to London," she told me during an interview, "and the fighting seemed to be north anyway, so I walked the other direction, toward the Mole."

She walked along the River Mole, a winding, seemingly aimless creek. Along the banks she was hidden from most of the German units above. A few Wehrmacht troops might have spotted her, she thinks, but battle-pressed infantry do not have time for wandering civilians.

"There might have been twenty of us along the river bank, trying to stay out of harm's way. I was trying so hard to make myself small, to disappear, that I didn't see the clouds of gas so many survivors remember."

Maude Bruce suddenly felt her throat restrict, as if a hand had been clamped around it. "My first thought, actually, was

446

that a German had snuck up behind me and grabbed my throat. Then my lungs seemed to fill with fire, and I thought I'd been shot. I thought, this is what being shot must feel like."

She collapsed into the mud of the river bank. "As providence would have it, my face fell into a bushel of moss. I was never unconscious, I don't think. I turned my head once, and my nose filled with a sweet hay odor, and I knew it was poison. I pushed my face further into the moss."

The river moss acted as a filter. Maude Bruce survived. When she rose thirty minutes later, the banks of the River Mole were dappled with bodies.

The English way with happy euphemisms at times fails them. The hospital for the criminally insane at Royal Tunbridge Wells was named Royal Tunbridge Wells Hospital for the Criminally Insane. Interred there were four King George VIs, two Napoleons, at least one Mary, Queen of Scots, and ninety others.

I spoke with Dr. Robert Longstreet, superintendent of the hospital. "My assistants and I tried, we really did. We had more than enough gas masks, but not enough strength. As soon as we would get a mask on a patient, he would yank it right off. Many just could not understand the danger. We lost forty-five patients, many dying with their masks in their hands."

At another hospital, this one near Guildford, Edwin Perkins felt fortunate for his injuries. Perkins had been badly burned a day before. He had been placed under an oxygen tent. The toxic gas seeped through the hospital windows.

He remembered, "An orderly convulsed, coughing and clawing at his neck. One of the doctors rushed into the ward, and he fell, too. And I saw other patients writhe and cough and then be still. But I was immune to it, and it took me a moment to understand. I was under the oxygen tent. It saved my life once, and it saved me again."

Graham Gilmore was spared when he sealed himself inside his grocery's meat locker. "After about ninety minutes, my choice was clear. I had to risk stepping outside or freeze to death." Out he went, and the gas had dissipated.

Roger Crighton was director of the Wheelerstreet Cemetery and Mausoleum, near Godalming. When a shell landed near his west garden, a green cloud raced toward him in the wind. He locked himself inside the mausoleum. "The lichhouse saved me."

Clara Roe of Albury, three miles southeast of Guildford, rolled up the windows of her automobile and closed the vent. She told me after the war, "I saw a wisp of lime green air come through the vent, so I took off my blouse and jammed it in there."

I remarked that this was quick thinking.

She blushed. "I wasn't through removing my clothes. When a puff of it came through the floorboards, I removed my skirt and lay it over the boards, and sat on it. Then I took my stockings off and pushed them along the bottom of the passenger door to stop another wisp. I sat there as naked as I ever care to be for twenty minutes until the cloud cleared. I felt quite the doxy."

Wayne Sandon crawled through a manhole into a sewer in Royal Tunbridge Wells. "After gagging for half an hour, I thought to myself, no German gas can be as bad as this sewer, so I climbed out. The poison was gone."

Lord Walford hurriedly descended into the wine cellar of his country home five miles north of the Duke of Norfolk's castle at Arundel. "I felt entirely safe, even snug, in that dark, warm cavern, with my wine collection. Then, after five minutes, I decided my faithful servants deserved to join me. I emerged to find them madly running around coughing in this distracting manner, and I had to fairly tug them into the cellar. Five of us were down there for two hours. It was exceedingly close, and we had little to talk about. Now that I think about it, I should have offered them something to drink."

General Clay's toxic clouds burst forth along a north-south line roughly corresponding to the western borders of Surrey and Sussex. More poison clouds erupted along the northern German front, in a sweeping east-west arc twenty miles south of the Thames. The freshening wind both aided and hindered the gas, moving it along but also diluting it.

It might have been worse. English civilians hid in basements, under blankets and laundry, in closets and pantries, under rugs, in bomb shelters, anywhere that seemed proof against the deadly wind. Some of these spontaneous shelters worked, and many civilians had gas masks.

The gas dipped down here but not there, puddled in one home but missed the neighbor's house, streamed along one village lane but ignored another.

Most civilians had already moved inland. Only essential workers and the brave, ignorant, or foolish had remained.

Despite all this, the carnage was appalling. Latest estimates for noncombatant deaths due to the chemicals are approaching 22,000. The number of wounded is much higher, and may never be accurately determined.

At 5:30 that afternoon, General Clay said grimly, "Not one goddamn further inch of English soil is going to fall to the enemy, Jack. Mark my words."

He was right. His ghastly tactic stunned the Germans. Wehrmacht fatalities were staggering. Their front froze. The vaunted blitzkrieg shuddered to a halt, choking and thrashing.

24

My last council of war—unless one counts my current membership on the board of UCLA's student newspaper—occurred the next evening in the hole in the ground. Winston Churchill called us to order by tapping an ashtray on the green cloth.

I do not believe General Clay had the slightest idea whether this meeting would be triumphant or recriminatory. It certainly began badly, though, when Churchill nodded at General Barclay, who said, "We will have a moment of silence for General Crawford Douglas."

Clay's head snapped up. He had not known the Allied Air Forces chief was dead.

Barclay said quietly, "Douglas was killed in a retaliatory phosgene strike while visiting a forward base. The gas bomb was delivered by a Luftwaffe dive-bomber."

During that silent moment, Clay's eyes went from man to man, judging his support. I could not determine a tally.

Churchill ended the tribute abruptly, "General Clay, will you report?"

Clay began aggressively, "Our situation is vastly improved since last we met." He stepped to the map of southern England. "The German advance, which was gaining a mile of English territory every hour, is dead in its tracks."

450

Clay spoke for several minutes, repeatedly sweeping his hand across the map, wiping away the Wehrmacht. He concluded, "We believe the Wehrmacht divisions, including the 28th, 8th, and 6th Mountain, which were spearheading the encirclement drive, and many of the encircling second-wave reserves, including the 7th and 8th Panzer and the 20th Motorized, have ceased to exist as fighting forces."

I am not sure of this, but despite the solemnity in the room, I believe that Winston Churchill grinned demonically at that moment. With the pretense of planting his cigar in his mouth, his hand quickly rose to cover the smile.

Clay went on. "The German has suffered exceptionally high casualties. Those Wehrmacht soldiers who escaped with their health have been rendered almost useless by the sudden plunge in their morale. They no longer have the will to take your land."

"How do you know the state of German morale?" General Alexander asked.

"Interviews with POWs. Captured soldiers tell my G2 that the Wehrmacht infantry is morose and haggard, paralyzed by the sudden reverse."

General Stedman asked, "How many POWs do you have?"

"Too many to count. I suspect my men have snatched more Germans in the last twenty-four hours than have been captured by all prior Allied efforts in the war."

I swear Churchill grinned again behind his hand.

"We have noted that a generalized Wehrmacht retreat has begun. The withdrawal may not have been ordered by OKW, but it is the result of battlefield reality. We are also noting a peculiar phenomenon. Many of the Wehrmacht regiments and battalions seem to be acting independently of command, seemingly without coordination."

Arthur Stedman said, "We think we know the reason. Bletchley's direction finders report an abrupt end to the concentration of signals coming from a position southwest of Horsham. They conclude a major Wehrmacht headquarters was destroyed in the gas attack, a corps or even an army headquarters."

Applause or congratulations would have been too much to

expect from the British, who usually have chilled water in their veins, but this news should have produced at least a few clucks of approval. The room was leaden with silence. And, to my mind, it screamed with the as yet unasked question to Clay: Who authorized the gas?

The prime minister said, "We'll hear now from Captain Swarthmore."

The weatherman entered with a brisk walk I had not seen before. He quickly took his spot in front of the map. His dark eyes seemed to dance. He said, "I have good news."

Swarthmore outlined conditions on the channel, which continued to deteriorate. Swells were approaching seven feet, with twenty-knot winds that would hold for a minimum of thirty-six hours.

Churchill asked, "Are you saying that the German landing operation will be entirely interrupted"

Swarthmore replied with prickly pride, "I am a meteorologist, Prime Minister, not a sailor."

Alexander said, "We do not believe a single Wehrmacht regiment has been able to land since noon today. Certainly no armor can make it to shore."

After Swarthmore left the room, General Stedman reported on the enemy landing at Lyme Bay in Dorset, where the Wehrmacht's momentum seemed to have slowed in sympathy with the devastation on the main front. No gas had as yet been used in Dorset, but no British troops were without their masks.

Then Stedman outlined efforts to reinforce the Clay's AEF and the Canadian I Corps with British units from the north. Before the chemical assault, Second Dunkirk, the heroic and impulsive rising of the English citizenry to transport their soldiers, seemed foolish. But with Wehrmacht forward units in gasping, stumbling disorder, the civilian land bridge might make a difference, Stedman said. Rather than in precise military columns of march along narrow, Luftwaffe-pocked roads, the army was being moved south in wide waves by British volunteers. General Barclay shook his head at the wonder of it.

Lord Lindley finally broached the subject that had hung in the room like the gas itself. "General Clay, may I inquire as to your authority to use the chemical weapon?"

"I am commander of the American Expeditionary Force," Clay answered. "I ordered the gas."

The minister for coordination of defense pressed, "You intentionally misunderstand my question, General. Who allowed you to be the first in this war to use chemical weapons?"

General Clay spread his hands on the table, a gesture of endless patience and reasonableness. "My army was on the verge of extinction. I had no alternative."

"Your alternative would have been, at the very minimum, to consult with us," Clement Attlee said. "You took it upon yourself to breach a treaty that has kept the world free of chemical battlefields for two decades."

"Mr. Attlee," Clay responded, his voice still level, "had I not used the chemicals, von Rundstedt would right now be delivering his orders from the chair you are sitting in."

Lord Lindley said, "We should not engage in profitless speculation—"

Clay cut him off, "And all your asses would be in Canada by now."

"My dear chap—"

"This group would be a shamed, defeated, impotent government in exile, just like the Poles who issue their useless communiqués from London."

I noticed that the politicians, not the military men, were grilling Clay.

Lindley said icily, "You are aware, General Clay, that your Congress and administration are in an uproar. There are members of your Congress calling for your summary arrest. General Marshall is under intense pressure to resign because he chose you to lead the AEF. Even President Roosevelt is mired in controversy, with your newspaper reporters shouting questions at him and some senators claiming he must accept the ultimate responsibility for your acts and step down. The wire traffic between here and Washington has brimmed with it."

Attlee brought his chin up. "General Clay, one question has fairly consumed me since I learned of your use of the gas. Did you consider the English civilians who would surely perish? Did you give them a thought?"

Clay said softly, "I did."

Attlee asked in an old man's voice, "Do you in any way share our anguish over their fate?"

"I do."

This was inadequate atonement for Lord Lindley. "General Clay, there is a possibility you will enter history as one of its great military criminals."

"Horseshit. You gave me a job, and I did it. Now stop your whining."

Lindley blinked as if Clay had spit at him.

A code clerk entered the room and gave a message to the prime minister. Churchill's face darkened as he read it. He looked up, "General Clay, this is from Marshall in Washington. You have been relieved of command of the American Expeditionary Force. General Hargrave is now its commander. You have been ordered to Washington."

Clay's face was impassive. A long moment passed. Then his mouth twitched, and his eyes became glassy. He blinked several times. He was struggling with himself, I could tell. He inhaled slowly. When he pursed his lips—that expression I had seen so many times—I knew he was in control.

He reached for his Pall Malls and dropped them into his pocket. He gathered his papers, then pushed himself up from his seat. I rose with him. General Alexander nodded. I learned later that Alexander had spoken over the telephone with President Roosevelt and had encouraged Clay's removal. All eyes were on Clay, but, once again, I found them unreadable.

Clay walked to the door slowly, to hide his limp. He turned to them. "You people need some advice." His voice was as strong and as true as a warning tocsin.

Lindley cleared his throat, dismissing Clay.

"You may think your resources are depleted and your soldiers are exhausted, but you must pursue the enemy with utter ruthlessness into the channel. No battle is won without the coup de grâce. Do not make the mistake of thinking you have won anything yet."

Clay's hand was on the door handle when Winston Churchill said magisterially, "You are advising us not to make the error General Meade did after Gettysburg, in failing to aggressively pursue the broken Confederate army."

454

Clay's eyebrow rose. "Yes." Again his hand went for the door handle. But he paused and said, "Or, as a better example, the French failure to pursue the Austrians after Wagram."

"Or, even better, Marlborough's failure to vigorously pursue the French after Malplaquet."

Clay countered, "Or, better than Marlborough, General Howe's failure to pursue Washington into Manhattan Island."

Puzzled AACCS members looked left and right, left and right, following the match.

"What you are suggesting," Churchill said, his eyes locked on Clay's, "is that we act as Napoleon at Austerliz did, when he ordered his artillery to smash the frozen Satschan Pond, so the Austrians fleeing across it would break through and drown."

Clay came back with, "Or as the English did after defeating the Jacobites at Culloden, chasing them in a spree of death and mutilation."

The prime minister paused, his next volley on his tongue. But it would not come. His brows sewn tightly together, he stared at the fan on the wall, then at the damp end of his cigar. "Well, my memory has failed me for the moment."

Clay smiled briefly. "Then this meeting wasn't a total loss."

I followed him into the hallway. We were stepping up the stairs into the London weather when Clay said to me, "He gave me that one."

"Pardon, sir?"

"He let me win, as a gift. And you can write in your goddamn diary, which will likely prove the ruin of me, that I said so."

General Clay had nothing to do with the British victory that followed, so I have little to report. The storm lasted three days, during which few German men or supplies landed and Luftwaffe sorties were severely reduced. The phosgene and the tabun and the weather worked together to cripple the Wehrmacht's operation. Then the British army crushed it. Ten days after they landed, the last German was thrown off the island.

But not to return to the beaches would leave General Clay's

455

ledger unfilled. He met the enemy there, and it is fitting I describe how the invasion ended there.

Winston Churchill and General Stedman took Clay's advice to heart, or, more probably, they were of the same mind all along. There was no repeat of Dunkirk, where the Germans strangely let a British army escape. The beach fighting was less a battle than a vengeful melee. I interviewed a number of German survivors.

Sergeant Waldemar Rasch, who had seen his entire ten-man squad fall rushing up the beach, witnessed the same thing when he returned to the beach. "Even though the seas had lessened, the evacuation was chaotic. The beach resembled a crowd at a rally, thousands of soldiers milling about. There was nothing to do but wait for a ship or a barge. All that we held of England then was the beach, a narrow band between the water and the British. And the British were angry."

American units had received the brunt of the invasion and had been pulled off the line. The pursuit was made by the British. After the slapdash rush south, many British soldiers could not find their regiments. They fought in spontaneously formed units.

Rasch was ten feet from the surf, in a line of riflemen waiting to climb onto a barge. His new squad had seven men left. Then a shell landed at the waterline. "I believe it was just one piece of shrapnel that tore through five of them in line, ripping through the first soldier's groin and rising as it blew back, through four more, then ripping off a portion of Hans Handlisch's head. He had been standing in front of me. With them all down at once, I was next in line to board. I did so quickly."

Alwin "Ajax" Oesten piloted a forty-foot French riverboat that normally plied the Seine. He told me, "We were using everything that floated, and that shallow-keeled boat wasn't made for chop. I put it right up to the surf, then swung hard to port, and signaled the waiting soldiers to board. I wasn't expecting them to come all at once."

Infantrymen frantically waded out to the boat, some casting away their rifles and kits to climb aboard. "Forty or fifty of them suddenly grabbed my starboard rail. I yelled, but they wouldn't let go of the boat, and it listed. That made it easier to climb on, and when they did, the boat tilted further. Finally, it foundered, rolled right on over. A few, including me, jumped free, but many drowned under the hull."

Able Seaman Gustav Foerster was a deckhand on a Kriegsmarine tug. Before the invasion his barge had hauled gravel, so it was easily capable of sustaining the weight of the three hundred soldiers he was taking home. "I thought we were clear of the carnage," he told me later. "We were churning away from the beach, leaving the turmoil behind, when an artillery shell struck the barge athwartships. When the smoke cleared, a few soldiers were standing fore and aft on the barge, but nobody in the middle, just pieces of them, and the barge was awash in blood."

At Pevensey Bay, Sergeant Hugo Brinkmann was pushed into the sea by a mass of soldiers. "It was like the bread riots during the panic in the early thirties. A weaving, pulsing throng, pushing and pushing. I was pressed deeper and deeper into the water. I don't think those at the back of the pack knew we were in trouble. They shouldered those in front of them to get away from the beach fire. Some soldiers were trampled under foot, others forced into the water."

Struggling against the tumultuous mob of soldiers, Brinkmann threw away his gas mask and scraped off his boots. "We were packed so tightly that I couldn't bend to get out of my pack, so I cut it off with my knife. Just as I did, my feet no longer touched the bottom and waves washed over my head. All around me were the thrashing and gasping and crying of soldiers. Many drowned before they could break free of the horde. I was pulled under by desperate hands, but I kicked free, and kept kicking until I was away from the pack. A barge glided by, and several soldiers pulled me on board."

At Rottingdean, just east of Brighton, the remnants of Corporal Max-Eckart Schuur's company, once a spirited unit of 2nd Battalion, 28th Infantry Division, attempted to surrender. Schuur rigged a white flag made from a flour sack to his rifle and with three others crept to the crest of a hill and waved the rifle back and forth.

"There was a pause in the Tommy fire," he recalled. "They yelled something at us. I stood up slowly, still waving the rifle.

The others put their hands in the air. Just then, Lieutenant Pruess ran toward us, cursing and waving his Luger, calling us cowards."

The Wehrmacht had been ordered never to surrender. Some officers, fresh to the front, were still burning with the spirit of the Fatherland. "Pruess yelled that we were traitors and wagged his pistol in front of us. I said, 'Lieutenant, haven't you got eyes? We are one minute away from being annihilated.' He turned red and sputtered something, then brought up the pistol. I believe he was going to shoot me."

He did not have the chance. "I smashed the butt of my rifle alongside his head, and he collapsed. We left him there, the fool. I held up the white flag again, and my friends and I walked toward the British line."

Bernhard Schenk was pulled onto a minesweeper, then in turn helped others behind him. When the boat was filled rail to rail with soldiers, the pilot threw the throttle forward, and it churned away from the beach. "I thought I had escaped. My joy at leaving that hellish island made me forget the shells overhead and the soldiers we were leaving behind. I wanted to dance. I was free. Then a heavy machine gun found our boat."

A steady stream of bullets turned the pilothouse into chaff. The wheelstation and the pilot disintegrated. "The mate rushed to the wheel, but there was nothing remaining to control the ship. The boat was out of control."

It veered right in a long circle, toward France and freedom, then toward the open channel to the west, and finally, agonizingly, back to the English shore. It powered over Wehrmacht soldiers, living and dead, then rammed the shore.

"I jumped into the surf, and swam away from the beach. I was picked up by a motor torpedo boat a few minutes later."

Lieutenant George Quedenfeldt's platoon had survived almost intact the entire invasion. Thirty-five of them entered the channel water toward a Kriegsmarine supply ship fifty yards offshore. The ship's mate had signaled that it could get no closer to the shore. The platoon began swimming, stronger swimmers helping the weaker.

Quedenfeldt told me, "We were halfway there when a British

458

machine gunner opened up. The water boiled with bullets, and my soldiers began bursting apart. The water seethed with bullets and blood. A bullet ripped off my left arm just below the elbow, and a corporal pulled me along. Only twelve of us made the boat. The screams still wake me at night."

Rudolf Liebe won a bronze medal in the hundred-meter freestyle at the 1936 Olympics in Berlin. Artillery and rifle fire had chased away most of the Kriegsmarine ships and barges. Liebe had been pinned to the ground in a dune thicket near Dymchurch. He told me after the war, "The air overhead sang with British shells. I looked up, and I swear the sky was rippling with all the projectiles. If I stood, I would have been mowed over by random shots. But I saw the last ship pull away from the shore, leaving me. I had to take a chance to reach it."

Liebe sprang upright and sprinted toward the water, stumbling over bodies and waving an arm to alert that last ship. "They either did not see me or decided it was too risky to bother with me. I waded into the surf, then dove forward. My arms glanced off a body. I started stroking to sea, but every few seconds I'd bounce into another body. All around, the water was squirting with shells. I was awash in bodies, more dead German soldiers than waves, it seemed. Germany's best, a sea of them, rising and falling with the swells." Liebe swam for six hours until he was pulled from the water by the crew of the *Erwin Wassner*, a Kriegsmarine submarine depot ship.

Liebe believes he may have been the last German soldier to leave British soil.

25

I was the last person to see Wilson Clay alive. Two days after being removed from his position as the American Expeditionary Force's commander, he and I were in his Grosvenor Square flat packing his belongings for his journey home. Our gas masks were nearby. The Luftwaffe had dropped several phosgene and mustard gas bombs on the city, but Londoners were well prepared, and there were few casualties. Rain was falling against the window.

Clay was packing his military treatises into a sea trunk when he looked up and said, "Jack, I haven't had much to do these past few days, as you know."

"Yes, sir."

"So I read your journal."

I was aghast. "Sir?"

"Even though it makes me appear a pompous know-it-all, it's fairly accurate."

"Thank you, sir."

"But how about doing your old commander a favor by omitting reference to my so-called Mystery Flight with Lady Anne. The public can do without that."

"I will, sir." There was a time when my word was my bond. An accurate account is of more consequence.

460

Wee Wee was sleeping at the general's feet. Before she died, Lady Anne had sent the pekinese in her Bentley to the general's London flat, maybe as punishment. They had taken a liking to each other.

He continued, "How many times have I busted you in rank this past month?"

I laughed. "Twelve or thirteen."

"What a nightmarish, topsy-turvy army career you've had."

I laughed again.

"Well, your roller coaster ride isn't over yet." He fished a small envelope out of his pocket. He opened it. "Here are your silver birds. In what may be my last official act in England, I've promoted you to full colonel."

I was nonplussed, then thrilled. He brusquely removed my silver oak leaves and replaced them with the eagles.

I said, "You can bet I'll push through the paper on this right away."

"I already have, Jack." He patted my shoulder and said, "And just remember, if Napoleon had been born two years earlier, he would have been Italian, since Corsica was ceded to France just before his birth."

I nodded. To this day, I have no idea what he meant by that.

He returned to his packing. He was not a collector of mementoes, and he had little more than the few articles he brought to England. He picked up the copy of *Bartlett's Familiar Quotations* he used for writing speeches and tossed it to me. "I'm giving this to you. You need it more than I do, I'll guarantee you that."

He carefully wrapped his framed family photographs. He stared for a long while at one of his wife. Then he abruptly said, "Jack, invading England was the German's first mistake. It won't be his last. We'll see the end of him, and it won't be long."

As in so many other things, General Clay was correct here, too. As all world citizens know, with less than a year to recover from the debacle of the English invasion, Hitler next swept into Russia. From that moment, his days could be counted. Bloodied and softened on the endless Russian steppes, the Germans could not mount an effective defense to the Allied

461

D-Day invasion, launched from the very English shores the Wehrmacht had briefly held. I wish Clay could have celebrated the war's triumphant end with the rest of us.

Several questions dogged me while I compiled this narrative. The first was whether the general's relationship with Lady Anne Percival colored his battle judgment. Her tragic end is clear evidence that it did not. He knew she would be at her country home, and he knew the poison cloud would sweep over it. If he were capable of causing her death, then it is inconceivable anything she did in her life would have influenced his conduct of the battle.

Another question was the prime minister's role in the use of the gas. I do not have any more proof than I have already set forth. In the hours before the chemicals were released, Clay conferred over the telephone with Churchill after having waved the rest of us out of hearing range, something he had never before done. At our last Defense Committee meeting, while some were searching for the guilty, the surreptitiously smiling Churchill seemed ready to dance a jig at the Wehrmacht's appalling fate. I also believe General Clay had been intensely loyal to the prime minister from the moment Churchill resisted pressure to dump Clay. It would have been true to General Clay's character to gain approval from Churchill, then deny Churchill knew anything about the use of the gas to spare the prime minister the political strife.

About seven o'clock that evening, I noticed that General Clay's packing had slowed. He was taking longer and longer to do less and less. He was being exceedingly careful, gently blowing dust off a few books, polishing a silver picture frame with his sleeve, scratching the back of Wee Wee's neck. He was acting like a man with nothing to do and nowhere to go.

He looked up from a small album of photographs and said, "The only goddamn thing of any worth my father ever taught me was that if there's enough blue in the sky to make a pair of sailor's trousers, it'll be good weather tomorrow."

"Sir?"

"Well, he didn't teach me enough, it looks like." He placed the album in a trunk. "Jack, you know me better than anybody but my wife. Do you know why you and I get along so well?"

462

I was immensely gratified. "I have a few ideas."

"Spare me them," he replied. "We have the same perspective on history. You can grasp why I did what I did."

"I can?"

"No general worth a damn is going to scratch his ass while the enemy runs over him. You didn't see me scratching my ass, did you?"

"Not once, sir."

He limped toward me, holding an envelope he had drawn from a back pocket. "I want you to give this to my wife."

A bell of alarm sounded. "You are leaving tomorrow for Washington, sir. Why don't you take it with you?"

"It's a new draft of my will. With the Luftwaffe out in force, trans-Atlantic crossings are risky. No sense having that document and me on the same flight."

I took it from him.

He reached for his uniform jacket. "I'm going to Mayfair to pay my respects to General Crawford's widow."

I rose and started for the armoir.

"No need you coming along," he said. "I'll be back shortly."

He had not had a driver since being removed from command. He also had little use for my services. Still, I found his going out alone unsettling. He deserved an entourage.

I bid him goodnight and returned to packing his trunk. After a few moments it was full, so I strapped and locked it, then returned to a book I had been reading.

At 8:30, I was startled by a booming knock. I crossed to the door and opened it. Two American MPs were standing there. One said, "Colonel Royce, there's been an accident. It's General Clay. Will you come with us?"

The blackout hid London as we passed through the city. I do not have a clear memory of that drive to Hyde Park. I did not see the crumpled car until our jeep had stopped. A rescue truck was there, as well as an ambulance and another military police jeep. But no one was frantically rescuing the occupant of the car, no prybars or winches or the loud orders of rescue organizers, so I knew what I would find. Wilson Clay, so conscious of the past, had just entered it.

The automobile, an Austin, had smashed into the trunk of

463

a roadside tree, thrusting the radiator back to the firewall and propelling Wilson Clay through the windshield and against the tree. His body lay on the crushed hood. Blood covered much of his head and had matted in his hair. I bent close. His eyes were open and unseeing.

I bubbled, "General Clay, please, no."

An MP casually lit a cigarette and said, "He's about as dead as I've seen anybody, Colonel."

A memorial service was held in the remnants of Westminster Abbey three days later. Winston Churchill and General Stedman attended. The general's body was then flown to Washington, where it was buried in the military cemetery at Arlington. I took Wee Wee home with me to California. Six years have passed since the night General Clay died, and I still grieve for the man.

He may have taken his own life. Investigators determined his car was traveling close to sixty miles an hour when it hit the tree. And the envelope he gave me did not contain a will, but a letter to his wife. Margaret Clay told me later it was a love letter. I could not ask to read it, so I do not know if it was a good-bye letter, too. I have no idea why General Clay would have me deliver the letter if he thought he was going home the next day.

On the other hand, the roads that night were slick from the downpour. Street lamps had been extinguished for the duration. Londoners will attest to the hazards of driving during the blackout. And Clay was a fighter, unlikely to let a moralizing commotion in the States send him to his end. He would have viewed it as too easy.

I believe, and I prefer to believe, that his death was a mishap on a dark and slippery road. I have no more details, so I end my conjecture.

Some have suggested Clay's death, whether suicide or an accident, carried the scent of justice. He would heatedly reply—I can hear him dictating his response and ordering me to put it in my journal—that every great captain has learned from his predecessors. Charles XII from Alexander. Napoleon from Frederick. Foch from Napoleon. Clay learned from them all, and the lesson was that in defeat was disgrace.

His actions will be a source of controversy for years. For Wilson Clay, there was no debate, no hesitation. He was a soldier who would vanquish the enemy. He would not abide history recording him as a conquered warrior, and so it will not.